Books by Laura Bradbury

Grape Series

My Grape Year

My Grape Paris

My Grape Wedding

My Grape Escape

My Grape Village

Other Writings:

Philosophy of Preschoolers

my

grape

paris

my grape paris

LAURA BRADBURY

Published by Grape Books

Paperback ISBN: 978-0-9959173-0-9
eBook ISBN: 978-0-9959173-1-6

Visit: www. laurabradbury. com

I dedicate this book to my incredible liver donor, Nyssa Temmel. Without your courage and selflessness I would be—not to put too fine a point on it—dead. Every single one of the "bonus" days you gave me is a gift.

"...But Paris was a very old city and we were young and nothing was simple there, not even poverty, nor sudden money, nor the moonlight, nor right and wrong, nor the breathing of someone who lay beside you in the moonlight."

—ERNEST HEMMINGWAY, A Moveable Feast

chapter one

The only proof I had that I was supposed to be there in Paris was my temporary student visa and a badly photocopied letter from some unidentifiable administrative office of the Sorbonne.

I scanned the letter I clutched in my sweaty hand. It was the last week in August, but the oppressive humidity made it feel as though we were in the tropics—the perfect weather to be sunning ourselves in Biarritz or Brittany, not tramping around the dog poop-festooned streets of the 5th arrondissement of Paris.

What I could decipher from the letter stated that, after my arrival in France, I should contact my exchange year advisor, Professor Alix Renier-Bernadotte, at the address provided. Just an address. No telephone number or any other contact information. *She better be at home.*

We found Professor Renier-Bernadotte's apartment a few streets away from the building where I would be taking at least half of my classes. She lived on a narrow, cobblestoned street, just off a much larger street.

The building rose from the sidewalk in the stately style that was synonymous with Haussmann, the designer of modern Paris—gray stone and large symmetrical windows, fronted by ornate ironwork so Parisians wouldn't tumble out onto the street when opening their massive wooden shutters in the morning.

I was already intimidated by this Parisian professor who was supposed to help me register at the Sorbonne, and I hadn't even met her yet.

Franck and I had arrived that morning after more than fifteen hours of travel from Vancouver. This Inter-University Exchange gig—I was being swapped with a French student who would study for a year at my school, McGill University in Montreal, while I studied at the Sorbonne—was already turning out to be more challenging than it looked on paper.

I studied the name tags stuck in the brass buzzer plate mounted on the wall of the apartment building. They were blurred by age and rain. "Does that look like Renier-Bernadotte to you?" I asked Franck, who was lighting a Gitanes. I didn't know how he could smoke in that heat, let alone Gitanes—the cigarette equivalent of pungent Munster cheese.

He took a deep drag and leaned forward to peer at the name I was pointing at. "It looks to me like it says *Rognon-Betterave*." Kidney-Beets. He rubbed his stomach thoughtfully. "That gives me an idea. If we find a *brasserie*, they might have veal kidneys in Madeira on the menu. They're a classic dish at Parisian *brasseries, tu sais*."

I made a gagging noise.

"You think you don't like them because you've never tried them."

"I know I don't like Gitanes, and I haven't tried them either. I can't get past the smell. Same thing with kidneys."

"Completely different. Kidneys are extremely good for you as well as delicious. Smoking is a filthy habit I need to stop."

"At least we agree on that," I said, then nodded at the buzzers. "So, should I buzz Professor Kidney-Beets here?"

Franck shrugged. "You know my opinion. You should wait until your first day of school. All of Paris goes on vacation in August. Haven't you noticed how empty the streets are?"

"Still—"

"I doubt she's here, and even if she is, she won't answer her buzzer. I warned you not to expect the same welcome that McGill provides to the incoming French students."

That was a shame, because at McGill, the incoming French exchange students were treated like royalty. They were appointed a student chaperone as soon as they arrived in Montreal to help them with everything from finding accommodation to registering for courses to meeting other students.

A whole week of special events were put on for the exchange students freshly arrived at McGill. There were scavenger hunts so they could familiarize themselves with the campus and mingle with others, live concerts, and drinks events so their livers could adapt to Canadian beer and the cheap Czechoslovakian wine from the dépanneur. And meetings were set up with various academic advisors so they would have all their questions answered and their timetable completely in order before the beginning of term.

So far, there had been no welcoming committee for me at the Charles de Gaulle airport on our arrival, and the only contact name I had been given was Professor Kidney-Beets, supposedly at this address. As a result, I was pulsing with desperation to connect with her. She was my only shot at feeling less disoriented.

"I have to try," I said. I buzzed on the buzzer.

Nothing.

I buzzed again. Then again.

Franck raised one eyebrow at me. "Does the state of that name tag beside her buzzer look like that of a person who *wants* students to find them?"

Dignified silence was the only possible response to my boyfriend.

I peered up to the two windows on the fourth floor, where Professor Kidney-Beets' apartment was supposed to be if we had indeed chosen the right buzzer. A curtain twitched and a face dominated by a large pair of glasses glanced down, then the curtain drew shut again.

"She's up there!" I shouted in English, even though Franck and I spoke French together most of the time. "I saw her!" I pointed, just in case Franck misunderstood.

I went back and buzzed the buzzer five more times so there could be no doubt I wanted to see her. I was going to buzz it a sixth time, when Franck reached out and stilled my hand. "Ever heard of getting off on the wrong foot? I don't know who this woman is, but I would bet that it's not a prudent idea to piss her off before the school year even begins."

I stamped my foot and buzzed again three times. The curtain above didn't even twitch.

Franck took me by the shoulders and pulled me back from the buzzer. "I'm not sure how it is in Canada, but being so persistent when somebody clearly does not want to answer their buzzer is considered rude in Paris," he said gently.

"I'm not the one who is supposed to be advising students and then hiding away in my apartment, leaving them completely abandoned on the street, not knowing what to do or how to choose their courses or—"

Tears began to roll down my cheeks. Tears borne of too much travel and too little sleep, and overheating and frustration, and the fact that the reality of this whole year-in-Paris thing was already at loggerheads with my fantasies.

"Come on." Franck took my arm. "Let's go find a *brasserie*."

"I'm not eating kidneys! I won't!" I heard myself shout like a spoiled, overtired toddler.

"You don't have to," Franck said, stroking the back of my hand. "You're to rest your feet for a while, and there might even be chocolate mousse on the menu for dessert."

"We don't have any money," I wailed. "You're always telling me how everything is so expensive in Paris."

"Not the *prix fixe* menu at Paris *brasseries*. They're a bargain. Besides, a good meal raises one's spirits. That's priceless."

I let myself be led up the street, the hope of meeting Professor Renier-Bernadotte's abandoned—for that day anyway.

"Just so you know," I said, "I'll be ordering a carafe of chilled rosé."

"So young, yet so wise." Franck patted my shoulder.

chapter **two**

The *brasserie* Franck steered me into was just across from a square called la place Monge where, Franck informed me, a market was held three times a week. It was named, rather unimaginatively, Brasserie Le Monge.

A not unpleasant odor of wine and espresso, strengthened by cigarette smoke, hit me as soon as Franck ushered me through the door.

Inside, just to the left of the entrance, we passed a glassed-in *tabac*, where patrons could replenish their stock of cigarettes and rolling papers and bags of tobacco and such. The television suspended from the ceiling in the corner of the room broadcasted a horse race.

Underneath the TV, there was a cash register with a large and peeling PMU sticker affixed to its front and a stack of betting forms and a Duralex glass full of stubby pencils to its side. So, patrons came to Brasserie Le Monge to buy cigarettes and bet on horses. Where exactly had Franck brought me?

He breathed a sigh of delight. *"Bien, dans son jus."*

The Brasserie Le Monge was indeed—as the French expression goes—"steeped in its juices." It was no bourgeois haunt, that much was certain.

The scuffed wooden floors told the story of decades of regulars passing through the door, taking time to indulge in anything from a quick espresso to a risky racing bet to a glass of house red.

The *prix fixe* menu was scribbled on a chalkboard propped up on the zinc bar: *salade frisée* with *lardons* and a poached egg; then cutlets of turkey in a cream mustard sauce, accompanied by *gratin dauphinois*; then the cheese platter; then a slice of *tropézienne* cake for dessert. It also included a *café* and a half liter of house wine. I planned to drink most of that myself.

We settled at a table by the front window looking out across the street. Franck simply ordered two *prix fixe* menus with rosé.

With some skepticism, I inspected the rusty bracket holding the TV dangling from the ceiling in the corner and the dusty, loud workmen trading bawdy jokes with the heavy-set bartender who stood behind the bar. He seemed to anchor down the entire joint.

Even if we were in Paris, the epicenter of gastronomic wonders, this was the sort of dive where the food would be terrible. Would it even be safe to eat?

"I'm not so sure about this place," I said to Franck.

"Are you kidding? It's fantastic. The food is going to be incredible."

I glanced over at the wizened woman perched on a stool behind the *tabac* glass. She looked as though she suffered from an intestinal worm. "What makes you so sure?"

"Two things," Franck said, leaning back in his wooden chair and admiring our surroundings. "First, the tradesmen eat and drink here. They are a more discerning judge of good food than any Michelin Guide restaurant critic." This maxim had proved true for Franck and me in the past.

"Second thing?" I asked.

"Look at the décor—"

"Or lack thereof."

"Exactly. This place is probably almost exactly as it was fifty years ago. No hoity-toity new owner has come to interfere with a winning formula."

I wasn't entirely convinced, but I did try to push aside my apprehensions that my lunch at Brasserie Le Monge came with a side serving of botulism.

The rosé came first, and Franck poured both himself and me a generous glass. It was the surest method of galvanizing myself for the dubious meal ahead.

The waiter came and poured us each a second glass and left an entire baguette on our table. Franck grinned.

"See?" He was so sure of himself. More sure of himself, in fact, than I had seen him during our past two years together in Montreal.

I felt disoriented in Paris, but Franck had never acted more at ease. It unsettled me to feel as though, all of a sudden, I was the vulnerable one in our relationship.

Also, we were only supposed to be spending one year in Paris. What if Franck liked it so much he wanted to stay instead of returning to Montreal with me?

I took a few more sips of my rosé to drown my doubts. For a house wine, it was lovely. Chilled and crisp, with a dryness many rosés lacked.

The waiter brought our salads over. With the first forkful, I concluded that Franck's hunch concerning the quality of the food was correct. The egg was poached to perfection and boasted a deep orange yolk. I had eaten the traditional *frisée* salad with warm goat's cheese on many occasions, but this was the first time I had eaten it paired with a poached egg. The homemade vinaigrette was heavy on the vinegar—just how I preferred it. Its bite was the perfect foil to the unctuousness of the egg. The *lardons*—rectangular cubes of bacon—tied the flavors together to perfection. By the time I finished the salad and two glasses of wine, I was far more sanguine about the rocky start of our Parisian adventure.

When I was devouring my turkey cutlet in Dijon mustard sauce, it dawned on me that there weren't many women in the restaurant, with the exception of the wiry specimen who manned the *tabac* booth. I watched in fascination as she prepared people's orders—a certain number of boxes of a specific brand of cigarettes or so many pouches of loose tobacco and rolling papers—most of the time without them even asking for anything. She seemed to know ahead of time what most of her clients needed and had a private joke or ribald set aside to share with everyone who bought her wares.

Franck and I were attracting our fair share of curious looks.

"Everyone here seems to know each other," I whispered to Franck.

Just then, the waiter, or *"garçon"* in the language of French *brasseries*, put a large slice of *tropézienne* cake in front of each of us. I picked up my spoon and savored the *brioche* pastry filled with thick buttercream and studded on the top with irregular chunks of sugar. It was clearly made in house, as every spoonful melted in my mouth.

"Feeling better?" Franck asked.

I nodded. "Better."

"It's normal that everyone in here knows each other," Franck explained. "That's what it's like in Paris. Each little pocket of streets is its own little village. People go to the same *boulangerie* every day. The same *poissonnerie*. The same—"

"*Brasserie*," I supplied.

"Exactly."

The well-padded bald man behind the bar spent his time serving drinks and lambasting the two *garçons*, who were dressed in the traditional black with long white aprons tied around their waists. They remained unruffled in the face of his haranguing.

I leaned back in my chair, sipping my *café* and reflecting on the notion that Paris is essentially made up of small neighborhoods. That certainly made the city less overwhelming.

"Before we can settle in a neighborhood," I said, "we need to find an apartment to rent."

The *garçon* brought our espressos accompanied by a small individually wrapped chocolate.

"Don't expect it to be anywhere as easy as it was in Montreal," Franck warned, not for the first time.

"I know," I said, but that didn't stop me from dreaming about finding the perfect nest for ourselves among the Parisian roof-tops sooner rather than later.

Franck had organized for us to stay with his cousin Florent and his cousin's girlfriend, Pauline, while we searched for a place of our own. It was generous of them, and it helped us not to have to stay in a cheap hotel or hostel.

Still, when we had dropped off our luggage there that morning after Florent picked us up at the Charles de Gaulle airport, I discovered their apartment was located in a gray, soulless commuter neighborhood. It was far enough out of central Paris to qualify as the *banlieue*—a word that specifically means "the distant suburbs."

There was nothing remotely charming or Parisian about our temporary home, I had noted during our quick pit-stop. Florent kept gushing to Franck about how they loved it, though—how they could get more space for their rent money in the *banlieue* and how they easily drove out of Paris without having to contend with the notorious Parisian traffic jams.

He dropped Franck and me off at the nearest RER station. Maybe it was because I was exhausted, but I found the hour-long commute from the *banlieue* to Madame Renier-Bernadotte's apartment unpleasant in the extreme. Even though the train wasn't overly crowded in the late morning, it was festooned with dried vomit, graffiti, and other mysterious substances adhered to the seats.

A whiff of gloom fought with guilt in my head. My brain and heart were acting like spoiled brats. I should have been feeling immense gratitude instead of an overwhelming sense of disillusion at our temporary accommodations. Everything just felt so unsettled.

Despite downing my thick espresso in one gulp, my eyelids began to droop. I wondered whether it was rude to lay my head down on the *brasserie* table and enjoy a little après-lunch nap.

"About an apartment"—I tapped my fingertips on our table, more to wake myself up than to get Franck's attention—"I don't care if it's the size of a postage stamp. Let's look only in the center of Paris."

"Trust me," Franck said, signaling with a cocked finger to the nearest *garçon* for the bill. "I don't want to be stuck in some godforsaken *banlieue*."

I breathed a sigh of relief at that. Still, I just didn't get the impression that Franck shared my sense of urgency. He, in fact, rarely shared my sense of urgency about anything unless it had to do with a perfect croissant or any of life's other pleasures.

"Where should we start?" I said. "Are there any real estate agencies we could visit while we're in this neighborhood?"

"That's not how it works."

"How do you know?"

"I just know. The only way to find a place in Paris is to know people."

"Who do we know?"

"Nathanael and Jacinthe," Franck said. "Did you forget that we're invited over to their place for dinner tonight?"

"I don't know if I can make it. You slept on the plane, but I haven't slept since we left Canada."

"I'm sure we'll get our second wind by then," Franck said.

"I'm on my tenth wind."

Franck studied my face, with sympathetic eyes. "If I could find you a bed right now, *chérie*, I would. I would even love to join you. The problem is we don't have a key to Florent and Pauline's, and I know they both get back late from work."

I had found it odd that neither of them had left a key for us, but probably it just wasn't practical, or maybe they had simply forgotten.

I felt a stab of regret that Franck's other cousin who used to live in Paris had moved to Bordeaux the previous year. He was extremely easy-going, as well as always traveling for work.

"We'll stop by some of the real estate places on the rue Monge as we go down to the boulevard Saint-Germain to get our Metro, d'accord?" Franck said, with a twist of his mouth broadcasting his belief that this activity would only be useful in that it might appease me.

"Okay." I looked out the *brasserie* window. The mid-afternoon sun was beating down on the gray pavement.

"If I know you like I think I know you, I suspect that might be the only way to get you to believe me that real estate agencies are not the way to find an apartment in Paris," Franck added.

"We'll see." I clinked my spoon against my espresso cup as if I was daring him.

chapter **three**

Back out on the rue Monge, waves of hot air still shimmered above the sidewalks.

"I'm starting to understand why everyone escapes Paris until the day school starts," I said as we headed toward the cool of the Seine, only a block away according to Franck.

"I love Paris in August," Franck said. "The city is so peaceful."

I coughed at the exhaust coming from the bumper-to-bumper cars on the rue Monge. "This is your version of peaceful?"

Franck stopped and wrapped me in a tight bear hug. "*Ah, ma petite Canadienne*, you have some adapting to do. Most countries don't have twenty square kilometers of tundra for each inhabitant like Canada."

Franck was joking, of course, but there was a kernel of truth in what he said. I had far more acclimatizing to do than my boyfriend. He was French, after all, and had lived in Paris for several years before we met. Again, I felt at a disadvantage.

"Aren't there all the tourists in Paris in August?" I said.

"They stay in certain areas and rarely venture beyond their

circuit. We won't be bothered by them. We'll be spending time at places the tourists don't know about."

"I like the sound of that."

Neither Franck nor I are from Paris, but neither of us considered ourselves tourists. Perhaps that was a kind of subtle snobbery, but my goal for the year was to become as comfortable in Paris as I was in Montreal or Vancouver, and as quickly as possible.

We neared a sign that read *Immobilier*, denoting a real estate agency. We stopped and I carefully read through the ads posted on the window. I rapidly found myself squinting.

The prices were more than triple our monthly rent back in Montreal. The few blurry and crooked photos looked as though they had been snapped in a Russian gulag, complete with holes in the ground where toilets should have been and bare lightbulbs suspended from crumbling ceilings with fraying electrical wire. Clearly, the notion of "staging" a property had not yet broached French shores.

We stopped in front of another agency that showed more of the same. At the third agency, just near the intersection with the rue des Écoles, I turned to Franck. "Let's go in and ask them. They must have more to show than what's taped on the windows."

Franck reached out and held me back. "Trust me on this, Laura. These rental agencies are a waste of our time."

"What time are we supposed to be at Jacinthe and Nathanael's for dinner?"

"Seven. They made it early for us because they knew we would be tired."

I checked my watch. "Time is one thing we have, then. It's just past four o'clock."

Franck raised his eyes skywards. "All right, but I'm going in just to humor you."

"Duly noted."

"I guarantee we won't find anything in there."

"I need proof." I pushed the door open.

There were two men inside the real estate agency. The one seated behind his desk was daring gravity by teetering back in his desk chair. He wore a royal blue shirt and a daffodil yellow tie under a fitted, black suit jacket. *Très chic.*

He was looking at something on his computer screen and laughing. His colleague was perched on the corner of the same desk, also peering down at the screen through large, plastic-framed glasses that were neon green—not a color one would often see on a North American man. He was also taking deep drags on a cigarette.

"*Bonjour,*" I said.

Franck showed no inclination of stepping forward.

At first, both men shared an identical grimace. It was clear that they would have rather continued their fun without being disturbed by pesky clients. Finally, the one with the lime green glasses hopped up at gave us a funny little bow. "*Bonjour,* Monsieur, Madame. How can I help you?"

"We just arrived in Paris, and we're looking for an apartment," I said.

Franck didn't add anything. He was, however, watching the exchange with a wry smile, as though he had decided to just enjoy the entertainment.

"*Oh là,*" the man said, walking across the room. He sat behind his desk and waved at us to sit down in two modern plastic chairs positioned in front. "That is going to be difficult. *Très, très difficile.* Not only is there almost nothing for rent but, you see, it is August."

"What happens in August?"

"*Justement.* You've put your finger on it. Nothing happens in August."

"Why?"

"Nobody's here."

"You're here," I pointed out. "And him." I jerked my head toward his colleague.

"But we don't want to be here," the colleague replied as though this fact was obvious. "We greatly resent being here, *en fait.* If we could be on the Côte d'Azur right now, we would be."

Although this example of Parisian customer service was worthy of comment, I was determined not to be sidetracked. "There must be *something*." I turned back to the man helping us. "You can't tell me that in this large neighborhood of Paris there is nothing available to rent."

"You'd be much better off if you waited until the end of September to start looking, or better yet, mid-October."

"How much better off?"

"Not much," he admitted.

"We need something *now*," I insisted, haunted by memories of the gray swaths of concrete in the *banlieue.*

He clicked his tongue. "Like I said. Difficult. Some would say *impossible.*"

"Yes," I said, my voice stony. "I get that."

I made the mistake of glancing over at Franck. His quivering mouth confirmed that he was enjoying a rare diversion indeed. I debated the merits of giving him a kick in the calf.

The agent, with a deep sigh, slid out a plastic binder from a drawer in his desk and began to flip through it. His expression was beleaguered, most likely because of the Herculean effort I was obliging him to make.

"What's your budget?" he asked.

I told him.

He just stared at me. "You must be joking."

"No."

"But that's impossible! If you are looking in the *banlieue* perhaps...I'm sorry, but we don't have any listings for—"

"We're not interested in the *banlieue*," I said. "We'd like to be in this neighborhood. Well, within walking distance to the Sorbonne Paris III and Paris IV, in any case."

He shot an expression of disbelief over my head at his colleague behind us. Then he folded his hands on his desktop and treated us to a lengthy exegesis on why what we were looking for was *introuvable*—that what we were looking for did not exist.

"*Introuvable*," his colleague echoed. "Completely *impossible*."

They spent several minutes relishing the high treat of bemoaning how there was literally not a single apartment for rent in this neighborhood within our budget. I had forgotten how shared commiseration is a honed skill in France. I never had much patience for it.

I stood up. "This is a waste of our time. *Au revoir*."

The real estate agent jerked back in his seat and tugged at his yellow tie. His eyes were wide, most likely because I had the audacity to interrupt such an enjoyable flow of lamentations. "Before you leave, let me show you a few apartments at least."

"Ah!" I turned to Franck, triumphant. "So, there *are* apartments! See?"

The man slid the binder in front of me and flipped to a page of photos. Just like the window photos, these were blurry and crooked. The apartment, from what I could see, had a toilet right in the middle of the only room. He flipped to another page, and then another. My mood descended rapidly from triumphant to despondent.

"These places aren't even fit for human habitation," I grumbled, when on the fifth apartment *fichier*, I noticed a gaping one-foot by one-foot ragged hole in the plaster of the apartment beside the cracked window. I could make out the sky and some clouds through the hole.

"Many of them are not," the agent agreed, regaining some of his former jubilation.

"Thanks for your time." I stood and left before anybody could stop me.

Franck joined me on the street after a minute or two, during which, I saw through the window, he'd been bidding a more civil good-bye to the two men.

Franck reached over and took my hand in his. "It's not their fault."

"His yellow tie was unforgiveable." I began stalking toward the Seine once again. This day was not going at all as anticipated.

Besides the delicious lunch, we had accomplished *nothing* of what we had set out to do.

Franck led us down a street called the rue des Fossés Saint-Bernard, which was, I thought pettishly, an unnecessarily long name for a street.

"I know where to take you to cool off," Franck said. "You *and* your temper."

My feet ached. I could feel a blister forming on the back of my left heel. I dashed away a tear that had begun to form in my eye. "Whatever."

We walked past a strange modern development on one side of the street, and then about halfway down, I caught a glimpse of the Seine. The air didn't get any cooler near the water. It felt as though we were trudging through a steam oven.

"This is where Jacinthe and Nathanael live, so we'll be right near their apartment for dinner tonight."

At the end of the street, there was a shiny modern building that was made up of square glass and metal panels with intricate designs in each panel.

"What is this place?" I asked Franck.

"It's the Arab World Institute. Do you see those metal designs within the squares?" He pointed to the exterior of the building.

"Yeah."

"They are oculi that shift during the day depending on the amount of sunlight. Isn't that cool?"

"That *is* kind of cool."

"Come on." Franck took my arm and led me inside.

"We're allowed to go in?" I asked.

"Of course. It's a museum and a cultural center. It's open to everybody."

The space inside was just as beautiful as the outside, but Franck ushered me into the glass elevator and pushed the button for the top floor.

"Where are we—?"

"*Shhhhhh.*" Franck patted my shoulder. "You'll see."

At the roof level, he led me out onto a huge, whitewashed terrace filled with tables shaded by large, white sun umbrellas. Wooden benches topped with a multitude of brightly colored pillows were scattered around. An oasis in the middle of Paris... A breeze ruffled the bedraggled strands of hair on my forehead.

"Wow," I said.

"Before we sit down, come here." Franck drew me close to the wall at the edge of the patio, which went up to my mid-torso. I looked out to the vista of Paris spread out before me. The Seine sparkled in between all the *quais* and the bridges. The massive buttresses and spires of Notre-Dame on the Île de la Cité were the glorious centerpiece of our vista.

"This is one of my secret spots. See? No tourists." Franck stood behind me and encircled my waist with his hands. "When Paris becomes overwhelming down there"—his hand swept to encompass the streets clogged with cars below and the honks that now sounded far away—"just go up."

I hated being such a newbie in Paris, but I was suddenly tired of fighting that reality. "You're an excellent guide," I said to Franck, then leaned back into his chest and just enjoyed the beauty and the solid sensation of his arms around me.

chapter **four**

Between sipping our mint tea on the rooftop of the Arab World Institute and arriving at Nathanael and Jacinthe's for dinner, we didn't do anything strenuous. Franck could tell that I was near my breaking point.

After a good couple of hours lounging and cooling off above Paris, we walked over one of the nearest bridges across the Seine to Notre-Dame cathedral. It was blessedly cool and quiet inside, with the exception of clusters of tourists on guided tours. The space was so cavernous, however, that it never felt crowded.

As for me, as much as I loved admiring the stained glass windows and the myriad of Virgin Mary statues, the thing I really wanted to do was curl up on a pew and sleep.

By the time we retraced our steps and arrived at the door of Nathanael and Jacinthe's apartment building just across the street from the Arab World Institute, I felt as though my body had collided with an unforgiving brick wall of exhaustion.

I never had been able to sleep in airplanes, whereas Franck always slept on them. How was I going to make it through dinner?

I knew Nathanael from my time in Burgundy just after Franck and I had met, but I hadn't met Jacinthe yet. I wanted to make a good impression—I had no friends in Paris and I wanted to remedy that. It wouldn't be good for my relationship with Franck to content myself with being dependent on him for a social life.

We were buzzed into the building and, like a sleepwalker, I followed Franck into one courtyard and then another. I was beyond noticing much about the surroundings.

We walked up what seemed like an endless spiral of stairs until we arrived at an open door. Nathanael emerged, unchanged from the last time I had seen him.

"Laura! Franck!" He kissed us both warmly on the cheeks. Franck and Nathanael were good enough friends to greet each other that way, instead of with a handshake. Their friendship was yet another reason why I wanted to make a good first impression on Jacinthe.

"Our place isn't big," he warned us as he ushered us into a narrow hallway. "But we'll go into the main room."

As the hallways turned into the main room, I staggered and bumped against the wall. Two salt sculptures that looked Alsatian or German and had been hanging there fell to the wooden floor and shattered.

A slim blond woman came out of the bedroom, still in the process of twisting up her hair.

"I'm so sorry." I covered my mouth. I dropped to my knees and began picking up the pieces of the hardened salt dough. *Maybe I could glue them together?* But the pieces were shattered, crumbling, and plentiful. There was little hope of resurrecting them…or my future friendship with Jacinthe.

Jacinthe stood staring down at me for a second, her blue eyes a few shades paler than before.

I broke out in a cold sweat. *Nice first impression, Laura.*

"Don't worry about that." Jacinthe came over beside me and motioned at me to get up off her floor. "It's fine. *Vraiment.*"

"Just tell me where you bought them, and I can buy you new ones." I stood up, my hands filled with the pieces.

"My mother made them."

Franck had told me that Jacinthe's mother had passed away after a sudden illness just five or six months previously. I couldn't seem to find the words for how bad I felt, but I had to try. "I feel terrible—"

"Don't. I shouldn't have hung them there. It wasn't a good spot."

Especially when you have a foreigner lurching around your apartment. Mortification robbed me of my French, reducing my words to an incoherent babble of apologies and self-recrimination.

Franck gently transferred the crumbling chunks out of my hands and pushed me down in one of the four red chairs set around the round wooden table.

He disappeared and returned shortly after with his hands empty. "Laura didn't sleep much during the trip." Franck gave *les bises* to Jacinthe. "She hasn't slept much since we left Canada, actually."

"*Ma pauvre.*" Jacinthe gave me *les bises* with surprising warmth. She disappeared into the kitchen and returned with a bottle of Champagne. "This should help. Champagne helps *everything.*" She smiled at me and I smiled back. She was exceedingly kind, but that didn't change the fact that I felt like a complete ass.

"Franck told me that you work for Moët & Chandon, the Champagne company?" I said, trying to muster up my company manners.

"I do," she said. "The work is interesting, but the best thing is it seems that I have a limitless supply of Champagne left over from events at my disposal. Everyone who works there enjoys that perk."

"I'll bet."

Franck sat down beside me. "Nathanael told me that your office is on the Champs-Élysées?" he said.

"*Oui.* It's quite beautiful. I'll have to take you and Laura there and give you the tour sometime."

Unbelievable. She is actually contemplating seeing me again? Didn't I just completely torpedo my chance to make a new friend?

"We'd love that," Franck said.

Jacinthe put her flute down on the edge of the table. "Go ahead and open the Champagne, Nathanael. Before I sit down with you, I just need to check on the roast and grab something from the kitchen."

Nathanael settled in across from me. "So, the prodigal Canadian intellectual returns."

"I'm not an intellectual."

"What are you studying at the Sorbonne this year?"

"Medieval French, mostly."

Nathanael popped the cork out of the Champagne bottle. "I rest my case."

"Shut up," I said, but with a grin.

He filled the four flutes and then handed one to me. "I wasn't sure when Franck left to be with you in Montreal that I was ever going to see him again."

"I'm learning you can't ever truly take the France out of a Frenchman," I said, and embellished this remark with a dramatic sweep of my arm that knocked the flute Nathanael was in the process of filling for Jacinthe off the table.

Franck's hand flashed out. A bit of the Champagne sloshed on the floor, but Franck set the flute upright again and leaned down and mopped up the puddle with his napkin.

Franck let out the breath he'd obviously been holding. "*Décidément.*" This meant, in one concise French word, that I was more than unusually klutzy. I was still speechless over my boyfriend's breathtaking reflexes, but Franck gave me a knowing wink. I smiled to myself, with the secret elation I had found someone who found most of my failings endearing rather than irritating.

"*Ni vu, ni connu.*" Nathanael put a finger against his lips. *I didn't see anything, so I can't know anything.*

I dropped my head into my hands. "I'm a disaster. I'm not fit to be in anything but a rubber room with nothing breakable inside."

Nathanael peered into my face. "You *do* look exhausted. I can't remember when I've ever seen such tired eyes. Do you want to lie down on our bed?"

"More than anything," I said. "But then you'll never be able to wake me up again." Besides, Jacinthe had obviously gone to the trouble of preparing a nice dinner for us. It would insult every notion of French hospitality to miss it completely. I drank my Champagne, and even through my fatigue, its deliciousness registered. Maybe the little bubbles would perk me up.

They did, for a while.

I enjoyed my second wind through the first course of home-made zucchini-and-basil soup, and through the red wine, and most of the way through a beautiful *rôti de boeuf* with an ancient grain mustard sauce soaked up by fingerling potatoes.

I was halfway through my second glass of red wine and my fifth forkful of potatoes when I hit the wall for the final time.

My eyelids and head dropped. I couldn't stay awake a moment longer. I felt immense relief when my head hit the table. The prongs of my fork were digging into my cheek, but that didn't mar the utter bliss of falling into a deep, dreamless sleep.

I was woken up by Franck's hand shaking my shoulder, hard. I heard a strange grunting sound that might have come out of my mouth. My head jerked up from the table, followed by a thread of drool. *Where am I?*

Franck's hand wiped my mouth. "You've been drooling," he said. "We've been trying to wake you up for the last five minutes. We thought we'd lost you to oblivion."

"*Quoi?*"

I looked down at my place setting and noticed a large wet splotch on the tablecloth and little rolled up balls of the yellow paper napkins Jacinthe had set her table with.

"We may have been trying to wake you with napkin balls," Nathanael admitted.

"I tried to stop them," Jacinthe said.

Had I just fallen asleep in the middle of the nice dinner she had prepared? "Did I snore?"

Jacinthe and Nathanael merely exchanged glances, but Franck said, "Loudly."

"Oh God."

Franck put my denim jacket around my shoulders. "Nathanael is going to drive us back to Pauline and Florent's."

"Thank you," I said. "I know it's far and—"

"Don't mention it." Nathanael waved my words away. "There's no way we could let you take the RER in such a state. You'd be robbed blind."

Franck shuffled me out. "I'm so sorry," I called back to Jacinthe over my shoulder. "For...you know, for me this evening."

"Don't worry about it." Jacinthe came over and gave me the *bises* by the doorway. "You need to sleep. I'll see you the day after tomorrow."

I had no idea what she was talking about, but I would find out...*after* I slept.

chapter five

The next day was a Saturday. After waking up on the click-clack, the fold-down couch, in the middle of Florent and Pauline's living room, we decided we would spend the day seeing if we could help Florent and Pauline around their apartment.

Pauline sent us for groceries with a long list, and we bought exactly what she wanted, even though it took us a while. We paid for it all ourselves. Even though we were shocked at the price of food in Paris compared to Montreal, we wanted to contribute to expenses. After all, we were sleeping in their living room.

Florent and Pauline's place was small, like most Parisian accommodation. It consisted of their bedroom, a tiny bathroom, a tiny kitchen that could only fit two people, and a living room with the couch-slash-bed we were sleeping on.

The day passed quickly. We vacuumed the floors, did some laundry, and organized ourselves for the week to come. As we were folding laundry, mostly Florent and Pauline's, Franck told me that he had arranged for us to go into Paris the next day to help Jacinthe paint their new apartment. She and Nathanael were leaving their little *pied-à-terre* on the rue des Fossés Saint-Bernard and had just signed a lease for a more spacious apartment on the bourgeois Right Bank, he explained. The entire conversation about that must have occurred over my sleeping, snoring self the night before.

"It was rude last night to fall asleep, wasn't it?" I said, folding up a pair of Pauline's tiny lace underwear.

"It was…let's say…unconventional."

"I don't know how I'm ever going to look Jacinthe in the face again."

Franck put the T-shirt he had just folded onto the bed and wrapped me in a hug. Being in his arms and surrounded by his familiar scent made me feel at home, even in this new, bewildering place.

"You were powerless against it," he murmured into my hair. "What could you have done? Besides, you were highly entertaining."

"Why? Because I was sleeping?"

"Yes, well…you fell asleep in the middle of your plate. I had to move your head to the tablecloth, and we cleaned off the sauce and squished potatoes out of your hair. There was the snoring. Also, the napkin ball game we devised was *très amusant.*"

I rolled my eyes. "So, I was, in fact, the life of the party."

"Yes."

"Fabulous."

Franck squeezed me tighter. "Don't worry about it. They're our friends. They won't hold it against us." He kissed my neck just below my earlobe.

"Jacinthe isn't my friend yet. After last night, I highly doubt she'll ever want to be."

"I'm not so sure. In any case, if you do become friends, you will know for sure it's sincere. Look at it this way, your presence is extremely refreshing to all the Parisians. You're different."

"That's for sure," I agreed, not at all convinced, unlike Franck, that this was a good thing.

Pauline came into the room and squealed. "Look at you two!

So in love! So adorable! Franck, you just can't keep your hands off her, *n'est-ce pas?*" Pauline was small and, I was ashamed to say, too perky for my taste.

"No," Franck said, then proceeded to demonstrate by squeezing me tighter and giving me a kiss.

I slid away to continue the folding. There was something about Pauline that made me squirm—a saccharine sweetness that struck me as insincere. This realization gave me a surge of guilt for being such an inwardly ungracious guest. *She is letting us sleep in her living room*, I reminded myself. *She might be part of Franck's family one day.*

At around six thirty, Pauline disappeared into the kitchen.

I followed her. "What can I do to help?"

She was taking bowls of things out of the fridge. "The kitchen isn't big enough for both of us." She shooed me out with a flap of her hand, without looking at me, her voice completely different than when she had found Franck and me entwined. "I'm the lady of the house."

I laughed. "Trust me, I have no interest in being the lady of any house but my own." Even then, I was hardly what you would call the domestic type. When Franck arrived in Montreal, he had been disconcerted to discover the only thing I knew how to cook was tuna melts.

"Good," Pauline answered, shooting me a combative look.

I walked back into the living room, confused. She had been odd that afternoon, whispering things to Florent and pulling him into closed rooms. I kept feeling that we weren't exactly welcome. Perhaps she had been strong-armed into having us by Florent's mother, who was a leader of the extended family and a forceful woman.

Florent, I knew from my dealing with him in the past, was not the type of person who would go out of his way to make anyone feel at ease. I could never decide whether Florent was socially awkward or just couldn't be bothered to put himself out for others. He began to play a video game, while Franck and I sat on the couch and cracked open a book each. Maybe Florent didn't even *notice* other people.

Franck went outside to have a smoke, and I grabbed my book and followed. We sat on a beaten-up wooden bench on the far side of the pea gravel courtyard. Franck had found a rusted Orangina can to use as an ashtray.

"Is Florent always like that?" I asked.

"Like what?"

"Like he just does what he feels like doing and doesn't feel any social obligation to make small talk or interest himself in others?"

Franck ruminated on this for a minute or two. "I guess. That's just Florent. Does it bother you?"

"It makes me feel like we're in the way."

"I wouldn't think of it like that. If he had to pay attention to us, then we *would* be in the way for Florent. Seeing as he can just treat us like we're invisible when he wants to…I think for Florent that means that we're not inconveniencing him."

I tried to work that out. I had been brought up with the idea that no matter how unsocial I was feeling, it behooved me to act pleasant. However, I had learned a valuable lesson during my first year in France when I was an exchange student hosted by the Ursus Club of Beaune. There is such a thing as being too compliant, and sometimes it is impossible to make myself and others happy. Sometimes, I have to choose. I had chosen Franck, our possible future together, and my happiness, even though it left many of my Ursus hosts angry and disappointed with me.

Pauline appeared in the doorway to the courtyard. "Yoo-hoo! What do you think?"

I blinked. What in the name of all that was Holy was she wearing?

When I had last seen her in the kitchen, she had been wearing jeans and a tight T-shirt. Now she was kitted out in a sheer, red net teddy trimmed with black lace, complete with scanty, red net underwear, red garters, and red fishnet stockings.

She executed a turn for us so that we could take in the full glory of her outfit. "À table!" she said. "Dinner is ready." She disappeared back inside.

Franck and I remained speechless for a few seconds.

"Did I imagine that?" I finally asked Franck.

"No. I wish you had, but *non*."

"What the—?"

"No idea…none whatsoever."

I couldn't seem to get up from the bench. "I'm scared to go inside."

"Me too."

After several minutes, Franck got up and pulled me to standing.

"We really need to get our own place," I said.

"Agreed."

We reluctantly went back inside. Florent was sitting at the table, looking more interested in the food his wife was bringing in from the kitchen than her lingerie.

I recognized the platter full of Mémé Germaine's quiches immediately by their beautiful crusts and heavenly scent. Franck's grandmother rarely let her grandchildren leave after a visit without several bags of her frozen individual quiches to take home with them.

Pauline had whipped up a *salade frisée* to go with it, which was, of course, the perfect accompaniment. She was a good cook. I wondered if wearing lingerie was the secret ingredient to her vinaigrette.

Once she had put the salad bowl on the table and handed Florent the serving tongs, she executed another little spin in front of me. "What do you think?" she asked.

I didn't know where to look. "Um…well…I honestly don't know what to think."

"But you must recognize where it's from!"

My best guess would have been Adult Film Stars R' Us, but I didn't really want to say that out loud.

"You *must* know," she urged, her voice tinged with impatience.

Why on earth would she think that? I looked at my denim cut-offs and linen tunic top. *Is she blind?*

"I have no idea," I said. "I don't own anything remotely like…that."

"I was sure you would know, being American."

"I'm Canadian, remember?"

She gave a pettish shrug. "Poor Franck. Men love this kind of lingerie, you know. You have to make an *effort*, Laura."

I glanced at Franck, whose face displayed the same horror I felt. Florent was intent on serving himself salad. Neither of the men present appeared captivated by her outfit.

"It's from Frederick's of Hollywood!" she said, doing an odd sort of curtsy. "Isn't it amazing? So *American*. Don't you have anything from Frederick's of Hollywood?"

"No."

"Are you sure?" she prodded.

"Absolutely."

"How is that possible?" She pouted.

"A gross oversight on my part, I suppose."

The only vague association I could make with Frederick's of Hollywood was to do with porn. With all the beautiful lingerie available in France—you could buy La Perla bras in the grocery store, for heaven's sakes—why would anyone would want to send to America for such vulgar stuff?

"The package just arrived yesterday."

Her outfit looked highly flammable—I considered warning her to watch herself near the gas stove in the tiny kitchen.

"My sister sent it to me."

It started to make sense. Pauline and her entire family idolized her younger sister who had left France to live out her version of the American dream. She was a trained hairdresser and was now working as a hair stylist and drove a Harley-Davidson. Apparently, she also favored lingerie from Frederick's of Hollywood, which was far more information than I ever wanted to know about anyone.

I studied Florent. He was intent on cutting up his quiche. Maybe he was the reason why Pauline felt she needed to serve dinner in her underwear to get attention.

Franck was casting furtive glances between Florent and me while studiously avoiding looking at Pauline. His lips were twitching now. *Please don't let him laugh.* I had no idea how Pauline would react if he did, but I had a feeling it wouldn't be good.

Luckily, Mémé's quiches were delicious. Trust her to save the day from afar.

I asked a lot of polite questions about Pauline's sister and about how she was doing, and about Pauline's own job in tourism, promoting the Vosges region of France to Parisians.

Florent finished his first quiche, then reached over and took another and polished that off too. He got up and disappeared into the kitchen, emerging with a plastic container of French pudding called Danette—beloved by elementary school children all over France. He literally had not said a single word before or during dinner.

He scooped his pudding with his spoon directly from the container, devouring it, without asking anyone if they wanted any. He left his dishes on the table, then went back to playing his video game. I felt sorry for Pauline, sitting there, ignored, all trussed up in her negligee.

"We'll take care of the dishes." I reached over and patted Pauline's hand. "Thank you for dinner. It was delicious. You go relax."

"Really?" she said, her eyes wide with genuine surprise. She acted as though she was used to getting zero help from Florent. I felt even more sorry for her.

The dishes didn't take long, and after they were done, I suggested a walk to Franck to escape the bizarro world we had unwittingly entered. Maybe Pauline and Florent needed some time on their own. Maybe Pauline's plan was to seduce Florent? I wasn't sure, but if it was, the poor girl had an uphill climb ahead of her.

I considered floating the idea of searching for a hotel in Paris to Franck, but then remembered we didn't have the money.

Once we had exhausted the topic of Pauline's behavior, we traced the deserted streets for a long time, encountering the odd stray cat but not much else. Unlike Paris itself, this neighborhood seemed to have no cafés or restaurants, and no kebab shops, even.

"So…painting at Jacinthe's tomorrow?" I said.

"Yep," Franck said.

"Can't wait. Normal people."

"Yes," Franck agreed. "Normal people would be a refreshing change of pace."

But then I wondered—after the way I had acted at their place the night before, would Jacinthe consider *me* a normal person?

chapter **six**

The next day, we took the long RER ride from the *banlieue* to the place du Trocadéro, a large tiled plaza that commanded a majestic view of the Eiffel Tower. Unbelievably, Jacinthe and Nathanael's apartment was only a stone's throw from this spectacular Parisian view.

It was still early. We had fled the apartment before Pauline and Florent emerged from their bedroom. My mind was still trying to make sense of their behavior, but all I could conclude was, whatever their reasons, the atmosphere of their apartment made me squirm.

All the buildings in the *quartier* we were now in were significantly more majestic than the neighborhood where we had been trying to buzz down Professor Renier-Bernadotte.

There, the people were different too. There was a profusion of chicly dressed women with dyed blond hair, carrying small dogs in Louis Vuitton or Prada bags. They all wore heels (the women, not the dogs). Dog poop festooned the sidewalks.

"Nathanael is sick at the idea of living on the Right Bank," Franck said as we walked along their street, hand in hand, searching for their apartment building.

"Really? How do you know that?"

"He told me two nights ago when he was driving us home from dinner at their place. You were fast asleep beside me, deaf to the world."

"What could Nathanael possibly have against this neighborhood? It's gorgeous."

"He would far rather live in seedy squalor on the Left Bank. This move will seriously dent his image as a bohemian anarchist intellectual."

Franck's friend Nathanael—who he had met when they attended the Sorbonne together—had always been ambitious, and that ambition had quickly fixed on TV. He had moved quickly up the ranks and was now what they called *un grand reporter* in France—a roving journalist who was flown in to various war-torn countries and countries in crisis to report. Nathanael thrived on the element of danger and the implied heroism of his job.

"In Paris, whether you live on the Right Bank or the Left Bank is important," Franck said.

True, the privileged and staid feel of the Rive droite did not exactly scream "rebel journalist."

As for Jacinthe, however, it made complete sense on the surface that she would live on the Rive droite. She worked as an *attachée de presse* for a luxury Champagne company. Her job consisted of organizing and attending events, such as the introduction of the new Champagne vintage on a boat in the Seine and the Louis- Vuitton show during Paris fashion week. All of that fit in perfectly with the Right Bank. It also made me feel more than a little intimidated to see her again.

Franck found their building, which boasted an ornate metal doorway that must have been ten feet tall. It was painted with a fresh coat of shiny black.

He found their name on the buzzer panel and rang.

A few seconds later, Jacinthe's voice crackled through the intercom. *"Allô?"*

"It's us," Franck said. "I hope you have paintbrushes for us."

"Génial! Montez!" She buzzed us in.

We walked through the passageway where the caretaker, or *"gardienne,"* had her apartment, then came out into a sunny courtyard.

"Coucou! Up here!" I shaded my eyes to look up and saw Jacinthe waving down at us from a window on the fourth floor. "I'll wait for you at the top of the elevator!"

"Quiet down!" an old voice emanated from another one of the windows—it was a muggy day and they were all open.

I thought I could see Jacinthe rolling her eyes even from that distance. "As you can see, there are far too many *vieilles peaux* who live here!" she exclaimed down to us, obviously making no effort to quiet her voice.

I stifled a laugh. *"Vieille peau"* is a highly derogatory insult to crotchety elderly people, translating directly as "old skin." I was starting to revise my previous conclusion…maybe Jacinthe didn't entirely fit the profile of the Right Bank either.

"That's a singular method of making friends with her new neighbors," I said to Franck.

He laughed. "That's one of the reasons I missed France so much," he said. "You don't have to be polite if you don't feel so inclined."

This was only one of many such "why I love being back in France" comments Franck had made since landing in Paris. We had both wanted to come back to France for a year, but Franck's motivations were different than mine. After struggling for two years to find his place in Montreal, he missed his homeland. Once again, I pushed away my fear that after another taste of French life, Franck might not want to make the trek back to Montreal when the school year was over.

We made our way into the second lobby, which was tiled with blue and yellow tiles in an intricate pattern. It was lovely and cool in there compared to outdoors—it was shaping up to be a hot day for painting.

A winding staircase to our right, covered with a plush, red carpet running down the middle, beckoned us upstairs. In the circular heart of the staircase, there was an old-fashioned, open cage-type elevator that looked as though it dated back to the same era as the Eiffel Tower.

"Do you think it's safe?" I wondered out loud as Franck pushed back the accordion metal door. Getting stuck in an elevator was just one in my stable of irrational fears.

"They do get stuck sometimes," he admitted. "They're old, but it's an open cage. If you scream loud enough and long enough someone will hear you eventually."

I supposed his words were meant to be reassuring.

He clanged the door shut and pressed number four on the old-fashioned keypad. With a series of unnerving clicks and squeaks the elevator slowly carried us upwards.

Jacinthe, as promised, was waiting for us on the *palier*, or "landing," of the fourth floor. She gave us *les bises*. "Did you finally get a decent sleep?" she asked me, sounding sympathetic.

"Yes. I don't think I'd ever been that exhausted in my whole life. Again, my apologies for my trail of carnage."

"Franck explained that you had spent the whole day apartment hunting and trying to track down your contact at school as soon as you got off your flight. You shouldn't have allowed that," she said to Franck, a challenging look in her eye. "What were you thinking?"

"But Laura insisted," Franck said.

"That's no excuse," she said. She looped her arm through mine and ignored his protest. "I can't believe we get you for a whole year," she said to me as she led us along the carpeted hallway toward their new apartment. "How is it working out staying with Florent and Pauline?"

I thought of the Frederick's of Hollywood dinner ensemble. "Educational," I said.

I so badly wanted to regale Jacinthe with the epic weirdness of the night before. I could just tell she would enjoy the absurdity of the whole situation. Still, I hesitated. I didn't know Jacinthe that well yet. Besides, Pauline and Florent *were* allowing us sleep on their couch. I also didn't want to embarrass Franck by gleefully gossiping about his family, as tempting as it was. Still, the need to share a good laugh with Jacinthe over the Pauline escapade almost won out.

"Fine, I guess," I said. "It's just a long way back and forth to their place." I felt a spark of pride at my restraint.

"Ugh," Jacinthe said, opening up an ornate, white door with her key. "I can't imagine living out there in the *banlieue. Quelle horreur.*"

We stepped into a large, bright apartment. Half the wallpaper was scraped off the walls. A good thing, as what remained was an orange-and-chartreuse floral that had accumulated years of tobacco stains and other substances that I decided I would rather not know about.

"As you can see, *on a du pain sur la planche*," Jacinthe said. She opened sliding doors to an equally big room. She was right about having the work of a Trojan ahead of them. This room had ugly wallpaper too—wide, yellow and purple stripes—but only one strip of wallpaper had been removed so far.

"This *was* the room Nathanael was working on." Jacinthe sounded exasperated. "He was sent to cover some stories in Bosnia yesterday. Although he tried hard not to act relieved, he was fooling no one. Turns out he'd much rather be shot at by snipers than scrape off old wallpaper."

I laughed appreciatively at that.

"Don't worry," Franck said. "We'll help you. Laura and I have done this before." We'd already renovated two student ghetto-style apartments in Montreal.

"You two are saving my life." She squeezed my arm.

I clapped my hands together. "OK then. Show us where we can start."

She led me into the bathroom, where a large pail of paint, a roller, a painting dish, and a few paintbrushes sat, untouched. The walls in there weren't so bad. They were just painted a white that had turned grungy over time.

Jacinthe used a wooden stir stick to open the can of paint. A beautiful pale mauve color was inside. I let out an involuntary sigh. "That's one of my favorite colors. So calm."

"I'm glad to hear you say that. The person in the paint store made some comments about it, and I started to have my doubts. Can you start painting in here?"

"Sure," I said. "But first, do you want me to do the ceiling?" I had learned the hard way that ceilings always had to be painted before the walls. This ceiling was high—about ten feet tall. It would require a ladder and a large pole that I could stick the roller onto—it would be awkward and messy.

"The ceiling looks fine to me." Jacinthe shrugged. "No need to paint it."

I was happy to hear that. The ceiling looked quite clean, at least from my distance.

"It's fine," Jacinthe said once more, as if trying to convince herself.

"Yes. Besides, who spends their time looking up at ceilings anyway?"

"*Exactement.*" Jacinthe nodded.

"Leave me to it."

Jacinthe went out to Franck, and I could hear them confer about the best way of tackling the main two rooms. I checked that the paint was oil based so that it didn't need an undercoat, then dipped the finest tipped brush in and began painting a straight edge above the high floorboards.

chapter **seven**

My mind wandered in that aimless, pleasant way it did when I was absorbed in painting. It was a wonderful antidote to the chaos of the previous few days.

I wondered idly how much Nathanael and Jacinthe had to pay in rent for this place per month. It was not only in a wonderful neighborhood but was also spacious as far as Parisian apartments went. I couldn't ask Jacinthe, though. People in France generally find discussing the topic of money ill-bred as well as boring.

I felt another stab of longing for a place for us to settle in Paris so we could truly start *living* there.

Would Paris be a city where I might want to make a permanent home? Of course, there was the problem of having to go back to Montreal to finish off my fourth and final year of my undergraduate degree at McGill. *But if Franck decides he wants to stay here after this year is up...*

That year was not only a crossroads for me but also a critical juncture for my relationship with Franck. That scared me.

Fully absorbed by the myriad of directions my life could take,

I lost track of time until Jacinthe came into the bathroom, followed by another woman with pursed lips and hair pinned back in a chignon so tight it made her eyes slant.

"Laura!" Jacinthe surveyed my progress. "I can't believe you've painted so much already!"

I gazed around me. I had painted three walls during my ruminations. "I must be on a roll," I said as I stood up and stretched. My jean shorts, T-shirt, and hands were festooned with mauve paint. I smiled at Jacinthe's friend, but she glared back at me with what looked like suspicion.

"This is Alexandrine Montdidier." Jacinthe introduced me. Alexandrine raised an expectant brow. Expectant of what?

I leaned forward to give her *les bises* at the same time as she stuck out her hand. I'd passed the point of no return with *les bises* and, besides, my hand was covered with wet paint. Alexandrine accepted *mes bises* like a fourteenth-century martyr. What could she and Jacinthe possibly have in common?

"Franck just told me that you guys are looking for an apartment," Jacinthe said. "Do you think you might be interested in the place we're moving out of?"

I had been so exhausted that night that I couldn't conjure up many memories of their current place. Still, the location would be perfect. It was walking distance to school and Notre-Dame and the Seine...

My imagination took off, and I envisioned Franck and me waking up in the apartment to rain splattering on the windows and the bells of Notre-Dame ringing.

"It could be *exactly* what we need."

Alexandrine rolled her eyes. "Your tiny place on the rue des Fossé Saint-Bernard?" she said to Jacinthe. "Who in their right mind would want to live there?"

"We would," I said.

"The Marais or Montmartre are the only decent places to live in Paris." Alexandrine sniffed. The address of Nathanael and Jacinthe's new apartment didn't fall within these parameters. Alexandrine was not known, I imagined, for her diplomacy.

"Luckily not everyone's looking for the same thing," I said. "I want to walk to school, and your place would be perfect."

"You're still in *school*?" Alexandrine stared at me as if I had just said I dine on small children for breakfast.

"Yes."

"Laura's quite the intellectual." Jacinthe smiled at me. "She's in her third year of university, and this year she'll be studying medieval French. Can you believe that? It puts my two years of business school to shame. You didn't do any higher studies either, did you Alexandrine?"

I was overcome with affection for Jacinthe.

"Well…we'll see how it goes." I laughed.

"Medieval French? *Vraiment?*" Alexandrine looked at me with disbelief. She lit a cigarette. "Why on earth would you want to do that? *C'est complètement bizarre.*"

"We Canadians are strange," I answered airily. "I don't know how to explain it to a *Parisienne*. Anyway, I should get back to painting before I lose my momentum."

Jacinthe shot me an apologetic look. "Alexandrine has come over to help too." She took Alexandrine's arm and steered her out of the bathroom. "Let's see what we can find you to do in the other rooms. Laura seems to be fending just fine for herself in here."

I sighed with relief when Jacinthe closed the door behind her. Hopefully, most of the people I would meet in Paris would be like Jacinthe, not Alexandrine, I thought. But Jacinthe wasn't originally from Paris, I reminded myself. Did that make a difference?

As I applied more of the beautiful mauve paint, my mind circled back to Franck.

The four months we had been separated between the time I left Burgundy after my exchange year and Franck moved to Montreal were torture—the doubt that we would find a way to be together, the longing, the miscommunications on the phone…

There were some great things too—getting letters in the mail and preparing packages to send him, then that wonderful day when I went to pick him up at the Mirabel airport…and the days, weeks, and months after we were reunited.

But could we last a whole year on different continents?

I was still excited about our year in Paris, but now, over top of the excitement shimmered the worry of what would happen with Franck and me at its end.

I jumped in surprise when Franck opened the door to the bathroom.

He surveyed my handiwork. "Looks fantastic. You haven't lost your touch."

"*Merci*. What have you been doing?"

"Stripping wallpaper in the kitchen. I swear to God, they used the blood of sacrificial goats, or maybe superglue, to stick it on."

"Slow going?"

Franck nodded.

I motioned at him to shut the door. When he did, I whispered, "Is Alexandrine still here?"

"Yes."

"Did you meet her?"

"Of course," Franck said.

"Was she a total cow to you too?"

"Not really...wait...you *do* know who she is, right?"

I put down my paintbrush in the roller dish. "Besides a cow?"

"You mean you don't recognize her name?"

"Should I?" I asked.

"Her father is one of the most famous men in France."

So *that* explained her expectant look when we had been introduced.

"Benoît Montdidier?" Franck said. "The name means nothing to you?"

I shrugged. "Nope. Nada."

Franck stared down at me as if he couldn't believe what he was hearing.

I was always amazed and entertained by French people's assumption that the fame of French celebrities spread far beyond France.

"He's probably the most famous living French philosopher at the moment. He has a TV show called *Grandes Pensées*. All the greatest writers and intellectuals are invited as guests, but Montdidier himself is probably more famous than any of them."

I pulled myself up and perched on the rim of the white, iron bathtub. "Definitely never heard of him. I can't say my first impression of his daughter was good though."

"She is a typical Parisian bourgeois. I was disappointed; she seems nothing like her father. He comes across as warm and *sympathique* on TV."

"She was the opposite of charming to me."

"I'm sorry." Franck sat beside me on the bathtub and slipped his arm around my shoulder. "If I had known, I wouldn't have let you deal with that alone."

"It's OK. I'm tough."

Franck pulled me closer to him. "I know."

"I looked up at him. "What do you think Jacinthe sees in her as a friend?"

Franck shrugged. "People are mysterious. Also, we don't know Jacinthe well, yet."

I loved what I knew so far, but Alexandrine gave me doubts that maybe my first impression had been wrong. But then, who was I to be going on first impressions? Thank God Jacinthe hadn't.

"What does Jacinthe have her working on?" I asked, amused at the idea of what would happen to Alexandrine's chignon if she was truly put to work.

"Actually, it's rather amusing. Jacinthe is ripe for murder."

"I need details," I said.

"She told me that Alexandrine insisted she wanted to come over and help, but instead of stripping the wallpaper, she's been wandering around the apartment criticizing everything."

"Ha! Poor Jacinthe, though…"

"When she's not criticizing, she's suggesting a constant stream of what sounds like *très* expensive improvements from *très* exclusive tradesmen. I think Jacinthe was about to go nuclear, which is why I came in here to check on you."

"To hide?" I laughed.

Franck leaned over and gave me a kiss. "Yes. Maybe to make out with you a bit too."

"Not because you missed me?"

"What did I just say? I wanted to make out with you. Same thing."

"Not really," I said.

"*Ma petite pédagogue.*" He traced a line down my cheek with his fingertip. "You have a lavender streak here. It suits you."

"I've never painted without getting it everywhere."

"My lovely mess," he said, then we fulfilled the purpose of his visit until we realized we either had to stop or lock the door.

"The locked door will raise suspicion," I pointed out.

Just then, I heard Jacinthe calling for Franck.

Franck sighed, and I looked at my watch. "We should probably grab the RER back to Florent's soon. Pauline might have made dinner for us."

I groaned. "Please God, let there be no Frederick's of Hollywood fashion show tonight. I think I may still be traumatized from last night."

There was a knock on the bathroom door.

Jacinthe poked her head in. Franck and I were sitting, innocently now, on the bathtub rim. "Were you hiding from Alexandrine?"

"It sounded like you guys needed to have your argument without an audience," Franck said.

"I wish she would just leave," Jacinthe said, then she looked around some more. "Bravo, Laura! You're almost finished."

"I'll definitely be able to finish it off tomorrow," I said, banging down the lid firmly on the can of paint so it didn't dry out. "Where should I wash out the paint brushes?"

"In the kitchen. Come with me, I'll help you."

Alexandrine was standing in the middle of the kitchen, smoking a cigarette and squinting her eyes as she inspected a large crack in the plaster ceiling. "You'll have to fix that, and not just paint over it," she said. "I know of a wonderful plasterer. He did my parents' château in Normandy."

Jacinthe then turned to me so only I could see and rolled her eyes. "After all your help today, the least I can do is invite you out somewhere to dinner," she said.

Alexandrine turned on Jacinthe, her eyes full of reproach. "You're already committed to me tonight! How could you forget? I've ordered the specialty pasta and sauces from that exclusive Italian craftsman. Zoë and Momo and Caroline will be there. You promised me last week."

Jacinthe flushed. "I forgot."

"No worries," I said. "I'm sure Florent and Pauline are already waiting for us. It would be rude not to show up without giving them any notice."

"Surely there's enough pasta if Franck and Laura come," Jacinthe said in a low voice to Alexandrine.

Alexandrine's eyes flitted between Franck and me. I had a strong suspicion that if we didn't come as a unit, she would have invited Franck. "Certainly not. I ordered just the right amount."

"It's fine." Franck squeezed Jacinthe's shoulder. "We'll be back tomorrow, bright and early."

"I have a better idea," Jacinthe said. "How about we meet first at the apartment on the rue des Fossés Saint-Bernard and you guys can have another look, and then we can come over here together?"

"I can meet you there too!" said Alexandrine.

"No," said Jacinthe. "Our old apartment is too small for the four of us. I'm beginning to have my doubts that even this one is big enough."

When we were out on the pavement once again, tears pricked my eyes. I wiped them away.

"Bitch," I said. "I hope all Parisians aren't like that."

In the apartment, I had found Alexandrine more amusing than awful, so why did her rudeness get to me now? Maybe it was the combination of her blatant exclusion of us plus the idea of heading back to the *banlieue*...

"You were right. She *is* a bitch," Franck said. "She's one of those women that feels threatened by other women. She was horrible to you and charming with me...well she tried to be charming, but failed."

"Really?"

"She may have been trying to flirt with me, but she's so unappealing it is hard to tell. Do you know what?"

"What?"

"I think she's threatened by you."

I looked down at myself. My skin and clothes were covered in paint. I was sweaty from working so hard. My hair was pulled up in a simple ponytail with a black elastic. "You must be joking."

"No. She realizes Jacinthe likes you. Plus, you're pretty, charming, much younger than she is, and obviously brilliant. Don't forget you also have the exotic allure of being from the Wilds of Canada."

Franck managed to make me laugh with this last bit. "I have to learn how to capitalize on that."

Franck squeezed my hand. "No need. You already do."

"It still didn't get us invited to the exclusive pasta event."

"Did you actually want to go? It sounded deadly boring to me."

"No, but it hurt to be excluded. I can't explain it."

"I can. You're in a completely new city. You're vulnerable. I know exactly how you feel."

"Is that how you felt in Montreal?" I asked, not sure I really wanted to know Franck's answer.

"Often, yes."

chapter **eight**

We arrived at the rue des Fossés Saint-Bernard earlier than expected the next morning. The RER times were hard to predict, but everything had run unusually close to schedule. No strike threats, mysterious stoppages on the tracks, or unexplained delays.

Thankfully, the previous evening, Pauline had been dressed in normal clothes—or if she was still wearing her Hollywood lingerie, at least she had put normal clothes over top.

Florent had even been unusually chatty—or chatty for him anyway. He'd asked us how the apartment search was going, then went on to enumerate all the benefits of living in the *banlieue* while Franck and I nodded politely, more than ever committed to finding a place in the center of Paris.

"Wonderful," I muttered, looking at my watch and calculating we had arrived at Jacinthe's forty minutes early. "Look what time it is."

"Having time to kill in Paris is never a problem." Franck took my hand, and we continued down to the end of the street to a café, where Franck stopped, announcing that it looked "*bien dans son jus*", meaning worn and slightly grimy, the way he preferred his Parisian establishments.

He opened the door and ushered me in. There was a well-worn zinc countertop and wooden chairs and tables that showed years of use and patina. On each table sat a chipped, yellow Ricard ashtray. The air was already dense with smoke and the smell of espresso.

Franck sidled up to the stools on the zinc countertop. "Let's have their *sur le zinc.*" This literally meant to have our coffees served "on the zinc" countertop of the bar. I concluded this was a typical Parisian moment, so I pulled out a stool beside him and leaned my elbows on the counter.

"We haven't had breakfast," I reminded him. We were still trying to give as much space to Pauline and Florent as possible, so we had left before they'd even finished their showers.

"I'm sure we can remedy that," Franck said.

Even though many of the patrons were zipping in and sucking back an espresso without so much as sitting down on a stool, Franck and I ordered a basket of croissants, jam, butter, and two big *cafés au lait.*

When the man behind the bar set this all down in front of us, I sighed. *"Parfait."*

I flipped back the red and white checkered cloth that covered the pastries. Steam rose from the basket. I picked up a croissant. It was warm and crispy under my fingertips. "It's still piping hot," I said. "How did they do that?"

"They're from the *boulangerie* next door," Franck said. "They just run over and grab them whenever anyone orders any. These must have been straight out of the oven."

I put mine down on the little, brown ceramic plate and ripped it open with my fingers. More steam came out, as well as the aroma of pure butter.

With my knife, I scraped off a curl of chilled butter—so pale it almost looked white—from its little glass bowl and spread it on. It melted almost instantly. I added a generous spoonful of strawberry jam on top and then tore a piece off and bit into it.

I had to stop breathing for a second to appreciate the gastro-nomic perfection of the sweet, buttery, crispy combination. "If we get Nathanael and Jacinthe's old apartment, I may be tempted to come here *every* morning."

"One thing Paris does not lack is fresh croissants," Franck said. "We never could find decent ones in Montreal."

My heart twitched. It made me uneasy to hear Franck com-pare Montreal unfavorably with Paris. I didn't like the image of Franck coming here alone for croissants if he stayed and I went back.

Franck dipped his croissant into his *café au lait*. "Try this. It makes it even better."

"That's possible?"

It was. The creamy coffee soaked into all the nooks and crannies of the croissant, and even though the odd glob of jam dropped into my *café au lait*, it only enhanced its flavor.

It would have been prudent to stop at one croissant because, to be that flaky and delectable, a lot of butter had to be involved, but there were two more in the basket, as well as chunks of a fresh baguette sliced in half. It would be a travesty, I decided, to leave them.

I reached for another croissant. "This is dangerous." I indi-cated the basket with my chin. "You know me—I rarely back away from a challenge."

"Look on the bright side," Franck said, picking up a second croissant for himself. "This way we can skip lunch."

"It's just good economics; we've paid for the basket full of croissants and baguettes whether or not we eat them all."

"Exactly," Franck agreed, through a mouthful of baguette. "Wise budgeting."

"Just think... if we get this apartment, I can walk to school. We're right beside the Seine. Right behind the Île Saint-Louis and Notre-Dame, and right near this supply of fresh croissants... it has *everything*."

Franck paused spreading butter on his croissant. "You need to realize that even though this apartment is our best shot, even then it's not going to be easy. The landlord has to agree. Let's just keep our fingers crossed he hasn't promised it to anyone else."

"I never thought of that."

"Don't think of it right now," he said. "First, eat."

By the time we met Jacinthe at the door of the building, we were feeling so replete with pastries and *café au lait* that there seemed to be no room left for despair.

We gave her *les bises*, and she pressed a four-digit code on the keypad and the door magically swung open.

"I'm so sorry about last night," she said. "Alexandrine was a *pétasse*. I don't know what came over her. I mean, I know she can be prickly at times, but I never expected her to be so rude to you. I was mortified."

I'd been upset the night before, not to mention mystified by Alexandrine's hostility, but at about three o'clock in the morning, I had decided she wasn't worth my angst.

"I *do* worry about it," said Jacinthe. "To think you had spent all afternoon helping me and are newly arrived from Canada, then to be faced with such a shrew... As soon as you left, I let her know what I thought of her behavior. I believe she will be more amendable next time you see her."

We have to see her again?

It was as if Jacinthe had read my mind. "We work together, and she's always been extremely kind to me. I've seen her act like a bitch to other people, but generally they were people I didn't like either," she explained as we crossed the first courtyard. "That all changed last night. I didn't go to her stupid pasta dinner. Trust Alexandrine to make something elite out of pasta."

"You didn't go?" Franck said.

"No," said Jacinthe. "*And* I told her where she could shove her fancy raviolis."

We burst out laughing.

"What did you eat in the end?" I asked.

"I went a couple of streets over and bought a kebab. I ate it and then went right back to stripping wallpaper. I got to an easier part where it was coming off in big hunks. Or maybe my anger made me more efficient. Either way, you'll be surprised to see how much I got done."

In the first courtyard, the street noises were still faintly audible, but when we passed into the second, it seemed almost as quiet as the vineyards around Villers-la-Faye.

This building was fantastic, I realized now that I was fully awake. It was charmingly old without feeling snobby or pretentious, and impeccably clean to boot.

"Just through here." Jacinthe ushered us into the typically Parisian apartment lobby, which had polished, patterned cement floors, a circular staircase, and a metal elevator (almost identical to the one in Nathanael and Jacinthe's new apartment building) in the middle. I caught myself thinking that this place felt like home, then stopped myself. We hadn't secured the apartment. We hadn't even communicated with the landlord.

"Stairs or elevator?" Jacinthe asked. "It's on the fourth floor, if you remember." She winked at me.

"I don't," I said. "Sadly. Let's take the stairs." I still wasn't one hundred percent confident about old Parisian elevators, and besides, the gracefully swooping circular staircase appealed to my romantic side. I felt a powerful urge to ascend it in a silk peignoir or ball gown, as per the characters out of my favorite romance novels.

The stairs were carpeted with a burgundy carpet that brought out the shine in the wood of the stairs and the bannister. Sliding down the bannister would be fun. It was smooth as silk under my palm and smelled of fresh polish.

"The *gardienne* in this building is superb," Jacinthe said. "We always got along with her. She's quite a bit better, I think, from the snarly old bag at our new place, who definitely seems to be part of the old guard."

We climbed up the stairs, and despite the already hot day, instead of hunched and sweaty and tired, I felt straight and cool and regal. There was something transformative about those stairs.

Jacinthe's door was just to the right of the *palier* on the fourth floor. As she was unlocking her door, a decrepit little man with a blue beret and a moth-eaten sweater emerged from across the hallway.

"*Bonjour*, Mademoiselle," he said. "Just off to buy my baguette."

"*Bonjour*, Monsieur Pierrepont," Jacinthe said. "How are you doing today?"

"*Bien, bien*," he said. With that, he made his shaky way down the stairs, clinging on to the sturdy railing for dear life. I wondered why he didn't take the elevator.

"That's our neighbor, Monsieur Pierrepont. He's lovely. I'm not entirely sure he can afford heat during the winter," she said. "He lives in one of the apartments that had rent control put on it just after the Second World War. The landlord, Monsieur Arseneau, is dying to get rid of him and the few others like him so he can jack the apartments up to market rate."

"That's terrible," I said.

We squeezed into a narrow corridor that was hardly big enough to fit the three of us. Soon, to our left, there was a tiny pocket kitchen with a sliding door. A regular door would never have fit.

"I'm happy to say that Monsieur Pierrepont hates Monsieur Arseneau so much that I often think it is the only thing keeping him alive. To spite him, Monsieur Pierrepont simply refuses to die."

"That's marvelous," I said.

"It is," Jacinthe agreed.

The hallway turned a sharp right after the kitchen, and to the left was just about the most cramped bathroom I had ever seen. The toilet was pushed right up against the shower, which itself didn't look big enough to turn around in. The sink was one of the miniature models that one generally ever sees only in Paris. The hallway opened up into the small room where I had knocked Jacinthe's decorations off the wall and where we had eaten dinner...and passed out, in my case.

The space was taken up by a round, black wooden table and four red chairs with woven straw seats. Against one wall, there was a black bookshelf. Directly beyond was a bedroom with a double bed shoved right up against the wall and an old wooden armoire squeezed in beside it and the far wall. There wasn't room for any other furniture. Making the bed, I decided, surely required a special technique known only to the French.

We would wake up in this little nest and start the morning slowly, maybe with a *café* and croissants from down the street.

"I love it," I said. "It's perfect." We didn't need more space than this with the entire city of Paris on our doorstep. "What do we need to do to get it?"

"It's not going to be easy," Jacinthe warned, echoing Franck's caution over breakfast. "The landlord takes joy in being difficult."

"But wouldn't it be easier for him to just have tenants who are ready to move in instead of looking for new ones?" I said.

"This is Paris," Jacinthe reminded me. "He wouldn't have to look for long. Do you have your *caution* ready?"

Caution? What is a "*caution*"? I raised my brows in a silent question for Franck.

"It's basically a security deposit," he explained. "In Paris, landlords have the upper hand, so they can pretty much charge what they want. How much do you think he'll want?" Franck asked Jacinthe.

She shrugged. "He wanted four months' rent from us, but he's nothing if not arbitrary, not to mention greedy…I would plan on six."

"Six months' rent?" I asked, stunned. In Montreal, the damage deposit was never more than a few hundred dollars. This would amount to *far* more than that.

"I'll contact him first," Jacinthe said. "I think it will be better that way."

"*Merci*," I said.

"Don't thank me yet." Jacinthe waved away my words. "Getting Monsieur Arseneau to rent to you won't be easy. Don't forget he's a vile man. Besides, after this, we're going back to my place to paint all afternoon, remember? We're more than even."

chapter **nine**

Paint all afternoon is exactly what we did. I had finished the bathroom and had made solid inroads in the kitchen by the time Jacinthe came and urged me to stop.

"It's already eight o'clock," she said, trying to wrestle my roller away from me.

I dodged her. "I just wanted to start in on the first coat of that last wall."

"No. No," she said. "You've done so much. *De toute façon*, we need to eat."

I looked down at my paint-spattered clothes. The kitchen was going to be a cherry red, and the combination of mauve and red paint all over me was arresting, to say the least. "I don't have a change of clothes. I can't go out to a restaurant like this."

"Don't worry," Jacinthe said. "I've got it all figured out. I'm just going to run out for a second, but start rinsing your brushes now so that you're ready to eat when I get back."

Once I cleaned up, I wandered into the front room, where Franck was doing the same. All the wallpaper was stripped off, and he had started to apply a white base coat.

I snuck up and pinched his bum. "Nice work."

He jumped. "Hey! Stop hitting on the tradesmen."

"Make me," I said and, when he tried to grab me, scuttled backwards, laughing. I kept sidling away from him, making a show of inspecting his work. "You got a lot done."

"It's satisfying. I enjoy seeing the progress in such a tangible way. I think maybe I deserve a reward."

"Hey! I worked hard too. We both deserve a reward."

Franck grabbed me. I squealed but, this time, let myself be caught. We were just settling in to our mutual reward when Jacinthe returned.

My first instinct—as a born and bred Anglo-Saxon—was to jump back, but Franck just held me tight in his arms. It was such a familiar place. It was my home.

Jacinthe carried a heavenly smelling bag under one arm and a grocery store bag in her other hand. She smiled at us. "Ah!" she exclaimed. "*Que c'est beau l'amour.*" I had forgotten how the French are never the slightest bit flustered by demonstrations of affection.

"What have you got there?" Franck asked her, still holding me.

"Last night, during my fancy pasta boycott, I discovered a gem of a kebab shop two streets over." Jacinthe set two stapled brown paper bags on the kitchen counter. "I just stumbled on it. It is the kind of place that I wouldn't have been surprised to have in the Latin Quarter but not in this arrondissement."

"The bourgeois have to eat too." Franck said.

"I know but...kebabs?" I said.

"Kebabs are delicious." Franck released me so he could help Jacinthe. "I'll bet the locals, with their miniature poodles in their handbags, sneak in there by the dozen to get their daily fix."

Jacinthe was glancing around the room. "I forgot. We don't have a table."

I held up a finger. "Wait."

I went into the living room, retrieved a box that had been full of paint cans and brought it back to the kitchen. I turned it upside down in the middle of the floor. "*Voilà!*"

"Brilliant," Jacinthe said.

We'll just sit on the floor," I added. "Tunisian style."

"Fitting of kebabs." Franck gave an improving nod of his head.

Jacinthe laughed and lay the three wrapped kebabs she had pulled out of the bags on our "table." "I had them put the super spicy sauce on all of them. Is that okay?"

"More than okay," I said.

We sat down on the throw cloths that were protecting the wood floors and began devouring the kebabs. The juicy, spiced meat and shredded lettuce and spicy sauce kept dribbling down our fronts—luckily our clothes were already beyond salvaging.

We had barely started when Jacinthe hopped up. "Wait. Wait! Don't eat another bite. I need to get us something to drink."

"I don't think I saw any glasses in the kitchen," I called after her. "I can go to the store and buy some plastic ones."

When Jacinthe came back from the kitchen, she had a role of paper towel (I was guessing for improvised napkins) under her arm and, in her hands, a bottle of Champagne and three lovely, hand-etched, bowl-style Champagne glasses.

"Where were you hiding those?" I asked.

"I brought them over as soon as we got the keys. A house isn't a home until you have a bottle of Champagne and flutes at the ready."

"That's a first-rate rule." Franck declared.

"How can you celebrate if you don't have Champagne?" Jacinthe set down the glasses. "*Voilà!*"

"Champagne?" I said. "With kebabs?"

"This isn't Champagne. This is Dom Pérignon. Dom Pérignon goes with everything."

Jacinthe turned the bottle so I could read the beautiful, shell pink label. It wasn't just Dom Pérignon. It was Dom Pérignon rosé. "Have you ever tasted it before?" she asked.

"No."

"Dom Pérignon rosé is the only thing I will drink with kebabs," Jacinthe said. "Once you try it, you can't go back."

Franck grinned.

"I'm sure," I said, rapidly developing an appreciation for Jacinthe's life rules.

Jacinthe handed the bottle to Franck to be uncorked. Franck, as a Burgundian, was adept at uncorking bottles, yet I was sure in her line of work Jacinthe was no slouch in the uncorking department.

Still, this was France. If there was a man present, he uncorked the bottle. It wasn't so much machismo as part of the subtle dance of Gallic gallantry.

Franck undid the wire cage on the top and popped the cork. He was holding the bottle over one of the *coupes de Champagne* so he wouldn't spill a drop.

He filled up all three glasses and we clinked. "*Santé!*"

"Here's to your new apartment," I said. "May it be filled with good friends, laughter, and lots of Champagne...scratch that... Dom Pérignon."

"*Tchin, tchin.*" Jacinthe nodded, the French way of saying "Hear, hear!" Hopefully we will be drinking Champagne soon to celebrate *your* new apartment."

"Fingers crossed," I said. Honestly, I didn't know how much more of the *banlieue*, Florent, and Pauline I could take.

The Champagne burst in my mouth like tiny stars. It was dry and fruity, without being the slightest bit sweet. As Jacinthe had promised, it was a sublime accompaniment to our Right Bank kebabs.

chapter **ten**

For the next few days until my school opened, we spent our days helping Jacinthe get her and Nathaneal's apartment ready. Occasionally we went to Madame Renier-Bernadotte's apartment and tried her buzzer again, but there was no response, not even a twitch of her curtain.

The day the school officially opened (I was at least given this rather crucial piece of information in the letter I had been sent by the Sorbonne), I still had no idea what I needed to do or where exactly I needed to be.

Franck and I decided to simply show up at Sorbonne Paris III—which was officially my exchange school even though I was taking just as many courses at Paris IV—by eight thirty in the morning.

The RER ride from the *banlieue* made for an early start yet again. I had never been a morning person at the best of times, but getting out of the *banlieue* was particularly rough. By the time Florent and Pauline had finished their showers, there was no hot water left. I only lasted long enough under the frigid blast to soap myself up and rinse myself off. We still had no key for their apartment, and I suspected that neither Pauline nor Florent had any intention of giving us one. This meant that we had about two minutes to get ready after Pauline and Florent finished their ablutions before we had to leave with them so they could lock up. We trudged to the RER station, shivering, dirty, and grumpy.

When we arrived at Paris III after several RER delays, I was shocked again at the esthetics, or rather lack thereof, of the place. I had the impression the designers were attempting to be modern, but the metal exterior was boxy and boring so that the school resembled a dilapidated office building.

"Why is this place so hideous?" I demanded.

"Because it was built after nineteen sixty-eight, *bien sûr.*"

"I don't get it."

"Paris was in total chaos in nineteen sixty-eight. The students and the unions banded together, and there were barricades in the middle of the streets, looting, cars being set on fire, a gas shortage, empty food shelves in the stores…the whole country wasn't sure how long it would last or whether it would end up being a civil war."

"So, they decided to put up a bunch of ugly buildings?"

"In a way, yes. The government split up the universities in Paris after nineteen sixty-eight as much as they could. They built new buildings that were designed to discourage students from sticking around after class was over."

"Then they wouldn't gather and plan revolutions and all that stuff?"

"Exactly."

I stared up at the run-down, block-like building that punctured my soul with its sheer ugliness. "Mission accomplished."

We saw we weren't the only ones with the idea of arriving early. The school—a virtual ghost town locked up like Fort Knox a few days earlier—swarmed with students.

There was a definite student "look," I noticed immediately. The girls had clipped their long hair back in messy updos, often with a pencil. They wore light cotton scarves wrapped several times around their necks, jeans, flats, and T-shirts. The boys were also in jeans, and leather shoes and T-shirts. Some of them were wearing linen or cotton scarves as well. Everyone except me was smoking.

We walked into the lobby, which I quickly decided was pretty much the most uninviting space imaginable. It also smelled of spoiled ham. Four ceiling panels had fallen down or been removed, giving a fine view of the insulation and wiring above. The walls were painted a dingy green. Cigarette butts and garbage wrappers littered the floor, despite the fact that the building had been open less than an hour. Was it possible they were left over from the day the school closed at the beginning of the summer?

"Is this place a jail, or a university?" I asked Franck over the hubbub and kissing sounds from students greeting each other after the long summer vacation.

"It's a university with the design esthetic of a jail."

"Where do you think I should go first?" I asked Franck, even though what I wanted to do was run out of the building screaming. This place was such a far cry from my daydreams that I could hardly believe it was located in Paris.

I had all my papers—my acceptance letter, my passport, my student visa, and the rest of it—but still I had no clue who I should be talking to in order to find out about my classes.

Franck headed over to a surly-looking woman sitting behind an opening in the wall with a little speaker thing set in the Plexiglas—exactly the same set-up as at police stations or the little payment huts on the autoroute. *Why does she need to be doing her job behind protective glass?*

Franck had to wait his turn. In the meantime, I tried to figure out where the other students were going and what they were doing. The ring of a bell could be heard over the din of conversation, but nobody seemed to react. Everyone just continued chatting as though it didn't matter. Perhaps it didn't.

After about fifteen minutes, Franck returned. "We're supposed to go to an office on the third floor. That's where the woman in charge of registering exchange students works."

"Sounds promising," I said. It was another hot day, and I was already overheating. There was nothing resembling functioning air conditioning in the building.

"But she warned me the elevators are all broken," Franck added.

"On the first day?"

"They've been broken for years, apparently."

"Stairs it is." I sighed.

We reached the third floor and quickly caught sight of a row of students slumped against the wall, fanning themselves with papers or binders. It had been warm and stifling in the lobby, but it was even hotter up there.

The students wore pained expressions, and I could see no sign of the line moving. *Please don't let it be here. Please don't let it be here.*

Franck walked to the door and read the name on the plaque. "It's here."

I studied the line. "I guess we better reconcile ourselves with waiting until the next Ice Age."

Just then the closed door burst open and a boy stumbled out, sobbing and shouting over his shoulder in Italian. This was accompanied with hand gestures that left no doubt that his meeting with the exchange coordinator had not been felicitous. He continued yelling the whole way down the hallway. I felt a sudden desire to learn Italian.

The next student in line stood up and hesitated before knocking on the door. He was a tall, blond fellow—he wouldn't have looked out of place in an authentic Viking outfit. How could such an imposing specimen be scared to enter the dragon's den? I wondered how many other students he had seen emerge from the coordinator's office in the same state as the Italian guy.

A curly-headed woman popped her head out the door. She surveyed the line of us students slumped against the wall and made an unmistakable sound of disgust—one which involved much phlegm and which only the French seemed capable of producing.

The air around her crackled with aggression. She turned to the golden god standing in front of her door. "Are you going to loiter there like *une cruche* all day? Don't tell me you can't speak French! Get in here, and you'd better have your *fiche d'inscription* with you or I may throw you out the window!"

The Viking was sucked into the vortex. The door slammed behind him.

I muttered *"fiche d'inscription?"* to myself at the same time as about ten other students.

"What is a *fiche d'inscription?*" I hissed to Franck. "I don't remember seeing one in my paperwork."

"You stay here and keep your place in line," he said. "I'll go downstairs and find out."

"What if it's my turn to see her before you get back?" I failed at keeping the panic out of my voice.

Franck surveyed the line of people in front of me. "It won't be," he said. "She seems to enjoy playing with her prey before devouring them."

He disappeared and I watched the coordinator's door, waiting for the Viking to be spat out.

Five minutes passed, then ten, then fifteen... I could make out raised voices, but they were muffled—the doors and the walls of the *tête du Programme d'échanges internationaux* were oddly thick in a building that otherwise looked as though it had been built with cardboard and sticky tack.

The door flung open and the huge, blond Viking backed out of it, knuckling tears from his eyes with massive hands. "But how can I give such a paper to you?" He pleaded. "It does not even *exist* in Norway."

"So, that is my problem, *hein?*" I heard her cry out. "I think not! NEXT!"

A thin Asian girl raised herself up from the floor and, visibly shaking, ventured inside. There was no need to wonder if the

coordinator would make her cry. Silent tears were already running down the poor girl's face.

I looked down the row of students. Roughly half of them were
teary. No air moved in the hallway. Sweat trickled down the back
of my neck. From fear or the heat? Probably both.

I lost track of time. There was no point in leaving—I had to
survive this gauntlet if I wanted to study here.

After the better part of an hour, I spotted Franck coming
back down the hallway, a sheath of papers in his hand. He had
been right, there were still three students ahead of me in line. I
hadn't been called in without him.

He passed the papers over to me. "Here's the *fiche d'inscription*. I had to stand in five different lines to finally get one."

"Excuse me," a boy beside me asked in stilted French. "Where
can I find that form?"

Franck told him and added, "I tried to get several copies so I
could give them out up here, but no matter what I said, they would
only give me one. You would think it was inscribed with gold leaf."

"Thanks for trying," the boy said, standing up. He raised his
fist and shook it *"Solidarité!"* he said to Franck, as if it were a war
cry. That guy was going to do well in France.

Every person in front of me then stood up and rushed downstairs, presumably to the office Franck had mentioned.

"I can totally see now why student protesters were a problem," I said. "But it's the school's own fault. What terrible treatment of—"

"You're next." Franck pointed at the door. "You'd better start
filling that out...*vite*."

Merde. He was right. I flipped through the four-page form,
found a pen in my bag, and started scrawling.

I had only filled out the first half—even then I had to leave
many empty squares where the questions didn't apply to my
case—when the door to the advisor's office opened again. *"Merde.*

Merde. Merde," I muttered and began to write even faster. The Asian girl stumbled out, sobbing now. She clung to the wall.

"Are you OK?" I got up and went over to her. She nodded without looking at me and waved me away.

"*Prochaine!*" the advisor's gravelly voice—I would bet serious cash that she smoked Gitanes—bellowed from inside.

Franck plunged in like a brave knight in medieval times. I continued madly scribbling on my *fiche* as I followed.

The advisor sat down behind the desk and thrust her hand out. "*Fiche d'inscription,*" she demanded.

"I've got it here," I said. "Just let me finish…it will only take a few seconds—"

"If you don't have a completed *fiche*, get out of my office." She pointed an imperious finger at the door. "Do not waste any more of my time."

She was tinier than her voice would lead one to believe. Small-boned like a bird. She wore huge black glasses, and a mop of black and gray streaked curls overwhelmed her small face with its pointy chin. She studied us with sharp black eyes, like a crow that had spotted a promising mouse on the ground.

"We're not going anywhere," Franck said, in a bored voice.

Her eyes widened with something akin to glee.

In the meantime, I continued to fill out my *fiche* while she was occupied.

"I will call Security," she warned. "They will get rid of you."

"You could," Franck said, "but I could tell them how every single student has walked out of your office in tears this morning. I certainly wouldn't lack witnesses."

"They wouldn't care. They have no love for students."

"Somehow, I doubt the security team has much love for you, either."

"*Comment osez-vous?*"

"Did I tell you I'm a journalist?" Franck lied. "And my closest friend is a *grand reporter*? He might be interested in this story."

She sat back in her chair and examined Franck through steepled fingers. "You're bluffing."

"You can take the risk and find out," he said. "Or you could just help my girlfriend here get enrolled. That *is* supposed to be your job, *n'est-ce pas?*" Franck passed her my passport, the letter from Paris III, copies of my transcripts from McGill, and all the other papers I had compiled.

"What am I supposed to do with all that without a *fiche d'inscription?*" She looked down at the pile disdainfully.

Just then, I filled in the final box. Sweat dripped behind my ears. I slid the *fiche* across the desk to her.

"Hmpf," she said, and cocked an eyebrow at Franck. "How did you figure out where to get one of these? Nobody else has so far."

"Charm," he said, with a mischievous smile.

And then...I couldn't believe it...the witch actually fought back a smile herself.

"Hmmmmmm...let's see if you have filled it out correctly," she said, picking my *fiche* up off her desk.

"You haven't filled out all the boxes," she said, flicking an accusatory glance at me, but then she moved her eyes back to Franck and watched him expectantly.

"The only ones I left blank are ones that didn't apply to me because I didn't go to *lycée* in France," I said.

Franck quirked his lips at the witch. "That makes perfect sense, doesn't it?"

"You have an answer for everything," she said to him in a playful tone of voice. She actually smiled back, revealing tobacco-stained teeth.

Oh my god. Was the witch *flirting* with Franck? I didn't know witches flirted.

Fifteen minutes later, I waltzed out of her office, not in tears, but with my course schedule in one hand and a laminated student card in the other. A new line had formed, and most of the students in it were slumped against the wall, feverishly filling out their *fiches*. They stared up at us in amazement. The witch actually accompanied us a few meters down the hallway and shook our hands. "*Bonne chance,*" she said to me. "Keep this man of yours in line."

"Actually, I might enroll for a course or two if I can squeeze it in with my job," Franck said.

"If you do, come and see me," she said, giving him a slinky smile.

She then crowed a funny little sound of satisfaction to herself before bellowing *Prochaine!* to the student next in line.

chapter **eleven**

"I can't believe you actually *flirted* with her." I shivered in faux disgust.

I was lying on my back with my head resting on Franck's lap in the peaceful Jardin des plantes, an old botanical garden that, Franck had informed me, was established in 1635 by Louis XIII's doctor as a medicinal garden. Where Franck learned tidbits of information like that was beyond me, but it was a haven of peace and beauty compared to Paris III's unsightliness.

We had settled at the base of a tree in the rose garden. The sweet scent of the late-blooming roses wafted over to us with the occasional breeze. The sun still beat down, but we munched on *jambon fromage* baguette sandwiches in dappled shade.

"It was sacrificial flirting."

"Still…"

"So, you start classes tomorrow…," Franck said.

"There's a blatant ploy to distract my attention from the whole flirting-with-the-witch thing."

Franck rolled toward me again. *"Bien sûr."*

I laughed.

"I can flirt with you instead. This is a most romantic setting, if you hadn't noticed."

"I noticed," I said, speaking the truth. One of the drawbacks of living in Pauline and Florent's living room was that we had zero privacy. That was starting to wear on both of us.

"I could make love to you right here," Franck proposed.

"In a public garden?"

"It's a public garden in *Paris*."

"Still...*ce n'est pas l'envie qui m'en manque*. We just need somewhere less...public."

"We need to get Jacinthe's apartment." Franck sighed.

"*Très, très vite*," I agreed. "Otherwise we *will* start breaking all the public decency laws."

We remained silent for a time, each trying to work through our mutual frustration.

"In the meantime," I said, finally, "I guess we may as well talk about school."

"Are you nervous?"

I picked a rose branch off the ground beside me and began to peel off the thorns. "A little. I saw no sign of Madame Renier-Bernadotte today. I wonder if she even exists or if she is just a mythical figure."

"My bet is mythical figure."

I finished my last few bites of sandwich, sat up, and brushed the crumbs off my shorts. I opened my backpack and pulled out my course timetable to look it over.

"*Introduction à Littérature Française du Moyen-Âge*," I read out loud. "Professor Renier-Bernadotte. According to this, I should be seeing her in the flesh in front of my first class, tomorrow."

Franck closed his eyes to take a little post-lunch nap. "I'll believe it when I see it."

I lay back down on my side, my head nestled in that perfect crook between his neck and shoulder—the spot that always feels as if it was made for me. I breathed in the smell of crushed grass and Franck's warmth under the minty scent of his aftershave. He stroked my hair until we dozed off.

I woke up to a pigeon pecking my ankle. I sat up and shooed it away.

Franck groaned. "What time is it?"

I checked my watch. "Two o'clock."

"You mean *quatorze heures*," Franck said. "Everyone uses the twenty-four-hour clock in France."

"Do you think the landlord is going to show up? I asked.

Jacinthe had phoned us the night before and told us she had arranged to meet with the landlord of her old apartment for him to inspect the place and hopefully give them the green light to getting their security deposit back. She thought if we should "happen" to arrive at the apartment at the same time the landlord was there, she could introduce us and the idea of Franck and me taking over the apartment.

"Tread carefully, though," she warned us. "For one thing, he only shows up about half the times he says he's going to. Also, he has a strange personality. He doesn't like to be coerced or feel like he's being hoodwinked by anyone. I've never met someone so suspicious."

"What was his name again?" I asked Franck as we brushed ourselves off and began to walk out of the garden and into the maw of Parisian traffic.

"Monsieur Arseneau."

"Monsieur Arseneau," I repeated, trying to commit it to memory.

"But probably it's better to pretend like we don't know his name," Franck added. "Remember how suspicious Jacinthe said he is? We have to act like this is a coincidence."

"Right."

Franck and I discussed strategy as we walked down the rue Monge toward the Seine.

"You take the lead," I said. I knew that, as a Canadian, I was almost pathologically unable to do anything but smile and act enthusiastic when interacting with a stranger. This made the French suspicious of my ulterior motives at the best of times.

As we made our way down the rue Monge toward the Seine, I

sent up a wish to the skies that this apartment would work out. I didn't relish the idea of having to take the RER into Paris every day to go to classes. Also, when the weather started to turn, where was I supposed to go?

The only sort of room in the university building that didn't appear to be either a classroom or an office was a ghost-town space that looked as though it might have been a cafeteria before a nuclear bomb or some other dystopian event blasted it out of commission.

It boasted what looked like the remnants of seats along a straight line of bar-height Formica. It would have been an uncomfortable but feasible place to sit, except the seat portion of the stools had been removed, or stolen, leaving only metal pipes, three-inches in diameter, sticking straight out of the ground.

Getting the apartment would solve all these problems. It was only a quick fifteen-minute walk from the school—ten minutes, probably, once I found the quickest route. I could settle into school, and Franck could find a job and have a semi-permanent address to use for his work resumé. Possibly the best part was that we wouldn't be the involuntary audience for any more Frederick's of Hollywood fashion shows.

We arrived in front of the building and buzzed Jacinthe's apartment. She buzzed us in right away. *Good sign or bad sign?*

We walked up the stairs to the apartment and found the door was propped open. A gruff voice emanated from inside. Something about its hard edge told me that this was going to be even more challenging than I had anticipated.

I knocked on the open door. "Jacinthe?"

She came into the hallway, her face flushed.

"*Quel trou du cul*," she muttered, *sotto voce*. *What an asshole.* "He's trying to convince me that the kitchen tile wasn't damaged when we moved in, which it was, as it clearly states on the état des *lieux*."

"Should we leave?" Franck whispered back.

"No. I think the time to catch him in a good mood is never." She beckoned us to follow her through to the tiny bedroom.

She introduced us to the burly man on his hands and knees

inspecting the floorboards. "Monsieur Arseneau, these are my friends who have just moved to Paris. They'll be helping us move."

Monsieur Arseneau took no notice of us or Jacinthe's introduction and continued to inspect the floor.

"As a matter of fact, they're looking for an apartment. Maybe they could just take over our lease on this one?"

This got his attention. Monsieur Arseneau stood up slowly and inspected Franck and me with sharp brown eyes.

"It's exactly what we're looking for," I said. "You see, I'm going to school right up the road so—"

Franck stepped meaningfully on my foot. *Why did I always feel the compulsion to talk to cover awkward silences?* I cursed the Canadian in me.

Monsieur Arseneau eyed me. "Where are you from? You're not French."

Is it that obvious? "I'm Canadian," I admitted.

"*Québecois?*"

"No. English Canadian."

"And you're French?" he asked Franck, but he clearly already knew the answer.

"*Oui,*" Franck said. "From Burgundy, like Nathanael."

"Can you provide references?" Monsieur Arseneau demanded. "And an *attestation bancaire*? And a security deposit of six months?"

I did some mental calculations. We simply didn't have that much money over there.

"Yes," Franck said.

"I'm going to raise the rent." Monsieur Arseneau rubbed his cheeks thoughtfully.

Jacinthe gasped. "But it was already high!"

He sent her a dark look. "I have a waiting list for this apartment, I will have you know, Mademoiselle," he said. "Besides, I don't like renting to foreigners. Nothing but problems. I prefer to rent to French people."

I wasn't entirely certain it was legal for him to say that, let alone discriminate against foreigners in such a way, but I certainly wasn't about to call him on it.

"But I'm French," Franck said.

"Yes, but you're with a Canadian." Monsieur Arseneau narrowed his eyes as he inspected Franck. "That makes you almost as foreign as your girlfriend. Besides, what if you break up? How will I get my rent then?"

"We came here together," I said. "We're going to stay together." Even as I said the words, I was faced with the reality that I didn't know anything for sure.

I hated not knowing if we would stay together after that year. I had never done well with uncertainty. We were still so young, as people never tired of reminding us. Were we just being naïve to think our relationship was for the long term? Actually, I didn't know for certain what Franck thought. Was it just me who was being naïve?

"If I had a hundred francs for every couple that has said that to me and then split," he said, "I would be a wealthy man."

Jacinthe cast him a hateful stare. He *was* a wealthy man.

"You can do the lease up in my name," Franck said. "Would that make it easier?"

"I may be able to find better tenants than you."

Jacinthe rolled her eyes. "These two will take over the lease without a day's break between our lease and theirs. That will save you money."

"How much is the rent?" Franck asked.

Monsieur Arseneau said a number that made me break out in a cold sweat. How could we ever afford that? But, then again, what choice did we have? It was still at least two thousand francs a month less expensive than any other place we'd seen advertised— ones that weren't nearly as nice or in such a good location.

"That sounds fine," I said. Franck raised an eyebrow at me, but I gave him a discreet nod.

"I won't make any decisions today," Monsieur Arseneau said. "I don't like being ambushed. Meet me here next week at the same time, and we will discuss it further."

"Next week?" I echoed. Seven days seemed like eons away. Seven more days of commuting, of feeling *de trop* at Pauline and Florent's apartment... "We could meet sooner than that," I said.

"You two may be dilettantes, but I'm a busy man," he said. "In the meantime, you need to get your paperwork together. I will phone you tonight about that kitchen tile, Mademoiselle," he said as a parting shot to Jacinthe.

Jacinthe stuck her tongue out at him when he turned to leave.

Once he had left, I rested against the windowsill. "*Quel connard*," I said. "You warned us…but…wow."

"As a matter of fact, that went better than I had expected," Jacinthe said.

"Are you joking?"

"No. He didn't say no outright. He didn't yell. He usually yells. I'm feeling more optimistic about your chances. He just likes to torture people."

What is with all these Parisians? First the exchange coordinator and now the landlord?

"It didn't sound to me like he wants to rent to us," I said.

Jacinthe shrugged. "I'm not sure he really wants to rent to anybody, but he *does* want the rent money. Can you imagine inheriting a building like this? The money it must bring in every month? It's beyond me why he's so miserable."

"What do you think about the rent?" Franck asked her. "We're still trying to adjust to the prices."

She shrugged again. "It's expensive, of course," she said. "But everything in Paris is expensive. It's probably market rate. It's quiet too."

"That's what I thought," Franck said, but then looked at me. "Still, it's far more than we had anticipated or budgeted for."

"Basically, you have to accept that, as a potential renter in Paris, you have zero power. The landlord holds all the cards," Jacinthe added.

Franck looked at me. "Do you think we can swing it?"

I grimaced. "Do we have a choice?"

"No. Not really."

"Welcome to Paris!" Jacinthe waved her hand with a flourish.

chapter **twelve**

The next day, Franck rode with me into Paris for my first morning of classes. The plan was for him to begin his job search while I plunged into the deep end of French university life.

If we were lucky enough to get the rue des Fossés Saint-Bernard apartment, we would be needing his salary sooner rather than later. It would also be close to impossible for us to secure the apartment if he had no job contract.

"Where are you going to start?" I asked him.

We were sitting on the RER, watching the gray *banlieue* zip by through the window. I had just caught a glimpse of Sacré-Coeur in the distance, shining white like a wedding cake on its hilltop of Montmartre. We'd arrive in the Châtelet - Les Halles station soon.

"I'm not sure, *pour dire la vérité*," Franck said, taking a drag of his cigarette. There was, ostensibly, a law against smoking on the RER, according to the heavily graffitied signs, but I always found myself in the minority as someone who didn't spend my entire commute puffing away. The RER stunk of a fun night gone terribly bad—stale cigarettes, wine, and urine.

Franck's vague answer unnerved me. Did he *really* have no idea where he'd like to work? He had a degree from the Sorbonne and was a hard worker; he could do anything he set his mind to. I fretted he would stumble into something horrible because he had no plan.

I attempted diplomacy. "Career wise, what kind of thing would you like to do?"

He arched a brow at me. "Career wise? I don't really think that way. I'm sure there'll be a job out there for me."

"But that's the approach you took in Montreal and, I mean… come on…telemarketing…taking polls at the airport…packing books into boxes…they weren't fun jobs."

Franck tapped his knuckles absent-mindedly against the grimy window. "I wouldn't say that. At the telemarketing job, I met Pascal, and he turned out to be a great friend. Remember when we went ice fishing with him and threw the freshly caught fish out onto the ice to flash freeze them?"

"Yes." We were light years from the topic at hand, but Franck was on a roll.

"If I hadn't gotten that job packing books, I never would have discovered that tiny café where I would have those amazing conversations with the owner while I ate her ham-and-bean soup. I could barely understand her accent from Gaspé, but that was a true Montreal experience. I never would have explored that area of town if it wasn't for that job. Also, I learned how to pack a box, which, you have to admit, has come in handy."

I shook my head, exasperated but afraid of opening my mouth for fear I would regret what would come out.

Franck narrowed his eyes at me. "What is it you want to say but don't dare say?"

"You need a *plan*." The words burst out of me. "You need to think strategically in terms of your career instead of just floating from one random job to the next—"

"We're only going to be here for a year," Franck said. "At least that's *your* plan. A career takes longer than a year to build. Do you actually *want* me to be thinking in terms of a long-term career in Paris?"

He had a point. A fantastic job would make his decision about returning to Montreal that much harder.

"I'm not sure I even *want* to find a career," Franck added. "I'm more interested in collecting different experiences. A career sounds—"

"Boring?"

"*Oui. C'est ça.*"

"Wasn't packing books boring?"

"I quit when I got bored," Franck said. "And I moved on to the polling company, remember? I like the freedom of always being able to change."

I squirmed on my hard, metal RER seat. How had this man who was so allergic to settling down in other areas of his life been able to commit himself to a relationship with me?

"I'm just going to see what life brings." Franck squeezed my knee.

I shook my head but didn't say anything further. My thoughts were such a tangle, and this conversation had ventured onto precarious ground.

The RER squealed to a halt at Les Halles and we transferred to the Pink Line that took us to the Censier - Daubenton Metro stop closest to my Sorbonne Nouvelle.

We popped out of the Metro exit beside an old stone wall covered in ivy and made our way to the rue Monge.

When we got to the Brasserie Le Monge, where we'd had our lunch on our first day in Paris, we saw that a market had completely overtaken la place Monge across the street.

What I felt like doing was meandering around the market with Franck, buying fresh cheeses and baguette and *pâté de foie* for lunch, instead of braving my first university class in France. Who was I kidding? I had almost failed French in high school. Even though I could now speak it fluently, what was I thinking when I decided I was skilled enough to participate in a real French university class? Panic made me feel as if I couldn't catch a deep breath.

"Do you have time for a *café*?" Franck paused at the door of the *brasserie*.

I checked my watch. I had given myself a ton of extra time, as usual, so my class didn't start for forty minutes. *"Bonne idée."*

Franck stopped at the *tabac* booth while I waited for him at the zinc bar. I watched as he chatted with the woman behind the booth and paid for his bag of Drum tobacco and rolling papers.

We ordered our coffees and perched on our stools, watching the customers flow in and out, buying cigarettes, placing bets on the horses, and drinking tiny glasses of chilled white wine. It was much busier than the last time we had been there—undoubtedly because of the market across the street—but still, the lady behind the tobacco counter and the man behind the bar seemed to know everyone.

I tipped my espresso cup to get every dreg of sugary, grainy goodness. "I'm just going to the bathroom," I said, and followed the WC signs at the back of the *brasserie*.

It had taken me a few months in France to figure out that "WC" in France stood for the very English term "Water Closet." I couldn't figure out why so many establishments and French people referred to it as the WC instead of *les toilettes*. Another mystery I might solve during our year as Parisians.

The sign on the women's WC must have been a relic from the Fifties. It featured the silhouette of a busty young woman with a full skirt and bouffant hairdo flipped at the ends.

I opened the door to the tiny room and stared with consternation at what I discovered inside. "What the—" I muttered.

There was no toilet. There was just a hole in the floor, with two footrests on either side. A chain cord hung down from the wall, with a cracked porcelain bulb at its end. I was not going to pee in a hole in the floor. No way. I didn't even know *how* to pee in a hole in the floor.

Franck was still at the counter when I returned, exchanging pleasantries with the large man behind the bar. I hopped back onto my stool.

I let them chat a few minutes, then consulted my watch. I really needed to find a bathroom. I tugged Franck's sleeve and smiled apologetically at the barman. "We should head to the school. It might take me a while to find the classroom."

We bid Franck's new friend *au revoir.* "There wasn't a toilet in the WC," I hissed to Franck as soon as we were on the sidewalk. "It was just a hole in the floor."

I was expecting shock or consternation, but Franck laughed. "*Une toilette turque,* you mean?"

"Those disgusting holes warrant a name?"

"Of course. They're called turkish toilets."

"Why? Is that how they go to the bathroom in Turkey? It was *literally* just a hole in the floor with weird foot rests."

"They're quite common in France, especially in *brasseries* and bistros *bien dans leur jus.*"

I made a sound of disgust. "Needless to say, I didn't use it."

"Why not?"

"I couldn't!"

"Of course you could."

"I had no idea where to even start!" I said. "That's not something they teach us in Canada."

"What about camping?" Franck asked. He knew I had grown up camping in forests and on remote islands in the Pacific Northwest.

"Going behind a log in the rainforest isn't the same thing as aiming into a filthy hole."

"At least you don't have to listen for bears or cougars lurking around when you use the turkish toilets in Paris."

This, as far as I was concerned, didn't even deign a response, despite the fact it was the truth. "I need to find a normal toilet before class starts." I stamped the sidewalk so Franck would start treating this crisis with the gravity it warranted.

"Peeing into a hole isn't easy for women, you know." I added, wondering if using turkish toilets wasn't one of those talents, like washing one's hair in a bathtub, that only French women were genetically programmed to master.

"I never considered that," Franck said.

"Of course you didn't; you're a man." This wasn't the first time I had railed against the comparative ease with which men can pee in a hole, on a wall, or basically anywhere they chose. "How am I going to find the toilets at school before going to class? If Madame Renier-Bernadotte actually exists, I can't be late for her class."

Franck cast me a skeptical look. "Toilets at the school?"

"They must be normal toilets at the school. There are laws about that."

Franck reached over and massaged the back of my neck as we walked. Needing to pee turned everything into a crisis.

When we arrived at the school, we found the bathrooms without much trouble. There didn't appear to be separate bathrooms for men and women. Maybe this was a post-1968, we-are-all-citizens-of-the-republic equality thing.

A bunch of girls were using the long, cracked mirror that ran above a row of sinks, but nobody was using the stalls. On closer inspection, the reason became obvious—not a single stall had a door.

I pinched Franck's arm and waved toward the row of doorless stalls. "What fresh hell is this?"

There were, I noticed on closer inspection, no toilet seats attached to the toilets. Not exactly pleasant, but I could work around that, unlike the door situation.

"I was a tad concerned this might be the case," Franck said.

"What!?" I spluttered. "Don't French people go to the bathroom? WHERE ARE THE DOORS?"

"The school probably got sick of replacing them, so they just don't bother anymore."

"But...proper bathrooms... that's a basic human right!"

"Perhaps it should be, but it's clearly not at la Sorbonne Nouvelle."

"Where do the students go to the bathroom then?" It simply didn't add up. French students drank a lot of espressos in a day. I had seen them do it.

"Cafés," Franck responded.

"In those turkish toilets?"

"Yes."

"You think Paris is so great, but at least we have decent toilets back in Canada. This place is barbaric!" I burst out. I suppressed the chaser to that thought: *I want to go home.*

Of all the problems I had anticipated encountering in Paris, a dearth of proper toilets was not one of them. My first class with the alleged Professor Renier-Bernadotte was to start in ten minutes. I had no idea where the room was, and I was about to explode.

I felt like bursting into tears, but that wouldn't help. "I think I saw a café across the street," I said. "Will you drink another *café* at the bar while I use the bathroom?"

"Of course." I could tell from his expression that Franck felt sorry for me.

Five minutes later, we returned to the school, my plan having been a success. I made a mental note that the café across the street had an entirely acceptable *normal* toilet. I didn't think it was something that I was liable to forget.

chapter **thirteen**

My first class, Introduction to Medieval French, was in a large amphitheater. Franck gave me a kiss at the door and told me he would meet up with me in the café across the street in three hours. The one with the civilized toilet.

"Good luck with the job hunt," I said. The toilet crisis had supplanted that worry, but now it surged forward again. Franck turned and winked.

I made my way into the amphitheater. It was about a third filled with fellow students, but so far no one resembling a teacher had made an appearance. About halfway up the theater, I slid into a hard, molded-plastic seat that looked like it was fabricated out of pressed asbestos.

Luckily I'd brought a clipboard because most of the desk attachments had been ripped off. I took it out of my backpack and settled it on my knee. I wrote "Introduction to Medieval French" with a flourish on the top of my pad of paper. I wrote it again in French—*Introduction à la Littérature Française du Moyen-Âge.* I tapped my pen against the edge of my clipboard and looked around.

The girls still looked oh-so-very French with their hair pinned back in messy chignons, and their tight jeans, minimalist tops, and artfully tied scarves.

No other girl seemed to have a backpack. Instead, each had brought either a large Longchamp or a Louis Vuitton handbag. Wouldn't that be impractical once we had to start lugging around textbooks? Maybe French girls had some magical way of doing that, the same way they managed to go to the bathroom in turkish toilets (or to not ever need to go to the bathroom?). More mystery.

There was an effortlessness about French girls my age that I envied. In comparison, I felt less put together, more awkward, and less sophisticated.

I was twenty-one years old and caught between who I was (a Canadian student) and who I aspired to be (a young Parisian-ish woman). Maybe I could figure it out during the year.

The boys were mostly eyeing the girls, or perfecting a look of existential boredom. About half the students, I noticed, were smoking. I was amazed that students could do that inside the school building, let alone inside the classrooms.

People came and went, friends and acquaintances bumming cigarettes and greeting one another with kisses. I didn't know a soul. I was aware from my year in France, back when I was eighteen, that French friends took time and persistence to cultivate.

I started to doubt again whether Madame Renier-Bernadotte existed or was merely a figment of Paris III's imagination. Maybe she'd expired in her apartment over the summer and nobody had discovered her body yet. I felt a twinge of guilt about all my doorbell ringing, but then again, there had been that twitching curtain and the phantom face in the window...maybe her ghost?

A few students were leaving, apparently having decided they had waited long enough. How long did a student wait for a professor to show up there at the Sorbonne Nouvelle? I was pondering this question when a woman about sixty strode down the aisle on the opposite side of the amphitheater. She had auburn hair cut in a razor-edged symmetrical bob and chic glasses with arresting, black plastic frames. She was dressed entirely in black linen—a tunic and loose-fitting pants, which were fashionably wrinkled. The whole ensemble was set off by a chunky amber necklace and matching earrings.

"*Bonjour, la classe,*" she said, after taking a few moments to set herself up behind the lectern at the front. "I will be your professor. My name is Docteur Renier-Bernadotte."

She was alive! And she had a doctorate! I wished there was some method of communicating this urgent information to Franck that second.

Docteur Renier-Bernadotte crackled with intellectual energy, yet when I looked around at my fellow students, most of them were smoking lethargically, failing to see how impressive this woman standing in front of us was. I got an inkling of why Docteur Renier-Bernadotte opted *not* to open her door to students.

"As you know, you are not allowed to smoke in here," she said. "However, I am an academic, not a *gendarme*, so do what you want. I'm here to impart my—if I may say—vast knowledge to you. I am not here to enforce arbitrary rules. Tedious."

Interest dawned on the faces of the students around me.

"Also, I think I should tell you that, out of all the people beginning this class today, only about half of you will get a passing grade. I'm a demanding teacher and a rigorous marker.

"I refuse to chase you down to get you to hand in essays. If you don't show up to write an exam, it will not impact my life in the slightest. If you don't study or come to me for help if you cannot grasp the material, that is your issue. If you are not interested in learning, you might as well leave right now."

At McGill, every student would have stayed in their seats. It would have been viewed as impossibly rude to get up and leave. The French students had no such compunction. Five of them got up and left. *What about not giving up? What about following through on things you start?*

"*Bien,*" said le professeur. "*Bon débarras* !" After remarking that it was an excellent thing that the garbage had decided to take itself out, she thrust a thick stack of papers at the student sitting nearest to her. "Pass these out."

A few students began to groan at the thickness of the hand-out. Professeur Renier-Bernadotte looked up sharply and, with a mere flash of her eyes, cut them off mid-groan. "That is the list of books you will need for my class. You will notice that I have translated three of them. Don't think you can get away with not purchasing the original medieval source material. One of the central things I use to evaluate my students is their ability to translate from the medieval texts to modern French. It is essential you practice working off the medieval texts to learn this skill."

My written French was far from perfect...could I really hope to keep up with French students for whom French was their native tongue? On the other hand, the subject, not to mention Professeur Renier-Bernadotte, fascinated me.

I had always been a sucker for history, especially the Middle Ages. It was in France that I had really felt the history of the Middle Ages come to life, with its medieval *châteaux* that one walked or drove past every day everywhere in Burgundy.

"I will tell you right now," the professor continued, "teaching is not my first love. Translating these ancient texts is my passion. Teaching is merely to pay the bills, so if you don't want to learn, don't waste my already limited time and, more importantly, my limited patience."

It was a novel experience for me to hear someone talk so openly and candidly about their deepest passions—especially those as obscure and poorly remunerated as medieval literature.

Professor Renier-Bernadotte glowed with something that I wanted to access for myself. I wanted to live with that same passion for something—something that had nothing to do with practicality or Franck or anything else, something I cultivated uniquely for my own pleasure.

"So, those of you who want to learn from me, go buy your books, and I'll see you back here next week. I'm going to my office to ponder the meaning of a sentence from the original text of *Tristan et Yseult*. Don't come to me with stupid questions. I won't take kindly to being bothered."

My mind full, I walked out of that class and up the stairs to my next class, Nineteenth-Century French Literature, mulling over Professeur Renier-Bernadotte. She truly didn't seem to give a toss what people thought of her. How liberating.

After that class, I went to the café with the decent bathroom to meet Franck. An hour later, I found myself thinking that I really needed to find a place to kill time between classes until we could get our own apartment. Even though hanging out in Parisian cafés figured highly in my daydreams of what life in Paris would be like, my bladder and my budget could only handle a limited amount of espressos in a day.

When Franck arrived, I lost no time telling him that Professeur Renier-Bernadotte *did* exist.

He settled in beside me. "Café?" I shook my head no.

"She was brilliant," I continued. "Confident. Took zero crap from anyone."

"She was worth the wait?"

"Definitely."

"I had a crazy teacher when I was at the Sorbonne," he said after he had ordered. "He taught philosophy and was completely deranged, but nobody ever missed one of his classes, even if they were prostrate with pneumonia. None of us knew what he was going to do next. His big thing was real-life enactments, such as urinating in the corner of the amphitheater to illustrate our reaction to someone contravening society's norms."

"In one of those beautiful old amphitheaters at the old Sorbonne?"

"*Oui.*"

I laughed. "That must have thrilled the janitors."

"One day, we came into class to discover that he had constructed a full-sized, fully-functioning guillotine. He even used vegetables to demonstrate that it worked, and did it ever... We all had to vote who among our fellow students would have their head chopped off at the end of the lesson. We weren't entirely sure our teacher wouldn't go through with the execution—there was no question he was unhinged—or whether this was just a ploy to introduce some topic like fear or self-sacrifice or cowardice for discussion."

"What did you do?"

"Somebody must have slipped out and ratted on him, because as he was tallying the votes, the security guys came in and dragged him away."

I leaned forward. "And his guillotine?"

"They took that away too. Sadly, he never came back after that day, and they replaced him with another teacher who was a bore."

"Any teacher would be boring in comparison."

"True. But even though he was crazy, or perhaps *because* he was crazy, what he taught stuck in my head. I received an incredible grade in Philosophy that year. He was one of the best teachers I ever had."

When I thought back to my favorite teachers, constructing a historical killing machine in class was not something that came to mind.

"How did the job search go?" I said.

Franck toyed with the sugar cube on his espresso saucer. "I went to the Pôle emploi first thing, but there's not much out there. I did grab a few job descriptions that sounded interesting."

"What kind of jobs?"

"Mainly journalism."

That sounded promising. I waited for further details, but none seemed to be forthcoming. I wanted to probe further but repressed the urge.

"I'm going to need to figure out a place to go between classes until we get our apartment," I said. "There's nowhere at school, and the park benches are going to be chilly in about a month or so."

Franck shredded his sugar cube paper, deep in thought.

"I have an idea," he said, after a time.

"What?"

"I'd like to surprise you. When is your next class?"

"Two o'clock."

"Do you have your student card?"

"Yes."

"Follow me."

We grabbed two *saucisson au beurre* baguette sandwiches from the *boulangerie* and ate them as we walked across the place Monge and plunged into a narrow, winding street on the opposite side.

I stopped in my tracks, captivated by the bustling, medieval road. It was lined with shops on either side selling fish, meat, cheese, and flowers, and pretty much everything else under the sun.

"What is this place?" I asked Franck.

"It's the rue Mouffetard," he said. "Hemmingway lived here at some point. Maybe Balzac too, but I could be remembering that wrong. It's one of the last remaining medieval sections of the city after Haussmann did his big remodeling of Paris."

I was riveted.

"This isn't where we're stopping today, though," he said, pulling my arm.

"We have to come back here."

"We will. It's in our *quartier*...or what might be our neighborhood if we get Jacinthe and Nathanael's apartment."

The wait until our next meeting with Monsieur Arnseneau felt like an eternity. But it wasn't as if we didn't have other things to do. I needed to buy books, figure out the rest of my classes, and find a place to go between my classes. Franck needed to find a job. We needed to go to the bank about the guarantee... The ground seemed to lurch under my feet. *Breathe, Laura. Breathe.*

Franck led me through a warren of alleyways that branched off from the rue Mouffetard. I had no clue where we were or where we were going, but I had learned that, in Paris, I could trust Franck when it came to directions. He somehow always discovered shortcuts that I doubted many born-and-bred Parisians knew about.

When we burst out into the open again, standing before us in all its golden glory was the pillared edifice of le Panthéon, the final resting place of Victor Hugo, Emile Zola, and Voltaire, to name just a few. The huge blocks of golden stone glowed in the sunlight, and the pillars and the cupola declared that this was a majestic place. It was built to be as awe-inspiring as the heroes buried inside, and it succeeded.

"Wow," I said.

"*Oui*, it's stunning," Franck agreed. "But it's not where we're heading." He pulled me along past it.

"But…," I protested. Franck ignored me.

On the other side of the *place* in front of the Panthéon we entered a building that was made of a similar creamy stone. Bibliotèque Sainte-Geneviève, with an arrow pointing up, was written on a sign at the bottom of a worn stone staircase.

At the top of the stairs we entered a space that robbed me of the ability to breathe. Paris was doing that a lot.

The ceilings were the height of many buildings. Two rows of intricate metallic arches ran down the length of the cavernous space, and underneath them were equally symmetrical rows of long, polished wood tables, each topped with eight precisely spaced study lights. The walls were covered with rows and rows of books.

While my mouth hung open, Franck chatted in hushed tones to a woman who sat at the desk by the door. He nudged me. "Laura? Can you get out your student card?"

It was possible that this was not the first time he had asked me to do this. I took it out of my wallet and passed it to him, unable to tear my eyes from the most inspiring library I had ever seen.

Franck and the woman continued to conduct their business. I paid them scant attention as I studied the stone arches that lined the huge curved windows equally spaced around the room. The metal arches looked as if they were designed in a similar motif to the metalwork of the Eiffel tower. Maybe Gustave Eiffel had left his signature there as well?

The woman pushed three sheets of paper in front of me for me to sign. "Mademoiselle," she prompted.

I signed where she pointed, then she whisked the paper and my student card away. Franck also gave her my passport, which he had been carrying on him for some reason.

"This place is…just…" I couldn't find adequate words.

"It's probably my favorite library," Franck said. "I used to come here when I was at the Sorbonne to study and read, or just soak up the atmosphere. It's open to all registered students in

Paris, you know, although you must get a separate library card for it. What do you think of coming here between classes?"

"*Parfait*," I said.

"Do you have one of those little identity photos of yourself?" Franck asked.

As a matter of fact, I did. I had taken several strips of them at the Photomaton machine in the Metro station. I'd been warned by Franck that I would need them for my various cards, *fiches*, and *dossiers* that were required of a student in France. I dug one out of my wallet.

Franck and the librarian completed the paperwork, so I just took deep sniffs of the scent of polished wood and old pages and worn leather.

Fifteen minutes later, I was the proud holder of a library card from the bibliothèque Sainte-Geneviève, which, as far as I was concerned, was one of the most treasured possessions I'd ever owned.

Somehow, even though Franck was no longer a student (although he would always be a Student of Life, as he enjoyed telling me), he managed to sweet-talk the librarian into making up a library card for him too, so when time permitted, we could hang out at the library together.

I parked the job search stress for the time being. I wrapped my arms around Franck and pressed my lips against his neck.

"What's this for?" he said. "Not that I'm complaining."

"I'm lucky to be with someone who wants to spend time in the world's most beautiful library with me. I just…I love you."

"*Je t'aime, aussi.*"

chapter **fourteen**

The next day, I had my first class at the old Sorbonne in an amphi-theater at Paris IV, the original Sorbonne building on the boule-vard Saint-Michel.

We had visited there three years before when we spent a short time together in Paris before I returned to Canada. When I had imagined going to school at the Sorbonne, the old Sorbonne was my fantasy. Reality, I was discovering, was usually more compli-cated than daydreams.

The classical entrance, made from the same creamy-gold stone as the Panthéon, rose in Grecian columns and was adorned with stone statues of studious-looking guys from ancient times. A gray dome topped the building, and the whole ensemble reeked of academic dignity.

Franck tried to lead me into the building but was stopped at the entrance by a guard. I showed him my student card and the guard said that, while I was permitted through the hallowed doors, Franck was not. He added something about the terrorist threat being elevated. Judging from the amount of people milling around wearing fanny packs and taking photos, I suspected the guards were more concerned about overzealous tourists.

Franck tried to sweet-talk the guard and even showed him his new library card, but the guard, unlike the librarian, proved impervious to his charm.

"I'll wait for you here after class." Franck squeezed my hand. "By the fountain."

I gave him a distracted kiss. "I'll be fine."

My class was indeed located in one of the massive amphitheaters. I took a seat on one of the worn wooden benches, about halfway up the rows. I stared up at the glorious frescoes on the ceiling. Even though they were surely painted centuries before, I was sure I could catch a whiff of oil paint.

It dawned on me that this was the exact amphitheater that Franck had snuck me into three years earlier, just twenty-four hours before I flew back to Canada. When I had sat there with him, I'd dreamed about coming back as a student. My dream had come true. Goosebumps rippled down my spine.

We are living together in Paris, despite the odds that have been stacked against us as a couple. We just couldn't break up at the end of the year. We had fought so hard to be together.

We'd said good-bye that time, not knowing if we would see each other again. My heart felt as though it was being wrenched in two. I couldn't even imagine what our good-byes would be like at the end of the year if Franck decided to stay in France. I didn't want to.

That thought felt like a knife being sliced across my sternum. I needed to turn my attention to something less painful.

The amphitheater was filling. Again, students were smoking, seemingly unperturbed by the damage their smoke did to the frescoes and woodwork. I seemed to be the only one in awe of my surroundings and their historical importance. I wanted to stand up and yell at everyone, "For God's sake, we're studying in the same school as Simone de Beauvoir, Saint Thomas Aquinas, Balzac, and Marie Curie. Some respect would be nice."

Maybe the wonder of French people would be triggered more by things like the vast swaths of virgin forest that covered a good part of Canada, the huge tree trunks, and the wild beaches with not a single soul upon them. Or is wonder viewed by the French as inelegant or unintellectual? I'd have to ask Franck.

The teacher, a male specimen who looked like he had been plucked from the back of a dusty cupboard of academia, came in and told us we would be learning about the myths of Amphitryon and Satan throughout French literature.

He didn't hold a candle to the charisma of Professor Renier-Bernadotte, but the surroundings made up for a lot. Besides, the reading list he handed out promised some eclectic course materials.

Franck was in the square when I came out, sitting on the edge of one of the three fountains. "How did it go?"

"*Bien.*" I sat down beside him. "I was in the same amphitheater you took me to three years ago."

"That's the one I thought it was. Is it still as beautiful?"

"Stunning. It got me thinking... Remember how difficult it was to say good-bye when I flew back to Canada?"

"It was awful." Franck slid his arm around my waist and drew me closer. "I took the Metro from the airport back to Paris and went directly to the consulate to find out how I could emigrate to Montreal."

"I never want to have to go through that again." My heart was pounding, but I tried to make my voice sound light.

"Why would you have to?" Franck asked.

"Well...if you decided to stay in France at the end of this year..."

Franck cast me a baffled look. "But it's the beginning of the year, Laura. Why are you ruminating over that now?"

"Because that's what I do. I overthink."

"Don't." Franck picked my backpack off the ground and slung it over his shoulder. "Instead, come and have a coffee with me."

I wasn't mollified. My worry, if anything, was stoked by Franck's words.

Seated at a table by the window in the café, I couldn't find the nerve to loop back to the end-of-the-year topic again. Instead,

I talked about my class. "I don't know what to expect from the course really, but the prof seems nice enough. Maybe a bit boring."

"*Quoi?* He didn't build his own guillotine?" Franck asked.

"Nothing that exciting. I think he is lost in the maze of academic life and has no desire to be found. By the way, is there a bookstore nearby? I need to buy textbooks for my classes. They didn't tell us where we should go."

"That's because everybody already knows. Gibert Joseph. Off Saint-Michel. That's where all students at the Sorbonne go."

The bookstore, just a few short blocks away, was easy to spot with its yellow awnings and students milling around in front. Everyone seemed to be, like me, armed with lists given to them by their professors. Harried staff were identifiable by their yellow shirts. They rushed around, apparently ninja-trained in the art of avoiding eye contact.

Franck figured out where we needed to go, and led me to a wall, where I plucked out a text on Madame Renier-Bernadotte's list, entitled *Érec et Énide*.

I ran my hand over the cover. This was a feast-for-the-eyes type of book. This one was the original text in medieval French, and the cover was lushly illustrated with gold-and-red medieval illustrations.

On the translated texts, Professeur Renier-Bernadotte's name was indeed front and center on the cover as the translator. To this pile, I added my books for Amphitryon et Satan and joined the long, snaking line of students at the cash register.

The students in line were complaining—about their profs, about their courses, about how crowded it was in the bookstore, about how the store had run out of an essential textbook, and about how they weren't allowed to smoke.

I made my purchases and stacked them lovingly in my backpack, then we escaped. On the sidewalk, I realized we were close to my favorite bookstore in Paris and, quite possibly, the world: Shakespeare and Company.

Plans for a languid Parisian evening before having to take the grubby RER back to the *banlieue* took shape in my mind: a long browse in Shakespeare and Company; a shawarma from Franck's secret spot in the Latin Quarter, eaten in the park near the foot of Saint-Michel; perhaps a stroll into Notre-Dame to admire the stained glass windows; and then an ice cream at Berthillon on the Île Saint-Louis... More or less, it would be a reproduction of the last few hours Franck and I had spent in Paris together before I went back to Canada three years earlier.

Before I could verbalize any of this, Franck took my wrist and checked my watch. "We really need to go to the bank before it closes," he said, "and figure out what we need to do to come up with a bank guarantee for Monsieur Arseneau."

I wanted to protest, but...short term pain for long term gain. Once we secured our apartment, we could do those Parisian things *every* evening if we wanted to. Well...except for the fact that, if we did indeed score the apartment, our "entertainment and eating out" budget would shrink to zero.

We walked along the boulevard Saint-Germain toward Jacinthe and Nathanael's old apartment on the rue des Fossés Saint-Bernard. Franck said that he had seen a Banque Nationale de Paris nearby and that it was best to start banking right away in a bank the landlord would recognize. We were already foreign enough.

Both Franck and I had our accounts at the BNP. Not *impressive* accounts, but we had worked hard for the money in them.

"Why do you walk so fast?" I said, gasping to keep up as we passed several cute little boutiques, which I noted to check out when we were more settled. Franck had two speeds—regular speed and Paris speed.

"This is the pace of Paris," he answered without breaking his stride. "If you don't go at the same pace as everyone else here, you get left behind."

Paris, in my mind, was a place where one should—on the contrary—slow down and appreciate things. Meandering was my modus operandi. This acceleration of my boyfriend was a shocking side effect of Paris life I hadn't anticipated.

When we arrived at the bank—way quicker than I believed

was humanly possible—I glanced at the *horaire* posted outside. Franck had been right to hurry. It closed in only half an hour, and I knew that the French didn't joke around when it came to knocking off work at the end of the day.

We had to be buzzed in—that was one thing I was going to have to adjust to. In Canada, everyone just swans in and out of buildings, including banks. I knew, theoretically, Paris isn't the same, but it was still a bit shocking to think of employees being locked inside their bank and buzzing in customers one by one.

Inside, Franck went right to the *accueil*, where, thankfully, there was no line and a smiling young bank teller.

"*Oui?*" she said. "How can I help you today, Monsieur?"

"We are trying to secure an apartment on the rue des Fossés Saint-Bernard," he said. "We've just moved to Paris."

"Ah?" she said. "What building?"

Franck described the building, and the teller's brows shot up to her hairline.

"You know it?" Franck asked.

"In a way. The landlord does his banking here, as do many of his tenants." She blushed and lowered her voice. "I'm not sure I was supposed to tell you that. I'm new with this job."

"He banks here? Perfect. You see, we need a bank attestation that will show Monsieur Arseneau that we can pay the rent." Franck shrugged apologetically. "We've just moved from Canada, so we are new at all of this too."

I knew that Franck had rented apartments during his two-year stint at the Sorbonne, but I also happened to know that these places were better left unmentioned. They were dives in the truest sense of the word, located in neighborhoods rife with crime, prostitution, and every kind of street life imaginable. Even if references from those apartments hadn't been almost impossible to track down, they wouldn't have done us any favors with either our prospective landlord or the bank.

"Canada?" The teller's eyes shone. "I have always dreamed of going to Canada! *Les grands espaces.* Dogsledding. Snowshowing..."

I could tell from her glowing expression that we had already forged a link with her through Franck's mention of my birth-place. *Well played, Franck.*

Though I had never been dogsledding in my life and snow-shoed only a handful of times, I knew better than to disappoint the teller by telling the truth. If it meant we could get the apart-ment, I would be willing to say I lived in the middle of the tundra and my best friend was a polar bear.

"Laura is from there." Franck pushed me forward to show that he wasn't lying about living in Canada, and to prove it, he had brought a Real Live Canadian as evidence.

"I was born there," I said dutifully. "My whole family lives there."

"Why did you want to move *here*?" the teller asked, her eyes round. "Paris is filthy. People are rude…"

"You're not from here?" Franck surmised. Indeed, Franck had warned me many times that born-and-bred Parisians can't imagine living anywhere else. As far as they are concerned, Paris is the epicenter of anything that means anything in the world—anywhere else, even big cities such as London and New York, are hopelessly uncultured.

"I'm from Brittany," the bank teller said. "I just moved here with my boyfriend to make some money, but it's just for a couple of years."

"I love Brittany," Franck said. "I sailed around the coast a few times."

She smiled. "Now, what is Monsieur Arseneau asking for this time? From what his tenants confide in me, he is *très proche de ses sous* and is always finding ways to get more rent and bigger deposits. Not a nice man, from what I've seen and heard—*typique-ment parisien*—although I shouldn't be saying that." She looked around shiftily.

"We've met him. Your impression of Monsieur Arseneau is entirely accurate," Franck said. "He wants an attestation from the bank, assuring him that we have enough funds in our accounts to cover six months' worth of rent. Neither of us have that much in our accounts right now, but I figured maybe there was another way…"

Her eyebrows drew together. "With some other landlords, perhaps, but he's as suspicious as they come."

"*Zut.*" I came up with and mentally discarded several possible solutions.

"Perhaps your parents," she said to Franck. "Would they be willing to write you an attestation?"

Franck frowned. "Even if they were, it wouldn't do any good. My parents aren't exactly rolling in cash themselves."

"Does Monsieur Arseneau have the right to check our bank accounts or ask for a readout only once, or can he, for example, ask for that every month?" I asked.

"Only once, I believe," she said. "Unless you fail to pay your rent, and then I'm sure he would demand that."

"We're not going to fail to pay our rent," I said, with certainty. My conviction came not because our monthly budget allowed us to pay the rent at this point but because I would rather forgo food than fail to meet such an obligation.

Franck nodded. Even if we had to live on only baguettes—astonishingly cheap in Paris—we would pay our rent.

"How about if we pool all the money we've saved up in our Canadian accounts?" I said to Franck. "I could get my Dad to transfer the money into our account over here. That should make a big enough amount."

"You're going to have to pay transfer fees, and last I checked, the exchange rate is not advantageous for Canadian dollars," the teller said.

"There's nothing we can do about that," I said. "Do you think that would be enough to satisfy Monsieur Arseneau?" I asked Franck, who, I could tell from his darting eyes, was doing rapid calculations in his head.

The teller held up a hand. "I think that could work, but honestly the least amount I know about the details, the better."

Ok. We have a plan. Or the foundation of a plan, anyway. "Can you give me all the international codes necessary to make an international transfer into my bank account here?" I asked her.

"Just a moment," she said, and left to confer with a colleague.

"Quick thinking." Franck squeezed my shoulder. "But are you sure you don't mind having all our savings moved over here?"

It would leave our bank accounts in Canada depleted. This was all the money I had earned from organizing mini-courses throughout the year at the Student's Union at the McGill University, plus my pay as a custom's officer at the Port of Victoria over the four summer months. It was the money Franck had saved from working in Montreal and as a fishing guide up in the Queen Charlotte Islands near Alaska during the summer months. Almost every cent.

"I honestly can't think of any other way."

"Me neither," Franck said.

"We have to at least try." We needed a nest of our own, away from the *banlieue*, Pauline's lingerie, the long RER rides, the lack of privacy...

"It still may not work out, you know," Franck reminded me. "Monsieur Arseneau still may not even be satisfied with proof of money in our account."

"I know." My heart contracted at the idea of that apartment and the chance of a real Parisian life slipping through our fingers. "But even if we try and fail, at least we'll know we did everything we could."

Franck gave my hand a quick squeeze. "You don't give up easily, do you?"

"No." Surrender was not part of my vocabulary. I sometimes wondered if maybe my life would be a little more peaceful, and I a little less anxious, if it were.

The teller handed us a piece of paper with a bunch of extremely long and, for the moment, unintelligible numerical codes written on it with a fountain pen. Many people in Paris still wrote with a fountain pen, I was discovering. The *boulangère*, the man behind the bar at the bistro who wrote out our receipt by hand, now the bank teller...

"As soon as we've arranged things, we'll be back to see you," Franck said. "We'll be banking here all year."

"I look forward to that," she said, smiling at both of us. "Good luck with Monsieur Arseneau. I have a feeling you'll need it."

chapter **fifteen**

I telephoned my father collect to ask him to make the transfer on our behalf. In the exceedingly unaccommodating ways of banks, international transfers had to be made in person.

One had to experience the illogical nature of how things happened there in France to truly believe life is conducted so differently. Most of the time, I got the distinct impression that my father thought I was exaggerating or, quite simply, pulling his leg. He just couldn't digest the reality that a landlord could possibly be able to require such a scandalous amount of money as a guarantee.

Pauline paced back and forth in front of me, obviously not reassured by my promise that she and Florent would not be charged a cent for the call. It was an extra element of stress added to the already fraught task of explaining to my Dad why we couldn't wait until the Canadian dollar was stronger against the franc. It made me even more determined to be in our own place.

Finally, mainly because he trusted me, my dad agreed to exercise his power of attorney over our Canadian accounts and transfer the lump sum into our joint BNP bank account in Beaune.

When I got off the phone, I looked up to see Pauline casting me black looks. "I promise you will not be charged for that call." I wasn't able to keep the frustration out of my voice. "I made sure it was collect. If you are charged so much as a cent, we will reimburse you immediately."

She whirled around and stormed into their bedroom. "I'll make sure of that!"

That night, we were treated to another punitive lingerie fashion show at the already awkward dinner table. Her outfit was just as revealing, but black satin and royal blue lace this time.

We had to get that apartment, whatever it took.

The next morning, we were back on the RER, headed out for another full day in Paris—classes for me, and the employment office for Franck.

We were having dinner with Nathanael and Jacinthe that night. Jacinthe presented it as a celebration of Nathanael returning from Bosnia without any bullets in him. As all four of us were in that awkward phase between apartments and the weather still felt like summer, we opted for a picnic on the banks of the Seine. We arranged for a meeting spot just behind Notre-Dame.

Franck walked me to the door of my next class in a separate building of Paris IV, two blocks off Saint-Michel and only five minutes down from the old Sorbonne.

The building itself was medieval and the classroom inside was equally as old, as well as dusty and crowded. Tiny particles of chalk dust danced in the beams of light that shone through the single-paned, minioned window.

The course was the only English literature course I was taking in Paris. I had no choice—I had to take at least one English language literature class to remain in my English program at McGill.

I'd chosen this course because it was on Dickens, which I'd already read and studied extensively. I needed an easy course to balance out the challenges of learning medieval French literature.

The seats were made up of worn and narrow wooden benches that ran almost from one side of the room to the other. They were so shiny with use that I surmised they had been polished by students' bums for several centuries.

In front of us was a thicker wooden plank that had old ink wells every foot and a half or so, like those in the amphitheater. Sadly, they were empty.

There were no frescoes, I noted with regret. Maybe I was becoming as hard to impress as the French students.

A willowy woman who looked barely older than me took the spot behind the wooden lectern at the front of the class. She cleared her throat. Most people stared at her in astonishment, surely sharing the same thought: *how could she possibly be old enough to be our teacher?*

"Hello," she began in a plummy accent that was an odd mix of British toff and French. "I will be your professor this year, and I'll be teaching you three of the most celebrated novels of Charles Dickens."

To be taught Dickens by a native French speaker…this was guaranteed to be a unique experience.

She handed out sheets that explained we would be studying: *Great Expectations*, *A Tale of Two Cities*, and *David Copperfield*, in that order. I had studied all of them either in high school or during my first two years of university. This was going to be a cakewalk.

"I will warn you now," the teacher (though it was hard to think of her as that) said. "I am an extremely hard marker. This course won't be easy for anyone."

I wondered if she knew she had a native English speaker in the class.

We were dismissed after we were given our reading lists. I walked up the boulevard Saint-Michel and through the crazy maze of streets between the Panthéon Paris and the rue Mouffetard, then on to the place Monge near Paris III, where I had my next course, another medieval class taught by Madame Renier-Bernadotte. I wished she would speak medieval French for us. I began to daydream about what this might sound like, and became lost, venturing down several dead-end, cobblestoned alleyways.

I paused in the middle of a passageway that was so narrow that I reached both my arms out to see if they would touch the stone walls on either side. They did. My fingertips touched the rough coolness of centuries-old stone. I looked up. Crooked stone walls punctuated with aging wooden shutters gave way to a sliver of blue sky above.

That exact spot probably hadn't changed much since the Middle Ages. I almost expected to hear medieval Paris around me—shouts, a cart going by on the larger street at the end of the passageway, a skinny stray cat meowing...

And then I saw it...a large jet flying far overhead, leaving a trail of jet stream that transected the narrow slice of sky above. I was jerked, reluctantly, back to the twentieth century.

Eventually, I managed to find the rue Monge and the bistro with the turkish toilets. I even had time to nip in and grab an espresso, feeling for one of the first times since my arrival like the quintessential French étudiante, even though my heavy backpack didn't fit the profile.

En route to class, I passed by a *boulangerie* with an incredibly ornate frontage—lots of curlicues and peach and azure blue tones. It wasn't quite lunchtime, but the pastries in the window looked so appetizing that my stomach began to rumble. I *had* done quite a bit of walking, after all.

I opened the door and was welcomed by the jingling little bell that heralded the arrival and departure of each customer. I inhaled the heavenly scent of yeast and spun sugar with an undernote of vanilla.

The bakery was just as baroque inside as outside. Ornate gold trim highlighted a variety of panels, mirrors, and painted sections of the walls. The entire ceiling was a fresco featuring frolicking cherubim. I felt as though I was in an opera house.

My eyes roved over the row upon row of buttery croissants, flaky *pains au* chocolat, and a new type of *pâtisserie* that I had never seen before—a twist of flaked pastry with some pale yellow cream and chocolate oozing out the edges.

"*Bonjour,* Madame," I said to the *boulangère* and pointed at the mystery pastry. "I've never seen those before. What are they called?"

"They're a relatively new invention," she said. "They're called *torsades* because they are twisted. It is *pâte feuilletée* with pastry cream and chocolate baked inside. Can I get you one?"

"Yes," I said. "*S'il vous plaît.*"

She wrapped one up in azure-and-peach paper, exquisitely coordinated with the shop, and handed me the change from my ten-franc coin.

"*Bon appétit!*" she said.

"*Merci.*"

I walked the rest of the way to Paris III in a fog of deliciousness. As I tore the beautiful wrapping away, the crinkle gave way to pastry that was fresh and flaky and still slightly warm from the oven. The vanilla-flecked pastry cream inside was creamy and studded with dark chocolate melted just enough to give way under my teeth. It wafted off waves of vanilla, cream, butter, and chocolate nirvana. This pastry was a whole-body experience.

I sighed with utter fulfillment when I was finished. I scrunched up the paper and looked for a garbage can. I'd reached the front doors of the school and, while I noticed a copious amount of litter on the ground, there were no garbage cans to be seen.

In a situation parallel to the toilets, there stood rusty, green metal rings on posts where, perhaps, one time in the distant past garbage cans had stood, but now all that was left were the rings welded onto the poles so students could only throw garbage through a hoop like a basketball net. From the cigarette butts, squished beer cans, broken wine bottles, random pages of paper, and ejected ink cartridges from fountain pens on the concrete below the hoops, I would have wagered that this was a favorite pastime.

No wonder tourists always complained of Paris being dirty and smelling of urine. There were no usable garbage cans or toilets. I crumpled my piece of paper and shoved it into my already full backpack.

It might make all my books and papers inside smell of torsade, *but that wouldn't be a bad thing.*

chapter **sixteen**

I spotted Franck crossing the street—shamelessly jaywalking in front of a car, whose driver honked his horn at him. Franck spun around, shrugged, and smiled.

"How did it go?" he asked me, after giving me a kiss.

"Great. I think I'm a little bit in love with Madame Renier-Bernadotte."

"You're not still terrified of her?"

"Oh, I am. I have love and fear for her."

"How did it go for you?" I asked. I hoped that maybe he had found a job.

"Let's go to the Bistro first for lunch and I'll fill you in. Wait, do you need to find a bathroom first?"

Franck knew me well. There was nowhere to go at school, after all.

"I do," I said. "But I have to figure out the whole turkish toilet thing if I'm going to be living here for a year."

Franck put his arm around my shoulder and kissed my cheek as we walked. "I think that's wise. Not to mention brave."

We paused for a moment in front of the chalkboard in the window of the bistro.

"Yum," Franck said. "*Pâté en croute, sole meunière* with lemon, a cheese platter, and *tarte tatin* for desert. That will be worth learning how to master a turkish toilet."

"I don't even want to think about it," I said. "Let alone discuss it."

I went to the WC as soon as we were given our table. Procrastinating wouldn't help. I stared at the hole in the ground—my nemesis. How was I going to conquer this thing? *Come on. All Parisian women do it.* I had to learn too. I took a deep breath.

When I headed back to the table, I raised my arms in triumph. "Victory!"

"*Félicitations!*" Franck said. "That will make your year in Paris much easier. What took you so long?"

"I washed my hands for five minutes afterward."

Just then, the *pâté en croute* arrived. They served generous portions there, and the slabs were thick, surrounded with flaky pastry, and full of perfectly seasoned pork, with little sliced cornichons visible here and there.

Franck had ordered a half liter of white wine before the customary half liter of house red. We took our time to savor forkfuls of the cured, flavorful meat and the flaky, tender pastry. The white wine, lip-smackingly dry with a pleasant mineral quality, was the perfect accompaniment.

The *sole meunière* was perfection worthy of Julia Child—a pristine filet of deboned sole, coated in flour and fried in butter, then deglazed with lemon. It was served with fresh lemon slices and tagliatelle pasta. The lemon butter sauce—topped with freshly cracked black pepper—was soaked up by the pasta, making a dish so scrumptious that neither of us said a word as we polished it off and finished off the white wine.

When the waiter whisked away our empty plates, I leaned back in my chair and sighed deeply.

"I was right when I thought this place was worth trying, *n'est-ce pas?*" Franck lifted an eyebrow.

"Oh *oui*. I think that was the best *sole meunière* I've ever tasted."

The cheese platter was so heavy it took the *garçon* both hands to carry it over to our table, and even then, his slight frame was staggering a bit under its weight. On it were generous chunks of about twenty different French cheeses—everything from extremely moldy goat cheese plugs to firm, flavorful Cantal from the Auvergne region in the center of France.

Franck and I chose an assortment of cheeses each, although I took about twice as much as he did. I had been introduced to French cheese platters when I first arrived in Burgundy at seventeen, and I still felt as though I had a lot of catching up to do. The red wine and fresh baguette slices in the basket on the table were the perfect accompaniment.

For dessert, there was a vanilla-infused, caramelized apple upside down tart, a Parisian bistro classic called a *tarte tatin*. We finished off with a strong espresso each and then rolled out of the Brasserie Le Monge and toward the Gibert Joseph bookstore on boulevard Saint-Michel to buy the rest of my course books.

The line was as long as it had been on our previous trip, but even though all I felt like doing was curling up for an après-lunch nap, I reasoned that standing in a vertical position was imperative for my digestion after that Parisian feast.

After I paid, I found Franck, who was browsing the long sidewalk tables piled with books. "I guess we have some time to kill now before dinner." I checked my watch. "Three hours to be precise."

"I would suggest going to the library," Franck said. "But it's just too beautiful out today to be inside."

It was one of those late September days when it still felt like summer. Blue sky. Bright sun. As beautiful as the bibliotèque Sainte-Geneviève was, I also wanted to soak up those last warm days. "Is there a park or something nearby?" I asked. "I'd love to lie on some grass."

"Are you feeling sleepy after that lunch?"

"Maybe *un peu*."

Franck smiled. "I think I have an idea." He took my book bags and my backpack. "It's only about a ten-minute walk."

"Ok," I said. "You know, you don't have to carry my stuff."

"Yes, I do."

"Why?"

"Because that's the gallant thing to do. I should have taken them sooner."

I knew that perhaps I should protest the macho nature of this Gallic tradition but it melted my heart every time. It wasn't feminist of me, but I didn't really care. Anyway, since we met, it had never been just a one-way street. Franck didn't just take care of me; we took care of each other.

Ten minutes later, we were standing in front of a pair of massive wooden doors on the rue Monge, just a few blocks down from the bistro where we had eaten lunch. There was a metal sign to the right of the doors which said Arènes de Lutèce, except that the letters looked odd.

"What is this place?" I asked Franck. It didn't look like a park.

"Open the door," he said.

"I'm allowed?" I asked.

"*Bien sûr*. Even if you weren't, I'd recommend you do it anyway."

I pushed open the heavy door and found myself in an arched stone tunnel. On the far side of the tunnel, I could see a flat space where a few groups of men, many wearing berets, were playing relaxed games of *pétanque* on the gravel. Above them rose curved row upon row of extremely old, worn-looking stone benches…or seats maybe. They were set apart quite widely, and between them grew tufted grass. Above them seemed to be another flat area covered in grass with a tree here and there.

"Can you figure it out?" Franck asked.

"No," I said, looking around…unless… I examined the smaller stone tunnels inset in the stone wall that encircled the gravel half-circle…but it couldn't be, not right in the middle of a busy Parisian street… "It looks like an outdoor theatre of some kind," I said. "Kind of like an amphitheater."

"Mhm-hmn," Franck said.

"It looks old," I added. "Is it some sort of modern replica or something?"

Franck shook his head. "No replica. This is a Roman amphitheater left over from when Paris was a Roman town called Lutèce."

Left over? What did he mean? "You don't mean this is an original Roman amphitheater, do you?"

"*Oui*, that's it."

"One the Romans built?"

"I imagine it was the slaves who did the actual building. I'm
not certain if they considered themselves Romans or not. I should
have paid better attention in my history classes in high school."

"But...that's *incredible*," I said. "I mean, what's it doing here,
just off the rue Monge?"

"The more accurate question is what is the rue Monge and
the 5th arrondissement and the rest of Paris doing around this
place? After all, the amphitheater was here first."

"It's peaceful here," Franck continued. "A lot of people have
never bothered to open the doors, so don't know its existence. It
tends to be used mainly by people who live around here. I discovered it when I was a student here."

"So, we're standing in an *actual* amphitheater from the old
Roman city of Paris?" I just needed to be certain on this point.
"Not a reproduction? Like those are the actual Roman stones it
was built with?" I waved my hand around.

"Yes. But remember the Roman city wasn't called Paris; it was
called Lutèce. That's why this spot is called the Arènes de Lutèce.
Arènes is another name for amphitheater."

"Like 'arena' in English?"

"Exactly. They did a lot of sports here, as well as plays and
speeches, so maybe that's why they used the word 'Arènes.'"

The pea gravel crunched under my feet as I wandered around,
trying to wrap my head around the history. The clink of the *pétanque* balls called me back to the present.

"How did you know so much about Roman history?" I asked
Franck.

"By reading *Astérix* comics, like all good French children."

"So...there were tigers and stuff here? And gladiators?"

Franck pointed to the low, curved tunnels I had been inspecting before. They punctuated the bottom wall of the amphitheater periodically. "You see those tunnels? That's where the animals came out. Sadly, maybe slaves too."

I turned in a circle, taking in everything around me I could. "Unbelievable," I said. "If we get the apartment, I would walk by this on my way to school almost every day."

Franck nodded, looking bemused.

"Do you realize how incredible this is?" I asked him. "To be standing in the middle of an actual Roman amphitheater that is just…you know…behind a set of doors off a busy street?"

Nobody was charging admission. There were no security guards. It was just public space—just another neighborhood park, except for the fact that it was an *actual Roman amphitheater*.

"I don't think I will ever tire of showing Paris to you." Franck put his arm around my waist and led me up one of the worn stone staircases. *Where actual Romans must have walked in their togas!*

We found a tranquil patch of grass at the very top of the last row of stone steps (or were they seats? A bit of both, I supposed). We spread out our sweaters before lying down. Franck lay on his back, and I rested my head on his stomach and looked up at the tree branches and the sky. I could almost hear the sound of the Roman crowds cheering.

"I forgot to tell you about my visit to the Pôle emploi," Franck said.

I couldn't believe it, but between the lunch and the bookstore and this place, I had forgotten about his job search.

"How did it go?" I asked, closing my eyes. The sun was hot, and I was beginning to feel drowsy. I wasn't feeling in the correct frame of mind to talk about the job hunt. I was still too steeped in the past there to worry about the future.

"There's not that much out there, but I may have found something in journalism."

"Really?"

"Yes. It's a paper that covers trade shows in Paris. It pays decently, and they need someone quickly."

"Where is it based?"

"La Défense."

La Défense was the new, industrial area of Paris, with modern architecture. It felt completely different than Paris but was only a few Metro stops away.

"What do you have to do?"

"Do up a CV and then apply. I'll have to ask to borrow Pauline's computer over the weekend, I guess."

"Do you think that's going to be a problem?"

"No…it shouldn't be, but—"

"You're no longer sure of anything with her."

"Yeah."

"That makes two of us."

"Tomorrow is Saturday. I'll work on it then," he said. "The woman at the Pôle emploi said having a contract would help us with the apartment, even if it was only a CDD."

A CDD is a *contrat de travail à durée déterminée*. The French never use a concise term when a long, convoluted name is possible.

Basically, a CDD is a short-term contract, anything from one week to one year. That is how most French people begin work in France. Starting with a CDD that they never know will be renewed or not, they slog away for years to earn the Holy Grail of French employment—the coveted CDI—or *contrat de travail à durée indéterminée*. The CDI is basically a job without an end date.

France's strict employee protection laws mean that an employee with a CDI could rob the company blind, burn down the building, sleep with the boss's spouse, and be discovered hoarding body parts in their freezer, and *still* not be fired.

This, of course, is why all French people want a CDI, and why all French employers don't want to hand any out.

For a landlord, of course, a CDI would be the most compelling proof of employment, but seeing as CDIs were so few and far between in France, maybe Monsieur Arseneau would accept a CDD. Anyway, Franck having a job would be fantastic, no matter what. It was one big thing we could tick off our list.

"Are they hiring right away?"

"That's what the woman at the Pôle emploi said. All I can do is apply and hope for the best."

After a few minutes, Franck's eyelids had closed, and I could tell from the rhythm of his breathing that he was close to falling asleep.

"Maybe you should go there in person," I prompted.

"I probably will," Franck murmured. "Monday."

Within a few minutes, he was snoring softly, and I eventually dozed off too, dreaming of job applications and leases and French employers wearing togas and laurel wreaths.

chapter **seventeen**

A rousing cheer from the gentlemen playing *pétanque* woke us.

I checked my watch almost immediately. We had been dozing for almost two hours. The shadows of the trees above now stretched over us, but the air was still warm. I stretched my arms above my head. "I think we were more tired than we realized." I wasn't a napper, but I clearly hadn't yet adjusted to the go-go-go pace of Paris.

Our days in the city were long because of the RER ride on either end and because we had no home to go to during the day. I had also become intimately acquainted with the metal bar positioned right under my back as I (tried) to sleep on Pauline and Florent's click-clack. It would be paradise to go back to our own apartment and collapse into our own bed whenever we felt like it.

"We have to stop at the store on the way to la Seine to grab some things for dinner." Franck interrupted my daydream.

"*Oui*," I agreed, but didn't move.

"Comfortable?" Franck queried after a few more minutes. He couldn't move until I did because my head was still on his stomach.

"Come on, Franck. Get going," I chided. "Lazy-bones." I sat up with a groan and took a few seconds to soak in the timeless peace of the amphitheater. "I like this place," I said. "A lot."

"I knew you would." Franck leaned over and gave me a kiss. "And now it's our place. Get up, woman!"

We arrived at the appointed picnic spot on the banks of the Seine with our arms full of fresh baguettes, cheese, two *saucisson secs*, little red cherry tomatoes from Provence, and a box of *macarons*.

"I hope they've brought a knife," Franck said, looking down at our haul dubiously.

"I'm sure somebody will think of it."

The spot was at the tip of the Île Saint-Louis, looking down the Seine with our backs turned to Notre-Dame.

We had just settled in when Jacinthe and Nathanael arrived with three other people, two whom I didn't know, and one I unfortunately did—Alexandrine Montdidier—the queen of the exclusive gourmet pasta party. They all were carrying baskets and bags of food as well.

I wondered which was worse, spending the evening with Pauline and Florent or with Alexandrine. It was a toss-up. At least there were seven of us at the picnic, so hopefully, her noxious effect would be diluted.

We all said our *bonjours* and gave *les bises*, and Jacinthe and Nathanael introduced us to their two other friends: Emmanuel—who they all referred to as Momo—was a radio journalist; and Caroline—the tall, rail-thin woman—was his best friend and also a journalist. I didn't catch further details for her.

In giving the customary round of *bises*, Alexandrine kissed the air beside my face rather than my actual face—a pointed slight in France.

Momo, perhaps to compensate for Alexandrine's rudeness, nudged me and nodded at Franck. "He's delicious. Where did you find him?"

"Burgundy. I had to come all the way from Canada to Beaune."

Franck was busy talking to Caroline. Momo scanned him from head to toe. "It looks like all those kilometers were worth it," he said.

"They were." I smiled at Momo as Nathanael finished spreading out a huge blanket and waved at us to come and sit down.

At times like that— which happened so often, like earlier that day at the amphitheater—how could I ever doubt that Franck and I would be together forever? But if that were the case, why didn't he just reassure me? Why couldn't he simply promise he would return to Montreal with me at the end of the year? Maybe he didn't feel as sure as I did.

It wasn't just my decision to stay together; it was Franck's decision too. I cursed my lack of control.

"How was Bosnia?" I asked Nathanael. I had to think of something else besides the future or I would be bad company.

"Oh. You know. Terrible. Wonderful. Unreal."

"Did you get shot at?" I sat down on the blanket beside him.

"A few times, but nothing too close."

Jacinthe held up her hand. "Don't ask him the details, *s'il te plaît*. I don't want to know."

Momo settled down beside me. "Have you figured out yet that I'm gay?" he said.

"I thought that might be a possibility."

"You did?"

"Describing my boyfriend as delicious was a bit of a tip off, *tu sais*."

"*Ah, oui*, of course. It's just that I like to clear up any confusion right off the bat."

"No confusion," I said. "Zero problem either."

"I've tried to turn him," Caroline said, sitting across from us and mock pouting. "He would be the world's best boyfriend for me, besides...you know...the actual wanting-to-have-sex-with-me part."

"You don't have a problem with homosexuality?" Momo asked me.

Jacinthe laughed. "Momo. Give Laura a break. You just met her."

"I just like to know where I stand with people from the start," he said.

"Of course not," I said. "I'm Canadian. Live and let live— that's our motto."

"She's not Catholic either," Franck added. "So there's that too."

Everyone gasped, and I wasn't sure it was entirely in jest.

"Lucky you," Momo said, with feeling.

"Is anyone *not* OK with you being gay?" I asked in disbelief. It was the mid-Nineties after all, and Paris was one of the most cosmopolitan cities in the world.

But then I thought of a childhood friend of Franck's who had committed suicide when he was sixteen. Franck always believed that it was because his friend was gay and that this was considered unacceptable in a traditional Burgundian winemaking village at that time. Sadly, he was probably right.

"You mean, besides my parents and my siblings?" Momo said. "My entire family, actually?"

"I'm so sorry. That must be painful for you."

Momo surprised me by leaning over and giving me a kiss on my cheek. "I like you."

Caroline stuck her tongue out at me in jest. "You can't have him as your almost boyfriend," she said. "I've staked my claim."

I accepted a glass of Champagne from Nathanael. "I've got Franck," I said, leaning back into Franck's chest. "Trust me, my hands are full."

Momo gave Franck a lingering once over. "I'll bet."

Franck laughed.

Alexandrine hadn't said a word during this exchange, but now observed us with a face like a shriveled prune. She leaned over and whispered something to Jacinthe, who frowned at her.

"So how is school going, Laura?" Alexandrine asked me. "How quaint it must be to still be living the life of an *étudiante*."

"I'm only twenty-one, so it's an appropriate thing to be doing at my age."

She narrowed her eyes at me, clearly disappointed that she hadn't scored a hit. "And you're just at *le fac*, not *les grandes écoles*?" she queried in an unnaturally honeyed tone.

In France, *les grandes écoles* that teach politics and economics and spew out generation upon generation of France's politicians (not an effective system, I surmised, given the state of French politics) are far more prestigious, not to mention expensive, than the universities—including la Sorbonne.

"I study literature," I said. "They only offer that at *les facs*."

"Laura is an intellectual," Nathanael added. "She's studying medieval French literature even though her native tongue in English. *N'est-ce pas*, Laura?"

"I don't know about intellectual."

"You are," said Jacinthe.

"You're far smarter than me in any case," Franck said.

"I would say you're far smarter than any of us here." Jacinthe raised a defiant brow at Alexandrine.

I felt myself turning tomato red. I took a sip of my Champagne, which sparkled like twinkling stars under the pink evening light. It was delicious, although not as good as the Dom Pérignon rosé we had drunk to toast our kebabs. Still, it was a fine vintage of Moët & Chandon. I was becoming spoiled.

"There are a million different kinds of intelligence," I said. "I'm a hard worker and there's stuff I find interesting. Now, one of my profs, Madame Renier-Bernadotte, *she* is a true intellectual. I'd love to be like her. She's unrelentingly rigorous and passionate about her work. She's in the middle of translating the original texts of *Tristan and Yseult* to modern French. It's not the first translation she has done either—"

I looked at the faces around me and realized I had lost them. Oh yeah. Not everyone found medieval French literature as riveting as I did.

"So, Caroline," I said, "what kind of journalism do you do exactly?"

Two hours later, the sun had almost set over the Seine, and the *bateaux-mouches* carrying tourists from every country had turned on their lights as they swept by us.

The loudspeaker systems on the boats always mentioned the history of the Île Saint-Louis, Notre-Dame, the great flooding of the Seine, and how on nice evenings, Parisians liked to come and picnic on the banks of the Seine.

Tourists looked out their boats to our group as we lounged on our picnic blankets, still drinking wine and lazily nibbling on *macarons*. Crusts of baguette and emptied wine bottles were scattered around us.

The tourists probably thought we were a group of Parisians— well, most of us were, but I wondered whether I stood out like a sore thumb with my different clothes. My Levi's were a different cut than the French jeans, I wore my hair in a ponytail instead of one of those French twists, I hadn't wrapped a scarf around my neck when the sun went down...did I blend in? Probably not.

It turned out everyone except Jacinthe and me was a journalist. We chatted about people they knew in common and restaurants and their families. They asked Franck and me a lot of questions about Canada, and everyone pretty much ignored Alexandrine and her sour remarks. I wondered why, besides the fact her father was a celebrity, they bothered to hang out with her at all.

"The *bateaux-mouches* look magical at night," I said. I always found it amusing that the direct translation of "*bateaux-mouches*" is "fly-boats." Is that because they look like gigantic insects coasting along the surface of the Seine?

Alexandrine made a disparaging sound deep in her throat, as if she was hawking up an irksome bit of phlegm. "Ugh. They're for the tourists."

"I adore them," Franck said. "There's no better way to admire Paris at night."

"Let's go on one!" Momo said, sitting up from his lounging position.

"*Pitié, non!*" Alexandrine said. "If you do, I won't be joining you. In fact, I may never talk to you again."

"Now there's an excellent reason to go!" Momo stood up and brushed the crumbs off his jeans. I loved this guy.

We packed up our blankets and baskets, chattering like a bunch of excited children.

"We have to use the *bateaux-mouches* at the pont Neuf," Caroline said. "They're the best. Most of the boats are open to the sky on the second deck.

"Do you remember the time we stood on the pont des Arts and threw buckets of water over the heads of people in the *bateaux mouches*?" Nathanael asked Franck.

"I'd forgotten about that," Franck said. "I hope nobody does that to us."

"You would deserve it," I said.

"Bad karma," Jacinthe said.

"True," Franck and Nathanael said in unison.

Alexandrine picked up her things, muttering in a low voice about how juvenile we all were and how she couldn't believe we were going to go through with such folly. Nobody paid attention to her, except Jacinthe, who said to her at one point, "Alexandrine, either come with us or not, but don't just stand around complaining. Help me with this picnic basket."

"But where are we going to put all these things?" Alexandrine complained. "We cannot possibly take them on the boat with us. They'll think we're carrying a bomb. *Quelle galère.*"

"We're parked just above here," Jacinthe said. "We'll stop by the car on the way to the pont Neuf and drop off our things."

We did just that and walked across the Île de la Cité to the pont Neuf and then down to the *quai* to pay our fares for our evening ride on the *bateau-mouche* that was departing in fifteen minutes.

Momo's irrepressible mirth carried us all along. Even Alexandrine cracked something that looked like a ghost of a smile once in a while, which said something for Momo's capacity for spreading good humor.

Caroline ran onto the boat first and found us all seats together on the second floor, which, as she had promised, was open to the clear sky above.

Some hapless German tourists tried to take some of the block of seats Caroline was reserving for us and, as I was coming down the aisle toward her, I heard her telling them to get lost in no uncertain terms. They clearly understood barely a word of her French, but her tone was unmistakable. The Germans beat a hasty retreat.

The boat left the dock shortly afterward, and we pulled out onto the calm, black waters of the Seine at night. The monuments of Paris slid by one by one—the Louvre, la place de la Concorde, the Eiffel Tower, musée d'Orsay, Notre-Dame, the Arab World Institute (when we passed that, I sent up a wish to the skies that we would be soon living on that very same street, rue des Fossés Saint-Bernard). Every monument, the entire city core, in fact, was artistically lit up, allowing me to appreciate the architecture and grandeur of these monuments in a new way. We slid under each stunning bridge silently, interrupting lovers and nocturnal strollers.

Even Alexandrine was smitten to silence. It had to be the wonder of this ride...or maybe she was sulking. Either way, I didn't much care. Paris, for all its grit, busyness, and difficult landlords, was also magic.

chapter **eighteen**

That next Monday was a busy day. Franck and I had prepared his
CV over the weekend, despite Pauline's black looks and patent
resentment at lending her computer. Before my first class, we
had to go to the bank and print out our newly inflated account
balance (thanks to the transfer from Canada) for the next day.

We made sure to wait in line, waving people to go ahead of us,
until we could get the same young bank teller we'd had the week
before.

She printed out our bank balance, which now looked large
and healthy—at least compared to what we were used to. It worried me, though, that we were putting all our eggs in one basket.
This was the money that had to last us the entire year or at least
until Franck got a job. That had to happen sooner rather than
later, even if Franck didn't realize it.

"I just need to wait a few minutes for my supervisor to con-
firm that you can go ahead and access your transferred funds
right away."

"Great," I said. "Merci."

"Oh, that's him over there." The teller pointed at a man in a gray three-piece suit and a lime green tie.

"I'll go talk with him directly," Franck said and left us.

"We can chat in the meantime." She leaned over to whisper to me. "Most people in Paris don't, you know. They are always in a hurry. Have you noticed that? It is different back home. We use all of our daily errands to catch up with friends and family."

I nodded. "How long have you and your boyfriend been in Paris?"

"Four months...no...wait...five."

"How long did it take for you to feel settled?" I asked.

She laughed a bitter laugh that I was surprised to hear come from such a gamine-looking person. "I'll let you know when it happens. I still feel homesick. I miss my family, the beach near my house, and kouign-amann of course."

"Kouign-amann?" I tried to imitate her pronunciation but only managed a vague approximation.

"It is a specialty of my region of Brittany, the most beautiful of course, called le Finistère. It's basically a layered butter cake. Salted butter is also a specialty of Brittany."

"Sounds like I need to plan a trip," I said.

I became aware of the sound of a throat clearing, repeatedly and pointedly, behind me. I turned around and saw an old woman with a polished wooden cane, a wool jacket that I wouldn't have been at all surprised to learn was vintage Chanel, and a fox stole around her neck—the kind with the head still attached and beady fake eyes. It was at least thirty degrees outside. Mémé Germaine was always complaining that the older she got, the colder she got. Maybe Fox Lady had the same problem.

I turned back to the teller, who didn't hide the fact that she was rolling her eyes at me. "*Vieille peau*," she said under her breath, using the same expression Jacinthe had used. "Not her again. Nothing is worse than *les vieilles Parisiennes*."

She pointed to Franck, who was standing on the other side of the bank, having what looked like a pleasant chat with the teller's supervisor.

The supervisor tugged his spectacular tie and nodded at our teller.

"Looks like you've got your approval for the funds." She printed out the updated bank statement.

I picked it up." "Thanks again. I enjoyed our—"

Fox Lady thumped her cane on the floor a few times.

That, I decided, was my cue to leave.

As I made my way up to the New Sorbonne for my class, Franck grabbed a Metro out to la Defénse to see if he could secure the journalist job by harassing his potential employers.

The weather was overcast. It was still hot, but the gathering clouds made it feel glum.

I stopped at the window of every rental agency I passed on my way up the rue Monge. The prospects were heinous. There were barely any apartments available, and those that were looked like derelict firetraps or mini Versailles that were asking twenty times our monthly rental budget.

Before going to the school, I stopped in what was fast becoming my favorite *boulangerie* and bought myself a *torsade suisse* to cheer myself up. I took a few bites and immediately felt more hopeful. These pastries had mysterious powers. I even remembered to duck into the café near the school to order a quick espresso at the bar and use their bathroom before class. *Am I getting the hang of this Parisian thing?*

By the time I took a seat in the amphitheater to wait for Madame Renier-Bernadotte, I was riding a wave of irrational hope.

When Madame swept into the room, swathed head to toe in drapey black clothing, set off by a necklace made of huge chunks of turquoise, the class seemed to still be missing half the students. She closed the doors behind her with a bang.

The amphitheater was stifling—the air conditioning must have been on the fritz, or maybe this was another technique for discouraging students from hanging around the university and discussing the latest techniques in making Molotov cocktails. The room became even stuffier as the professor organized her papers on the podium. That fabulous necklace granted her a lot of license, but why couldn't she leave the door open to let the few paltry wisps of air circulate?

She instructed us to pull out both the medieval text and modern translation (that she had translated, *bien sûr*) of *La Chanson de Roland*.

Within seconds, the door creaked open—the hinges had clearly not been oiled since the 1970s, making it impossible for anyone to enter the amphitheater unobtrusively. I filed this away for future reference. Madame Renier-Bernadotte fixed a look of steel on the boy who was making a disastrous attempt at sneaking into class late.

"Get out," she said.

"*Désolé.*" The boy smiled what I imagined was his most charming smile and began to shuffle down the stairs that ran between the sections of tiered desks.

"I mean it," she said. "Get out. Don't bother taking one step further into my amphitheater."

"*Mais,* Madame…," he began, his tone cajoling. Now that he was alongside where I was sitting, I could see that he was tall and handsome, with thick lashes, big brown eyes, olive skin, and an impressive head of wavy black hair. "You must let me attend class. I'm only a minute late…it was the Metro. I promise it will never happen again."

I got the distinct impression that this guy expected his charm to work on women of all ages. I had seen attractive students, both male and female, get away with this sort of thing all the way through high school and my first two years of university. Unfair in the extreme.

In the meantime, five or six other students—also latecomers—had clustered just inside the door of the amphitheater, waiting to see how this played out before venturing any further.

"If you are here before me, you may come in," Madame Renier-Bernadotte said in a ringing voice. "If you are late—even so much as ten seconds—you will be disrupting my class, and I will not let you in. I have every right to bar late students in my class. Let us be clear on this point—I have *all* the rights. My class is a dictatorship, not a democracy."

The students, and not just the latecomers, started to protest in a muttered crescendo about late Metros, traffic jams, and so on, but Madame Renier-Bernadotte put up her hand, and their words died off mid-sentence.

"I would have thought university students would know the definition of a dictatorship," she said. "It means I'm in no way interested in what you have to say."

"Mais, Madame—" the boy pleaded.

She held up her hand. "Stupid boy, do you not even comprehend basic French? How on earth did you pass your baccalaureate?"

"But surely…just for today…"

"*Non.*" I wondered how she made her voice project so imperiously without a microphone.

The boy's face had gone from handsome to petulant. Maybe this was a novel experience for him, finding a female he could not cajole. "*Vous n'êtes pas très gentille,*" he said.

Madame Renier's shoulders drew back and her spine straightened. She seemed to gain a foot in height and more than that in presence. Her smooth cap of auburn hair glinted red under the lights illuminating her lectern. An image of a fire-breathing dragon flashed in my mind. *Merci Dieu*, I was not the person in her line of fire. Please, God, may I never be.

"Nice?" she demanded.

"*Oui. Gentille,*" the boy said, but his voice shook.

"Why on earth should I be *gentille*? she said. "Because I am a woman?"

She waited for him to respond, but his gaze had become riveted to his shoelaces.

"Let me tell you this once and for all. It has not, nor will it ever be, a goal of mine to be thought of as *nice*. Brilliant. Yes. Ambitious. Yes. *Gentille*? Bah!" She spat out the word. "Girls are still being brought up all over the world by parents who teach them that they must be nice. What a tragic waste of intellect and energy."

Like a master orator, she let this sink in for a moment.

She waved her hand toward the door of the amphitheater. "Now, all of you latecomers get out of my classroom. If you don't leave willingly, I'm sure I can find a security guard to eject you. If you want the privilege of learning from me, be on time. *Au revoir.*"

The cluster by the door scurried out, and the boy, the last to leave because he was the farthest down the steps, slammed the door behind him.

I turned back to Madame, whose eyes were still flashing. "As edifying as that was," she said. "It is time we got down to some work."

The next hour and a half were taken up with a swan dive into the deep end (at least for me) of medieval French literature. She used *La Chanson de Roland* as an example of an original French text that we would, Madame Renier-Bernadotte said—if we were not a complete dimwit and came to class—be able to read and understand by the end of the year.

"Flip to the first page in both the original and the translated versions of the text," she began. Everyone complied immediately, and I knew no one was going to ask her to crack open the door.

Despite the stuffy room, the minutes flew by as I experienced the rush of learning a new language that was also, paradoxically, a dead language. It was utterly foreign yet oddly familiar. Knowing English, I realized, helped. Many of the words could be decrypted by using a combination of French and English. It was like an obscure, linguistic treasure hunt. There are few things I like better than a treasure hunt.

My head was still with my newfound interest when I walked out into the bright day and cut across la place Monge and the rue Mouffetard to get over to my class on Dickens near the old Sorbonne.

I felt a glow of satisfaction every time I remembered Madame Renier-Bernadotte's tone when she spat out the word "nice." Her utter contempt for it rang of truth for me.

After all, that's what I had been taught too. Growing up, we girls were always expected to make friends, apologize even when we knew we were in the right, smooth over disagreements, and in essence bend ourselves to the will of others.

When I was a teenager, the second biggest compliment a girl could pay to another girl (after "you're gorgeous") was "you're so sweet."

Sweet! That word always repelled me in the same sickly way as "nice"—as if I were being forced to eat a jar of Nutella on my own.

Still, when I was a teenager, I aspired to be "sweet" and "nice," just like the other girls. The only other alternative was to be a "bitch," and nobody wanted that label. Bitches scared off boys and were the target of other teenage girls.

Did I still aspire to be "nice" even though I was twenty-one? I probably did, I realized with no small amount of horror. I wasn't a person who thrived on conflict—like most Canadians, I much preferred it when everyone got along—but still, I often stuffed down what I really thought to make life easier for those around me.

I had a lot of things about me that didn't fit into the tiny, squashed box of "nice." I was as stubborn as a mule. My thoughts were frequently opinionated and critical. Usually, my opinion on a person or a thing, once fixed, was hard to sway.

What would my personality be like if I were a boy? I couldn't help but think it would have been more outwardly forceful, instead of safely battened down with thick ropes of compliance.

Madame Renier Bernadotte made me want to shake off those ropes and release the not-always-nice person beneath. I needed to become more like her, I decided. I would have her in front of me all year as an example to emulate. With her, I had found a living example of a woman thriving in society on her own terms.

From my experience during the year I had spent in France when I was eighteen, I suspected that French women as a rule didn't feel the same pressure to be "nice" as their North American counterparts. It was a paradox that, for them, expressing precisely what they felt was never seen as unappealing. On the contrary, it was one of the things that made French women so universally intriguing. Having *"du caractère"*—meaning talking back, and being strong-willed, brave, and often a pain-in-the-ass—was considered enviable for them.

I hated how as a teenager I had felt that we girls were all shoved in a rigid mold—thin, pretty, nice, accomplished, sporty (but not in an unfeminine way)... When we didn't fit into that mold—and I didn't in many ways: I was always too curvy, never quite pretty enough, awkward, bored by sports, caught up in my own day-dreams most of the time—it was painful. Yet, I imagined most of the girls I went to high school with must have felt that they didn't fit either. Still, we all kept trying—starving ourselves, stressing ourselves, beating ourselves up about a fierce word escaping or about appearing weird...

How on earth did none of us have the revelation that perhaps the problem wasn't us; it was the mold?

Could I shed that mold for good this year in Paris? Like a turtle shedding its shell? I was a woman now, no longer a teenager.

I strode to my Dickens class, weaving in and out of Parisian traffic, intoxicated by a sense of possibility.

chapter **nineteen**

I was a few minutes early and took a seat near the front, determined not to act shy or unassuming as I had in the first class. Professeur Renier-Bernadotte had fired me up. I spoke English, goddamit, and I had read every novel Dickens had written and dissected quite a few of them in high school and during my first two years of university. I was not going to hide either my intelligence or my capacity to speak and write English under a bushel of modesty.

The class began on time, and the polished but young teacher began speaking in her strange English accent.

"*Great Expectations* is the first novel we're going to study," Professor Gabrielle said, her stance rigid. She asked how many of us had finished it (we were supposed to have finished it by then). Only a quarter or so of the class put their hands up.

"It's just so *big*," one student moaned in French, even though we were supposed to speak only English in that class.

"Yes," she conceded. "But it is a classic. Did anyone enjoy it?" She did not have the same authority as Madame Renier-

Bernadotte, but then again, maybe that could only be acquired with experience.

I was the only one to put my hand up. "Ah!" She looked relieved. "Can you tell the class why you enjoyed it?"

Normally, I would have said a few sentences, but emboldened by Madame Renier-Bernadotte's pride in owning her intellect, I launched into a detailed description of my favorite aspects of *Great Expectations.* For about five minutes, I discoursed on the themes of expectations versus reality, the palpable sense of long-ing that infuses Dickens's masterpiece, imagery of stars versus fire, and the famous characters of Miss Havisham in her crusty wedding dress and the diamond in the rough, Magwitch.

"*Merci,*" the teacher said when I was finished. She rocked backwards on her heels, as though stunned. "What is your name?"

"Laura. Laura Bradbury," I said, pronouncing it without a French accent.

"You are Anglophone," she said. It wasn't a question.

"Yes."

"Thank you for that…interesting…interpretation of the book."

She paused a bit on the word "interesting," imbuing it with a sense of skepticism. Or was it mockery? No. I had to give her the benefit of the doubt.

She drew herself even taller, as though readying herself for a fight. I had just said what I thought—nothing more, nothing less. Did she disagree with me?

"I thought only native French speakers were allowed in this class." A girl in front of me piped up. "It's not fair to us Francophones to have Anglophones here too. We can't compete." She, too, didn't bother trying to speak in English.

"There is unfortunately no rule against it," the teacher said, also in French, and eyed me pointedly. "Although it is true the large majority of you speak English as your second language, as do I. Rest assured I will be taking that into account when I am grading papers and exams."

I wasn't the slightest bit reassured. That was unfair.

I was being cast dirty looks from my fellow students, as if I had just been caught cheating on an exam. "I am taking French classes too," I announced to the room. "In fact, I'm taking three classes in medieval French, which, as you can imagine, is no cake-walk for me."

"So, you admit it," said one of the boys in my row. "This class will be easy for you."

That was what I had thought just minutes before, but now I had the sinking feeling that Professor Gabrielle might make it difficult for me.

"Not as hard as medieval French." I laughed, trying to show them that I wasn't a threat, then feeling disappointed in myself when I realized that, yet again, I was downplaying my abilities. Madame Renier-Bernadotte would never do that.

"Don't be too sure," the teacher said to me with a patronizing smile. "I will hold you to a higher standard than the other students."

That was discriminatory, but I was not going to degrade myself by whining about it. I would prove myself through my work.

Another girl at the front, with blond hair clipped back in a ponytail with an enormous red barrette bow, raised her hand tentatively.

"Yes." The teacher called on her.

"I'm Anglophone too," she said in a whisper of a voice. "My name is Grace. I'm also an exchange student." She turned around slightly and gave me a shy smile over her shoulder. "I've never read *Great Expectations* though."

I caught a soft Southern accent.

The teacher smiled at her kindly. "Welcome to our class, Grace," she said. "Where are you from?"

"Nashville, Tennessee," Grace answered. That explained the hair bow, which was an incongruous sight in Paris, to say the least.

The teacher hadn't welcomed me to the class.

"Please turn to page twenty-three of the novel," she said.

I was left wondering—had I emulated Madame Renier-Bernadotte wrong, or was being a woman like her in the world simply one battle after another?

It had not escaped me that the teacher was far more kind to Grace, who projected timidity and intellectual insecurity. If that was what it would take to be accepted, too bad. An unthreatening woman, if it meant dumbing myself down, was *not* what I wanted to become.

I took my time gathering my things after class. When I was done, I looked up to see Grace waiting at the end of my row. I couldn't hold Professor Gabrielle's behavior against this girl.

I smiled at her. "It's so nice to meet another exchange student."

"Oh! I'm so excited to meet another American too!" she gushed, reaching out and squeezing my hand. "I've been so lonely since I got here." She leaned in, enveloping me in a cloying cloud of perfume. "Paris isn't at all how I thought it would be."

I squeezed her hand in return and then slipped out of her hold so I could sling my backpack over my shoulder. "Actually, I'm Canadian," I said as we walked out of the classroom together. "I'm from British Columbia, though—the English part."

"Canada? How interesting. Do you hate it here too?"

I was taken aback by her question. We walked toward the corner of the boulevard Saint-Germain and the boulevard Saint-Michel, where a cute guy in a scarf but no helmet beeped the horn of his scooter as a Renault van cut him off.

I didn't answer right away. I hated living at Florent and Pauline's, although I knew I should feel grateful. I hated the RER. I hated what Monsieur Arseneau was putting us through to get the apartment and I hated the thought of how it would feel not to get it. I hated the noise and the pollution and feeling disoriented all the time. I also wondered, going on my opinion of Alexandrine, whether I hated native Parisians as much as the rest of France did.

But I loved *les torsades suisses* at the *boulangerie* and the crazy warren of twisted medieval streets between the rue Monge and the Panthéon. I loved the bibliotèque Sainte-Geneviève and the Arènes de Lutèce amphitheater magically hidden behind the door off the rue Monge.

The ride on the *bateau-mouche* along the Seine at night was spectacular. I adored being able to duck into a café for a delicious espresso served by a traditionally garbed *garçon* in his black pants and top with the long white apron tied around his waist. I loved catching glimpses of the Eiffel Tower throughout the day, and I loved the lunch specials at the Brasserie Le Monge, even if I resented the turkish toilet.

I both hated and loved Paris. Up to then, I hadn't been able to reconcile the two.

"I haven't made up my mind yet," I said, finally.

"Where do y'all live?" she asked. "I am *au pair*ing with a French family, but it's a nightmare. They treat me like a slave, and their children are dreadful. All they do is laugh at me and they're only six and nine! Can you believe that? They have no manners."

"Where does the family live?" I asked.

"In Neuilly," she said, naming one of the wealthiest neigh-borhoods in Paris. "Their place is nice, but they definitely are not. Where do you live?"

"My boyfriend and I are bunking in at his cousin's place in the *banlieue*. We've found the perfect apartment not far from here, just down by the Seine, but we're not sure the landlord will rent to us.

"You have a boyfriend here with you?"

"Yes. He's French. From Burgundy."

"You're *so* lucky. I had to choose between my beau and coming to Paris for the year. I chose Paris, so he broke up with me. Now I think maybe I made the worst mistake of my life."

"He made you choose?"

She nodded. "He's from a big Southern family. Very traditional."

"Still—"

"It sounds from what you said that you and your boyfriend are planning on living in this apartment together?"

"Of course."

"You'll be living in *sin*?" she asked, breathless.

I laughed. "I'm twenty-one. Besides, I don't buy into the 'living in sin' concept." I slowed down a minute to savor the scent of freshly cooked crêpes being made by the crêpe vendor we were walking past.

"But what did your parents think? And your church?"

I had to bite back another chuckle. "My parents weren't thrilled when I was nineteen and my boyfriend moved to Montreal to be with me, but they've accepted it now. As for a church"—I shrugged—"I don't have one."

"Really?" she asked, her eyes wide.

"Really."

"I'm so surprised by how many people here in Paris don't have a church. Everyone in Nashville belongs to a church."

"I guess most French people would consider themselves Catholic, but don't really go to church that much. As for me, I've not from a religious family."

"Paris is such a strange place." She dropped her head.

I checked my watch. "I have an hour before my next class. Do you have time to grab a coffee?"

"I'd love that more than anything. You're so sweet to ask."

Sweet was still a word I hated. I had no desire for anyone to think of me that way, yet somehow coming out of Grace's mouth, it didn't sound so bad.

chapter **twenty**

The next day, our plan was to meet with the landlord, Monsieur Arseneau, without Jacinthe.

"We are still fighting over the security deposit. It's getting nasty," Jacinthe told us earlier on the phone. "Trust me. My presence will not help your case. In fact, it's probably better to avoid reminding him that I introduced you." That didn't bode well.

Monsieur Arseneau was a full forty minutes late. Franck and I lingered in the second courtyard, perching on the edge of a flower planter that was, mercifully, in the shade. It was blazing hot outside. The summer was signing off with one last stifling Parisian heat wave. I pulled out my textbook for Madame Renier-Bernadotte's class later that afternoon, *La Chanson de Roland*.

I realized I had the medieval French version in my hands, not the translation. I was about to dig around for the translated text when curiosity got the better of me and I cracked open the book. I felt a compulsion to understand this new-slash-old language.

I began trying to decipher the jumble of foreign words in front of me. I lost all sense of time passing until Franck said, "I think that's him." He stubbed out his cigarette with his heel and gave me his hand to help me stand up.

"I have other people interested in the apartment, you know," Monsieur Arseneau said by way of a greeting.

He didn't even stop to shake our hands, which, in France, is grossly uncivil behavior. We hurried in his wake. Over his shoulder, he added, "And that friend of yours is wanting her entire security deposit back. *Non, non, et non!* I refuse."

He unfortunately had an excellent memory.

"We have the bank statement," I said. "We have plenty of money to cover the rent."

"We'll discuss this upstairs in the apartment," he said, gruffly. "Who knows who's eavesdropping on us right now. Most of my tenants spy on me. They don't know better than to mind their own business."

I looked up to the windows and saw the flutter of a few different curtains and a few shadows move past. I could hardly blame them. Who would pass up the edifying entertainment of Monsieur Arseneau raking a new set of potential tenants over the coals?

I both did and didn't want to go back up to the apartment. I wanted to see it again, of course, but I knew I would fall a little bit more in love. I had already started to care too much about it becoming ours.

It was becoming a real trial to commute for such a big chunk of each day, not to mention endure Pauline and Florent every evening. They never failed to ask us whether we had found an apartment yet and when we thought we'd be moving out.

Franck and I tried to do everything we could to be helpful—we paid our way and spent the least amount of time possible at their apartment. Nothing could change the fact, though, that we were camped out in the middle of their living room. No matter how many pains we took to make ourselves unobtrusive, we hadn't yet discovered the trick of disappearing completely.

We walked into the lobby, and Franck ushered the landlord and me into the black metal cage of the elevator then closed it. "I'll take the stairs."

Granted, the elevator was too small for three people, but why had Franck stuck me with Monsieur Arseneau in a contained space? He knew I always blurted out the wrong thing.

I became aware of how slowly the pulley system of the elevator moved, leaving me to make small talk with this man who seemed to suck up every particle of oxygen. "I love these old elevators," I announced. "They're so charming. We don't have anything like this back in Canada."

He eyed me with suspicion.

Shit. I wasn't supposed to remind him that I was a foreigner, was I?

He rolled his eyes at me. "They break down all the time. Costs a fortune to put in a new one though, so that's just the way it is."

"People get stuck in it?" I asked, uneasy. I didn't relish the idea of spending any more time than necessary trapped with Monsieur Arseneau.

"Constantly." He scowled at me. "People sometimes have to spend the night because the alarm button doesn't work." His tone held a note of pride.

"Ah," I said faintly, and prayed to the elevator gods. The thing was moving so slowly, we had only just reached the second floor. I was certain that every second we spent together decreased Franck's and my chances of getting the apartment.

Franck was waiting for us on the landing, looking not the slightest bit out of breath. He folded open the metal door for us.

The landlord scowled at him again and took a huge key ring out of his pocket to open the apartment door, then motioned us inside. "The tenants eavesdrop in the hallways too," he said, darkly.

What was the point of having all his money and all these apartments if Monsieur Arseneau was miserable and hated his tenants? Maybe he enjoyed being miserable. I contemplated this foreign concept for a moment. It wouldn't be the first time I had met a French person who seemed to make a hobby of discontent.

Monsieur Arseneau shut the door behind him and moved into the living room, the only room where there was space for the three of us.

"Bank statement." He held out his hand. Franck opened his bag and gave it to him. Monsieur Arseneau's eyes flicked over the printout. There was a lot of money in our account. How could he possibly object?

"This is passable, I suppose." He slid his eyes over to Franck. "Do you have a CDI yet?"

A CDI? Within weeks of moving to Paris? That was like asking if Franck had flown to the moon. Franck cleared his throat and managed to look earnest. "As you know, CDIs are extremely difficult to come by," he said. "However, I do have a job interview that I hope will result in a CDD."

"Hope?" Monsieur Arseneau's eyebrows bristled.

"I have every reason to believe it will result in a CDD."

"That's optimistic."

"I don't think so." Franck held his ground. "I think it's realistic."

"As you can see on the bank statement," I said, "the money is there to cover the rent for both of us, so—"

"Are you telling me how to do my job, Mademoiselle?"

"No."

Franck shot me a look that I read as clear as if he had spoken. I needed to stop talking.

"Most of my tenants have CDIs," Monsieur Arseneau said. "It would be extremely foolish of me to take on a new tenant without one when I have several people with CDIs who are lining up to snap up this apartment in a heartbeat."

But we provided what you asked for, you bastard! There was nothing I hated more than playing by the rules, then having the rules changed on me. It was torture to need something from someone who didn't play fair.

I looked around at the room and made the mistake of thinking how nice it would be to come back there between classes. I longed to wake up in a leisurely fashion and be able to walk to school up the rue Monge or along the boulevard Saint-Germain, maybe stopping to enjoy the ambiance of the roman amphitheater for a while.

How can we possibly sway him? Money clearly wasn't enough.

"We can move in right away," I said. "And pay rent for this month." It was the end of the month, so basically Monsieur Arseneau would be getting a free month's rent. A savvy negotiator, I was not.

He didn't respond right away. When he did, he said, "I'll think about it."

Irrational hope surged through me. Maybe Monsieur Arseneau never rented an apartment to anyone without enjoying stringing them along for a while, like a fisherman delighting in playing a flapping fish on his line.

Monsieur Arseneau left us shortly after that. He gave us no indication of how long he needed to think over our candidacy or when (or if) he was going to get back to us. Torture.

"Was I too desperate?" I asked Franck as we glumly made our way out to the rue des Fossés Saint-Bernard.

"Yes."

"*Merde.*"

"I don't think it made any difference." Franck reached up and rubbed the back of my neck. "We have no sway over him. That *connard* holds all the cards."

chapter twenty-one

The next day, Franck had his job interview in la Défense with the *Expo News* magazine. He met me after my second medieval French class—equally as intriguing as my first—with a huge smile on his face.

"I've been offered a CDD," he announced by way of a greeting.

I gave him a sound kiss. "Amazing! Should we call Monsieur Arseneau and let him know?"

"I'm going to do that right now. There's a phone in the Brasserie Le Monge. Let's go."

Both the *tabac* dame and the owner behind the bar gave us small nods as we entered. *Progress.*

As soon as I had perched on a stool at the zinc bar, Franck dropped his bag at its foot and went off to the old phone booth incorporated into the back of the café.

The phone booth was built for privacy as a separate wooden room, with a wooden bench, polished from use. A glass door enclosed the space and had a peeling, gold *Téléphone* decal adorning its front. Maybe the ancient turkish toilets weren't to my taste, but the vintage charm of the phone booth almost made up for them.

I ordered our *cafés*, and when Franck emerged, I raised my brow in question.

"He wants to see my job contract—" Franck began saying after he sat beside me.

"He doesn't take your word for it." This was a statement, not a question.

"No."

"Of course not." I muttered some choice French curse words under my breath.

"But I'll go to la Défense and pick it up tomorrow and take it straight to Monsieur Arseneau. You should come with me in case there's an opportunity to finalize things."

"Even if I have to skip class, I'll be there," I said. "If I think about it anymore, I'll be a complete stress case, so let's talk about something else." I waved my hand in an inviting gesture. "Tell me about the job."

"It's full-time." Franck tapped his fingertips on the zinc counter. "Grunt journalist work," he continued, "but if the magazine does well, maybe I could work my way up."

"That's fantastic," I said, and meant it. "How much are they paying you?"

Franck looked blankly at me.

"You *did* ask them what your salary was going to be, didn't you?"

Franck laughed, a bit self-consciously. "Actually, no."

"They mentioned it then?"

"No."

"What?" I said. "But how can that—"

"The subject just didn't come up."

"How could the issue of what they are going to pay you for your time *not* come up?" I demanded.

"Well...they didn't say anything and I guess I was just so pleased to be offered the job, I forgot to ask."

At that moment, the owner slid *cafés* across the counter to us. We had to pause our discussion while Franck found the right coins in his pocket to pay.

Annoyance boiled up inside of me at Franck's impracticality. I remembered Madame Renier-Bernadotte. *Nice.* That's what I was trying to convince myself to be—I had caught myself in the act. Why did I have to be nice?

Because I loved Franck and didn't want to hurt him, of course...that was an excellent reason.

Still, so much hung on his salary: the possible apartment (the *only* possible apartment); our ability to truly settle in Paris; the chance to make it back and forth to Burgundy from time to time; the prospect of us doing *any* traveling while we were there...

I stared into the black recesses of my espresso cup. Franck's salary even answered the question of whether we could afford to drink all these *cafés* we paid for daily. I played back Madame Renier-Bernadotte's rejection of "nice" in my mind.

"If you didn't ask about money, how do you know the job isn't merely a volunteer position?" I said, a hard edge to my voice.

"It isn't."

"But how do you *know*?'

"I just do."

"Even if you did," I said, "you don't know if you're earning ten francs an hour or a hundred."

"Ten francs is below minimum wage. It can't be that little."

"What was the point of calling Monsieur Arseneau if you can't even tell him how far your salary will go in covering the rent?"

"You're not being very supportive about this," Franck said, his mouth tightening in a way I knew well. "Can't I just be happy about *getting* the job for a few hours? I'll figure out the money thing later."

"No, I can't be supportive. The first question Monsieur Arseneau will ask is the amount of your salary. We could lose the apartment because of this," I said. "Later might be too late. It was a dumb oversight."

Franck jerked back so far he almost tumbled off his stool,

as though I had slapped him. "It's not always about the money," he snapped.

"No, but clearly is 'all about the money' to Monsieur Arseneau. Be practical for once in your life, Franck. To get the apartment we have to play his game. Being carefree basically means that you're off-loading the worry onto someone else."

"Who? You?"

"Yes. Me."

"You think that's what I do?" Franck looked appalled.

"Yes," I said. "At least that's what you're doing right now. Money is not all that's important. I'm not saying it is," I said. "But money does buy things like freedom to travel and the ability to pop into a café and buy baguettes at a good bakery whenever we feel like it. Money *pays the rent* and will be the only thing that convinces Monsieur Arseneau to rent us the apartment."

"I forgot, OK?" Franck said and took his pouch of tobacco out of his pocket and began to roll a cigarette with unwonted violence.

During this brief pause, my guilt rolled in like an unwelcome tide. Was I being unsympathetic? Was I acting like a shrew? I began to doubt what was justified and unjustified, true and false. How did Professeur Renier-Bernadotte do it with such assurance?

Being nice was easy for me. I had been so trained in being nice growing up that it was second nature. Expressing what I felt and *putting it out there* was the thing that took courage and effort. It made me feel guilty. Madame Renier-Bernadotte hadn't warned us about this.

Franck stood up and picked up his satchel. "You should get to class or you'll be late," he said, stiffly.

"I still have five minutes if I walk fast."

"No. Go ahead," he said. "I have things I need to do. I'll meet you at the Saint-Michel Metro, like we did yesterday."

I fought against the urge to back down and smooth everything over before he left. With Franck's family, it is never difficult to tell when they are angry. They all clamp their lips together and grit their teeth. It means, *bien sûr*, that you have hurt them grievously, but that they are being stoic and trying to withstand the excruciating emotional pain you have inflicted upon them.

"Fine." I grabbed my school bag and swept out of the café.

On my way to the New Sorbonne, it dawned on me that on Madame Renier- Bernadotte's door ringer there had only been one name—hers. By following her example, was I bettering my life or sabotaging it?

That evening, Franck was clearly holding a grudge against me and was evasive about where he had gone in the afternoon.

However, the next day when we met Monsieur Arseneau at the apartment to show him Franck's employment contract, Franck turned out to have the exact amount of his new salary to pass on as well. I tried to catch his eye and smile at him, but he wasn't ready to make peace yet.

Monsieur Arseneau sighed. "It's not an impressive salary," he said. "But I have a broken boiler to attend to this morning, so to save myself some time—not because I think you will be good tenants—I'll rent you the apartment."

I vibrated with joy and relief, and almost burst with the effort of keeping it contained in front of Monsieur Arseneau. I had never thought I could feel such gratitude toward a broken boiler.

Franck did a much better job of appearing nonchalant, perhaps helped by being in high dudgeon with me. "When can we sign the lease?"

"Tomorrow," Monsieur Arseneau said. "Bring your *pièces d'identité*, and your *relevé de compte*, *attestation bancaire*, and *chèque bancaire* for...then he named a truly obscene damage deposit amount.

"Will do," Franck said, unfazed—or at least pretending to be— by this daunting list. "What time?"

"Eleven o'clock," he said. That was right in the middle of one of Madame Renier-Bernadotte's classes, but this was one thing— maybe the *only* thing—that I would miss it for.

"We'll be here," I said.

"Don't be late." He waved us in the direction of the door. "Now, leave me alone. I have things to do."

"We won't be late," Franck said. *Ne vous inquiétez pas.*"

We hurried out before he could change his mind.

We waited until we were out on the rue des Fossés Saint-Bernard and Monsieur Arseneau was well out of sight before Franck and I gave full reign to our happiness.

"*Ouuuuuiaaaaaas!!!*" I shouted and leapt into his arms, causing him to stagger backwards. "We did it!"

Franck just hugged me tight and settled into a long kiss. "It's going to be *génial*," he said. "This neighborhood is perfect."

"You're not mad at me anymore?" I asked.

"I guess not," he said. That was impressive, as another trait of Franck's family is the tendency to hold grudges for preposterous lengths of time.

"After we fought yesterday, you went and found out about your salary?" I guessed.

"Yes," he admitted, with a sheepish smile.

"I felt guilty afterward," I confessed. "I was bitchy, but—"

"You were, but that's what lit a fire under my *derrière*. You made me so angry, but you were right. We wouldn't have gotten the apartment today if I didn't have that information; so, thank you. It's a good thing that we're not the same."

That, we definitely are not.

chapter twenty-two

Within five days, we had assembled a moving crew of Nathanael, Jacinthe, and Momo to help us settle into our new Parisian nest. There wasn't that much to move. It pretty much amounted to Franck and me and our suitcases.

However, after moving all their furniture to their new place, Jacinthe and Nathanael decided they didn't want most of it anymore and would give it to us, so we now needed to move it *back* from their new place on the Rive droite to our new (their old) place on the Rive gauche.

"I can't believe we didn't have the forethought to think of leaving all this stuff here rather than moving it twice," Jacinthe groaned. We were both carrying her red, wicker-seated chairs from the sidewalk and across the courtyards of the rue des Fossés Saint-Bernard.

"I know," I said. "But on the other hand, leaving the furniture would have made Monsieur Arseneau even more resentful of us, if that's actually possible."

"True," Jacinthe said. "That man is a miserable excuse for a human being."

"I can pay you for all of this," I said, as I dragged the chair into our Parisian nest. "You're literally giving us everything we need to furnish our apartment."

"Absolutely not." Jacinthe put down her chair. The guys were a few minutes behind us, carrying the unwieldy black bookshelf.

"I feel guilty taking all your stuff." Guilty, but at the same time incredibly grateful. After paying the scandalous security deposit to Monsieur Arseneau, our bank account was once again depleted. It was going to be a challenge to pay our rent every month, let alone buy stuff. Jacinthe and Nathanael's hand-me-downs were a godsend.

"Then there is one thing you could do," she said.

"What?" I asked.

"When you're able to help somebody else in the future—pass on some of your things to them. That's how I figure it should work. We help each other when we are able, and even though you don't necessarily pay back the person who helped you, you pass that help on to the next person who needs it."

"Promise." I decided I was adopting this philosophy immediately and permanently.

"Believe it or not," Jacinthe said as she peeked out the apartment door to see if the guys had appeared yet, "Alexandrine was incredibly generous to me when I was getting settled in Paris. We met at work, and she took me under her wing. That's why it bothers me so much when she acts like a snobby cow to you. She has a kind side that not many people see."

"Maybe I judged her too fast," I said, feeling magnanimous.

"*Non*. She's never been kind to you," Jacinthe said. "That's because she's jealous. She's possessive of her few friends."

Franck and Nathanael appeared, both sweating profusely and trying to manhandle the bookcase up the winding stairs without bashing the walls. Nathanael had a cigarette hanging out of his mouth, and I noticed the tip of ashes was perilously long. It would singe a big spot in the luxurious red carpet that went down the middle of the oak stairs if it fell. I suspected it wasn't too early for Monsieur Arseneau to evict us.

I wished again that we could use the elevator when moving our stuff and not haul it up three flights of stairs. Still, Monsieur Arseneau had made it clear when we signed the lease that the strictest rule in our new building was to not use the elevator for moving furniture or large objects. It was old and fragile, and he was far too cheap to maintain it properly.

I felt a rush of gratitude about the fact we were officially no longer living with Florent and Pauline. Things between us had gotten more stilted and awkward with every additional day under their roof. I was so thrilled to be out of there.

Jacinthe and I squeezed past our boyfriends, not forgetting to taunt them for their weak biceps, and went back out to the shaded courtyard and through the huge front metal lattice door to the street, where Momo was stationed, guarding our furniture. He was leaning up against the building, wall smoking a cigarette and watching the Parisians go by.

"Nobody is going to steal this stuff," I said. "I'm sure you don't need to stay outside here to protect our furniture."

Momo paused mid-puff. "You are joking, *n'est-ce pas*?"

"No."

"You are so charmingly naïve, *ma petite Canadienne*. Trust me, anything left here would be gone under twenty seconds."

"It's true," Jacinthe said.

"Hmmmm." I remained unconvinced.

"Anyway, I like this job," Momo said.

"It suits your talents perfectly," Jacinthe observed.

"If you're trying to insult me for being a layabout, you've missed your mark. You, of all people, know the pride I take in exerting myself as little as possible."

"I'll try harder next time." Jacinthe contemplated the pieces of furniture remaining on the sidewalk.

"Do you find people here on the Left Bank more attractive or those on the Right Bank? Momo asked us as we were evaluating the best way to carry the round black table. "I'm trying to decide."

"Left Bank," I said. "I've always preferred the bohemian type to a business suit."

"*Moi aussi.*" Momo nodded decisively. "Don't worry, Jacinthe. Even though you and Nathanael have moved in with all the bourgeois, I'll still visit you."

"I wasn't losing sleep over that," Jacinthe said. "You'd come to bum food and Champagne off us if we lived in Ouagadougou."

"Probably." Momo stubbed out his cigarette against the building wall. I scanned the street, but luckily there was no sign of Monsieur Arseneau.

We took a quick inventory of the furniture still sitting on the sidewalk. There were no smaller pieces left—only the round, black table. It didn't look extremely heavy, but Jacinthe eyed it with doubt.

"I'm strong," I assured her.

"From all that dog sledding?" Momo quirked a brow.

"*Bien sûr,*" I said. "I've been dog sledding since before I could walk, like all Canadians."

"*Bien sûr.*" Momo smiled at me.

"I'm strong too," Jacinthe said. "From hoisting all those heavy cigarettes to my lips. Come on, Laura, let's show the guys how to do it."

We lifted the table. At first it didn't seem particularly heavy. However, about halfway through the first courtyard, I discovered that round things are incredibly awkward to carry. Its curved edges left no place to really hold on to, and by the time we had crossed the first courtyard my muscles were trembling from the effort of not letting it slip out of my grip. The guys passed us on their way back out to the sidewalk, and Jacinthe and I, by silent agreement, both stopped griping until they were out of earshot.

I glanced over at Jacinthe, and I could see beads of sweat breaking out on her brow. When we got into the lobby at the foot of the stairs, we set the table down with sighs of relief.

I looked up the stairs. If getting the table over a flat surface was tricky, the stairs were going to be a nightmare. Jacinthe walked over to the elevator cage and pushed the call button.

"We're not allowed," I reminded her. "Monsieur Arseneau gave us a huge lecture about that." I noticed a brass sign posted beside the elevator that said it must not be used to move furniture, and pointed at it to underline my point.

"*Tant pis.*" Jacinthe shrugged. "We break the rules. So?"

"But what if he evicts us?"

"You've signed a lease. This is France. I'd enjoy seeing him try."

"I don't know…maybe it won't be so bad carrying this up the stairs. I bet we could do it."

The elevator reached the lobby with a clunk and, ignoring me, Jacinthe reached in to fold back the metal door.

I sighed. "Okay. I guess we're doing this. We're breaking the rules, and we haven't even moved in yet."

"It's important to start as you mean to continue." Jacinthe motioned at me to help her tilt the table on its side so we could pivot it into the metal cage. She jammed her foot against the folding door, and we began to roll the table into the elevator.

I pushed my side in, and after a few minutes of struggles, we awkwardly managed to fit the table in on its side and squeeze ourselves in as well. "I hope none of the old people are watching," I whispered to her as the elevator began to rise with ominous creaks and scraping noises.

"They are," she assured me. "They should be grateful. We're providing them with first-rate entertainment."

Somewhere between the third and fourth floor, the elevator halted with a jerk. Panic flashed through me like lightning.

"*Merde,*" I said, snaking my hand around a table leg to press the button for the fourth floor again. The elevator didn't budge. "Shit. Shit. Shit. It's because of the weight of the table."

Jacinthe shook her head. "*Non.* This elevator gets stuck all the time. It's ancient, and Monsieur Arseneau is miserly."

I remembered, but I doubted he would accept the blame in this situation. "What are we going to do now?" I muttered, more to myself than anything else.

Jacinthe began to laugh, quietly at first, but then louder.

"Why are you laughing?" I hissed at her.

"It's funny!" she said. "I mean, the *irony* of us getting stuck here with this table."

"It's punishment," I said, darkly.

She snorted. "Oh, come on...punishment for what?"

"Breaking the rules."

"Do you seriously believe God, or whatever is up there, cares that we're using Monsieur Arseneau's elevator against his wishes?"

Put like that, it did sound ridiculous. It was not as if Monsieur Arseneau was a prime candidate for God's benevolence.

"There are all sorts of good reasons for breaking rules," Jacinthe said. "Besides, who needs a reason?"

"But—"

"Breaking rules is just good for the soul."

I would have to consider this Gallic perspective on rules at some point—it merited further contemplation—but right then, stuck there in the elevator with our table, I wasn't in the mood.

"Listen for the guys," I said. "Maybe if they press the button on the outside it will work."

"Maybe." Jacinthe leaned back against the elevator wall. She lit a cigarette. We weren't supposed to smoke inside the building. Particularly, I imagined, not inside the elevator.

She must have seen me stare at her with round eyes. "We're already in trouble if he catches us." She flipped her blond hair. "One cigarette will make no difference. Do you want one?"

I wasn't a smoker and had no intention of becoming one. Still, while we were rule breaking, a part of me that I didn't know existed longed to binge on all the transgressions at once. Besides, there wasn't much else to do to pass the time until the guys materialized.

I held out my hand and took the Marlboro Light Jacinthe passed me under the table leg. I stuck it between my lips and leaned over the table for her to light it for me. I sucked some in and dissolved into a coughing fit.

"That's strong," I said through gasps.

"It's not, actually," Jacinthe said.

"I guess I'm not used to it."

We stood in silence, enjoying our cigarettes—or in my case,

I was enjoying the idea that I was rebelliously smoking a con-traband cigarette in Monsieur Arseneau's elevator. We devised a game of flicking our ashes down into the elevator cage, where they would only come in contact with metal.

Jacinthe flicked a big bit down and said, "There you go, Monsieur Arseneau. *Un petit cadeau* for you. Serves you right for being such a cheap bastard."

"He doesn't seem to have a large fan club," I observed. "Even the bank teller at the BNP told me that he was a jerk, and she's brand new."

"Can you imagine that?" Jacinthe asked. "Going through life and making only enemies? It would be almost as bad as going through life and making only friends."

"What's wrong with making only friends?"

"If you have no enemies...that's well...it's boring, isn't it? It means you never enter the fray. It shows a distinct lack of discrimination."

"But shouldn't we at least try to be friendly?"

"That's the most ridiculous thing I've ever heard. You must have realized by now that there are people out there in the world who are simply not friend-worthy."

I thought about that. "I guess that's one way of looking at it. One of my new profs at Paris III is this amazing woman. Brilliant. You should have heard her when a young student—a guy—reproached her for 'not being very nice.'"

"Did she give it to him?" Jacinthe asked with a grin.

I thought back to the scene. Goosebumps prickled my fore-arms. "It was majestic."

"I wish I could have seen that," she said, wistful. She took a few more puffs then peered out the cage. "Where are our men? They're taking a long time."

"Of course they are. We're stuck in an elevator. That's the way life works."

"True."

"You know, I was brought up to be nice to everyone," I mused. "Even if I didn't like them or they were acting like shits."

"You had to *pretend?*"

"*Oui.*"

"That's awful." Her blue eyes widened.

"I'm just realizing that now," I said.

Jacinthe made a sound of disgust. "*Quelle horreur.*"

"What I truly felt about a person or a situation didn't make much of a difference," I continued. "It was what I projected on the outside that was important."

"It was all about appearances?"

"Exactly."

"That sounds horrible. Like the worst kind of jail." Jacinthe rattled the metal cage of the elevator. "Not dissimilar to this, actually."

If it was, it was a jail of which I had only gained a glimmer of awareness since I came to France the first time when I was eighteen. I took another drag on my Marlboro Light and enjoyed breathing the smoke out slowly, contemplatively.

At the end of that first year in Burgundy, I had been forced to make a choice—a choice between being the kind of well-behaved girl my French host families wanted me to be and the kind of girl who would run off with Franck to Paris to see where our relationship could go. I couldn't have both.

I chose Franck.

Since then, I had continued to fight for my relationship with Franck against all obstacles, whether they be disapproving family members, friends, financial penury, or Canada Immigration. But I had never, I realized, had the nerve to break the rules for much besides Franck.

"Being nice becomes automatic," I said to Jacinthe. "I didn't even realize I was doing it until I got back here to Paris and noticed women here don't seem to feel the same obligation."

Jacinthe contemplated this. "I think French women feel an obligation to be seductive...and charming, but they are under no pressure to be nice."

"Is having to be seductive tiresome?"

Jacinthe shrugged. "No. It's like you being nice. It's ingrained in us from our childhoods, so I don't even think about it. French men also need to be seductive. It's just the way life works here."

"Huh."

"Are Canadian men taught the same thing?" Jacinthe asked. "To be nice all the time?"

I flicked my ashes down the cage as I thought on this. "I don't think Canadians are comfortable with conflict as a rule, so I think, to a certain degree, Canadian men have a default setting of "nice" too. It's definitely not as deep-set as for women though."

"The way I see it"—Jacinthe was blowing masterful smoke "O"s—"there's a world of difference between 'nice' and 'kind'. I try to be kind, but I'm not interested in being nice."

Jacinthe opened her mouth to say something else, but she was interrupted by the sound of Franck's distinctive laugh and Nathanael's answering chuckle.

"*Eh, les garçons!*" Jacinthe crushed the remainder of her cigarette against the metal cage. "We're stuck in here. Come save us."

chapter twenty-three

"*Quoi?*" Nathanael's voice floated from the lobby downstairs. "Where *are* you?"

"On that note," I called down, "where were you two? Why did it take you so long to come back up?"

"We had to go to the hardware store on the corner to get screws for the bookshelf to replace the missing ones," Franck said, his voice getting closer. I could hear his muffled footsteps on the carpet of the stairs. "Then…well…we thought we may as well stop for a *petit verre* of white."

"Slackers," I called down to them.

"We're in the elevator," Jacinthe shouted, in case Franck and Nathanael hadn't figured that out for themselves.

I saw Franck's feet first, then Nathanael's behind them.

"What the—" Franck asked when he saw that we were not alone in the elevator but accompanied by the large, black table and our Marlboros.

"We're stuck." I said. The elevator was clearly halfway between the third and fourth floors and not moving anywhere fast, so this piece of information, in retrospect, was perhaps superfluous.

"Since when did you start smoking?" Franck demanded.

"That is not the most urgent issue here," I said.

"Yes, it is."

"You smoke," I reminded him.

"But you don't. When did you start?"

"As it happens, I only smoke when I'm stuck in an elevator. Can you please try pressing the button from the outside on the fourth floor?"

"We're not supposed to use the elevator for furniture," Franck said.

"The table was really heavy," Jacinthe explained. "And you two were nowhere to be found."

"Don't even think of blaming this on us." Nathanael snorted with laughter. Jacinthe scowled at him.

"The table doesn't look that heavy," Franck said, eyeing it.

"Trust me. It is," I said. "It's awkward to carry. Enough idle chitchat. Can one of you please go and press the button outside the elevator on the fourth floor?"

"I'm going. I'm going." Nathanael climbed past us. "Anyway, I know who to blame for this. What did I do to deserve a girlfriend with such tricks up her sleeve?"

I noted he sounded proud rather than displeased. With a mighty creak that had me wondering for a few seconds whether the elevator was going to move upwards or plummet directly to the lobby below, the elevator began to move.

I breathed a sigh of relief. We were rising. "It worked!"

"You see?" Jacinthe said. "God wasn't punishing you for breaking Monsieur Arseneau's stupid rules. God just wanted you to take *un petit* rest for some good conversation and a Marlboro."

That was a unique interpretation of events, but a compelling one.

On the landing, an old lady emerged from her apartment two doors down from ours. I recognized her from the BNP bank. She was still wearing the skinned fox stole over her shoulders. Through the cage, I could see Jacinthe and I were the targets of her penetrating black eyes. "It is strictly *interdit* to use the elevator to move furniture." She stamped her cane for emphasis, just as she had done at the bank.

"*Vraiment?*" Jacinthe said airily, with an eye roll. "We had no idea. Thank goodness you are here to tell us the rules."

The woman eyed the cigarette stub I still held between my fingers. "There is absolutely no smoking in the elevator either."

"I just found this on the ground and picked it up," I said. "Litter these days, you know. *Terrible.*"

She huffed and narrowed her eyes at Jacinthe. "I know you."

"I believe you're mistaken," Jacinthe said.

"Hmmmpph." The woman muttered a lengthy diatribe about the manners of young people these days.

Franck and Nathanael opened the elevator door and quickly rolled the table into our apartment. They did not re-emerge. Jacinthe and I stepped out of the elevator. Jacinthe held the folded metal door for my critical new neighbor, Madame Fox.

"Madame," Jacinthe said, "you can step inside now."

Fox Lady tightened her vividly lipsticked, pink lips and entered, not breaking eye contact with Jacinthe until she had disappeared below our feet.

"I hope she gets stuck too," Jacinthe muttered as we joined the guys in the apartment.

"Now, now Jacinthe," Nathanael remonstrated, overhearing us. "She's just a little old lady. Be nice."

"Little old ladies are the worst," she said. "Especially little old Parisian ladies. Anyway, I'm not nice. Laura and I were just talking about that." She winked at me.

Jacinthe might have said she wasn't nice, but toward me she was one of the kindest people I had ever met. I thought back to the first night we met, when I was a stumbling, drooling mess and destroyed her apartment (now our apartment—it was funny how things worked out) and literally fell asleep in the middle of her carefully prepared meal.

Yet Jacinthe had never been anything but unwaveringly loyal and generous with me. Inviting me to be part of her group of friends—at picnics and dinners—and giving us almost all their furniture and not wanting to receive so much as one franc or thanks in return.

Maybe the difference between niceness and kindness is the first is an automatic response, whereas the second is a choice. If that is true, kindness has infinitely more value.

After a few more rounds of back and forth with the remaining bits and pieces of furniture and such, we all (except Momo) found ourselves in the apartment.

"Who else is getting hungry?" Nathanael asked as he and Franck finished positioning the red chairs around the table.

"Starving," I said.

"Me too," Franck rubbed his stomach.

"Getting stuck in elevators stokes my appetite," Jacinthe agreed.

"You've been to Batifol, right?" Nathanael asked Franck and me.

"No," I said. "What's Batifol?"

"*Ouuuuiaaaas*! Let's go to Batifol!" Momo chimed in. He must have sauntered upstairs when he realized he had nothing left to guard outside.

"Will someone please tell me what Batifol is?" I said.

"Batifol is our only—actually, *your* only now—neighborhood bistro," Nathanael answered, sitting down in one of the red chairs and crossing one leg over the other. "It's just steps away from the door of your new apartment."

"I think a celebration is in order then," Franck said. "Let's go."

We strolled down the rue des Fossés Saint-Bernard toward the Seine, which sparkled under the late fall sun.

On the corner was a large, typically French-looking bistro with a green-and-white awning and large block letters announcing "Batifol" outside.

We had a bistro on our corner—I was finally living *in Paris*.

To the left of it stood an enticing *boulangerie* that I would have to investigate.

Inside the bistro, there was the usual bustle of lunchtime diners and the traditionally dressed French *garçons* in their black suits and long white aprons. I sniffed in the welcoming scent of braised red wine and homemade French fries. Nathanael and Jacinthe were greeted like family, and they introduced Frank and me.

The five of us were ushered to a table near the front window on the Seine side, where we could sit back and watch Parisians drive like maniacs and run the red lights at the intersection. The faint background of beeping horns punctuated the hum of chatter.

On Jacinthe, Nathanael, and Momo's recommendation, we each ordered the traditional bistro classic of steak frites with a *frisée salade au chèvre* to start with, and what they all promised was an eminently palatable house red to wash it all down.

The salad was delicious—there was a reason why salad with broiled goat cheese on toasted *tartines* was one of my favorite things to eat (although that list was long and getting longer with every day spent in Paris).

I sighed in bliss at the peppery steak, which melted on my tongue. The french fries were home cut and served piping hot and studded with raw salt from the Camargue region in the South.

A wee, white ceramic pot of Dijon Mustard was quickly emptied by our group. Dijon tastes different in France than it does back home in Canada—spicier, stronger...infinitely better.

We ordered a second carafe of house wine and then a third, as there was much to celebrate. Franck and I were now living, just the two of us, in Paris. There we were, at a Parisian bistro near the Seine, just steps away from our very own Parisian *pied-à-terre*, laughing and enjoying ourselves with three French friends.

When the waiter brought dessert, in the middle of the table, he put down a massive silver cup—or bowl, actually—that looked oddly similar to the cup they awarded to the winner of Wimbledon. I touched the metal. It felt cool against my fingertip and was damp with condensation. The waiter brought a second cup and set it down beside the first.

"What's in those?" I asked Momo, intrigued.

"With the menu we ordered, the choice for dessert is either *mousse au chocolat* or *fromage blanc*. Here, both are á volonté."

All-you-can-eat *mousse* au *chocolat* and *fromage blanc*? I'd never come across all-you-can-eat *anything* in France, although all-you-can-eat buffets were a staple of my Canadian childhood.

"Incredible," I said, eyeing the cup.

"But you have to choose between the *mousse au chocolat* and the *fromage blanc*."

"Who says?" Jacinthe demanded.

"The menu, *mon amour*." Nathanael patted Jacinthe's hand.

"That's okay," I said. "I'm perfectly happy with just *mousse au chocolat* for today."

"We need to order some Champagne or *mousseux* with this," Jacinthe said.

Nathanael flagged down the waiter and asked what the restaurant stocked in terms of fine bubbly.

"We have a fine *mousseux* from Burgundy—"

"We'll take it," Franck said. "A bottle please."

I had to wait until the *mousseux* was brought to the table, ceremoniously uncorked, tasted and approved by Franck, and served to each of us in the flutes they supplied before I could dig in to dessert. It seemed like an eternity.

Finally, I picked up the silver spoon in the chocolate mousse chalice. It was to scale, meaning it looked like a soup spoons for giants. I put several spoonfuls of the dark, fluffy chocolate mousse into a much smaller silver bowl that the waiter had put in front of me.

My eyes must have been shining, because Franck nudged me and whispered, "Happy?"

I looked around the table. "How come nobody else is eating this yet?" I asked, dumbfounded.

"Because we're enjoying watching you eat," Momo said.

"Stop staring at me. Let me enjoy this without an audience. Come on." I gestured toward the silver chalices in front of them. "Serve yourselves and *mangez!*"

"Is that an order?" Nathanael asked.

"Yes."

I polished off one dish of the chocolate mousse and had started on my second. My French tablemates all served themselves sparingly and limited themselves to one bowl. Such restraint was admirable, but in my opinion, borderline insane. All-you-can-eat French chocolate mousse was made to be enjoyed like the glorious offering it was. This was hardly the time or place for restraint. Then again, I rarely seemed to feel that any time or place was right for restraint.

I remembered that French people don't equate quantity with quality. I took another spoonful and a sip of the cold, bubbly mousse. The mousse literally melted in my mouth. I savored the deep, creamy chocolatiness. *This* was quantity *and* quality. I wondered how long it would take for me to live in France before I began to subscribe to the "less is more" philosophy that seemed second nature to the French. Living within steps of Batifol, probably a *très* long time, indeed.

Just as we were waiting for our espressos to round out our feast, Franck left the table, and we all just assumed he was going to use the WC.

He came back just as we were served. A good fifteen minutes, after we had finished our *cafés* and when everyone at the table except me was enjoying a post-meal cigarette, Nathanael flagged down the waiter for the bill.

The garçon came over to the table. "*Mais*...it has already been taken care of, sir."

"By whom?" Nathanael asked.

"*Moi*," Franck said. "It's the least we can do."

So, that's where he had snuck off to.

"But I was going to pay!" Nathanael protested. "You two are just starting out."

"*Non*, I was going to pay," Momo argued. "I wanted to pay as a 'welcome to your new Parisian home' gift."

"Too bad. I've taken care of it."

"Well then," Jacinthe said, "all that's left for us to do is to return the favor next time. Trust me, there will be many times."

chapter twenty-four

We had almost been settled in our new apartment for a full week when Florent called and asked Franck if we wanted to meet him and Pauline that evening to go and eat an ice cream at Häagen-Dazs on the Champs-Élysées.

I'd been hoping

"Yes," Franck said, rubbing his forehead. "Still…Häagen-Dazs?"

It always struck me as bizarre that Florent thought the height of a Parisian experience was a bowl of Häagen-Dazs ice cream, which, I believed, was actually an American import.

In any case, despite our sorely restricted budget, Franck and I had bought them a fancy Cuisinart that Pauline had been lust-ing after, a huge bouquet of flowers, a box of chocolates, and a very nice bottle of wine as a thank you gift.

Pauline appeared delighted with the Cuisinart—a response that underlined the fact that we did not have much in common. I felt, in the end, that we had left them on perfectly civil terms. It had been uncomfortable to feel beholden to people who—when it came right down to it—I couldn't persuade myself to like.

Franck and I stood in front of the Jussieu buildings and

waited for them. I wasn't enthusiastic about spending an evening with them so quickly, but family was important to Franck. Even though this meant adorning my "nice" persona, I was willing to do it for him. Besides, maybe Florent and Pauline would be fine in small doses. Very small doses.

When Florent pulled his car into the parking spot we were saving for them, his face appeared oddly flushed. I could see through the windshield that Pauline's mouth was set in a scowl. They got out, the air around them crackling with an unresolved spat. Franck and I had been in that situation enough times with them for me to recognize the signs.

"*Bonjour!*" I said, kissing them both, pretending as if nothing was amiss.

"*Bonjour.*" Their lips barely touched my cheeks. *Probably still preoccupied with their fight.*

"Come up to our apartment," Franck said. "We can have an *apéritif* before heading out." Either Franck hadn't picked up on the tension or he decided to ignore it and jolly them along.

We walked across the street, and when we were on the sidewalk on our side of the street, I turned around and realized that Florent and Pauline hadn't followed us. They were still standing beside their car. Pauline was holding tight to Florent's arm and hissing something at him. Florent was shaking his head, but she yanked him closer and hissed with more intent, her eyes closing into slits.

"What's that all about?"

"I'd wager he doesn't agree with her about something," Franck guessed. "I never thought Florent was such a pushover, but I've noticed that Pauline always get her way."

"Maybe she didn't want to come tonight."

"Maybe." Franck shrugged. "In that case, they could have spared us." Perhaps I had overestimated Franck's love of this particular familial branch.

We waited by the front door of the building until Florent nodded, looking aggrieved but resigned. He turned to walk across the street toward us. Pauline had wiped the scowl off her face and was now smiling brightly.

"This is the building?" she said when they reached us.

"Yes," Franck said, picking up the thread as if that bizarre interlude hadn't just happened. "The location is perfect for us. Laura can walk to school. I'm close to the Metro line that takes me to my job at la Défense. We were lucky to find it. Also, it means that you two can have your click-clack back."

"I couldn't stand to live here," Pauline declared. "I mean, I'm sure it's perfectly fine for you two. I don't like the noise and the pollution and the crowds. I can't *bear* the center of Paris."

"It's good everyone doesn't want the same thing," I said.

Franck opened the door, and we led them across the first courtyard, then into the second one.

"It's unbelievably quiet," I said. In fact, it was far quieter than their place in the suburbs, but I was too polite to point that out. "The only thing that reminds us that we are in the center of Paris is the bells of Notre-Dame."

"Ugh," Pauline said. "Bells ringing all night? I couldn't stand it."

I couldn't think of a civil response. Hearing church bells is one of my favorite things.

"Stairs or elevator?" Franck asked once we had arrived in the lobby.

"What floor are you on?" Florent spoke for the first time since saying hello.

"Fourth."

"Florent, let's take the stairs," Pauline said, grabbing onto his arm. "I hate those old elevators. I'm always afraid I'll get stuck in one."

"Jacinthe and I actually did get stuck when we were moving in. It was hilarious."

Pauline shuddered.

"It looks like a well-cared-for building," Florent said, running his hand over the smooth, shiny, wooden bannister.

Pauline scowled.

"It is," Franck said. "Nobody messes with *la gardienne*. She runs a tight ship."

He opened the door to our apartment, all three hundred and seventy-five square feet of it, anyway. We couldn't all fit in the hall at once, so I hung back in the corridor, waiting for Franck to do the honors of showing them around. I knew that, given the size of the apartment, it wouldn't take long.

"It's so tiny!" Pauline cried. "Like a doll's apartment!" In fact, their apartment was only about a third bigger.

"We don't need much space," I said. "Not with all of Paris just outside our front door."

Pauline said nothing, but I could tell from the crease between her brows that my determined positivity was not the response she had bargained for.

"It must be *so* expensive." She sent a loaded look to Florent.

What is up with her?

"It's more than we wanted to pay." Franck joined us at the window. "But we couldn't spend the entire year camping out in your living room. We can't thank you enough for letting us do that, though. Hopefully we can pay back the favor one day."

"Yes, thank you both again so much," I said.

Pauline gave Florent an elbow in his ribs.

Florent cleared his throat, his face crimson. "I'm glad you mentioned that," he said with a false air of nonchalance.

Mentioned what? Franck and I traded bewildered looks.

"Pauline and I have done up a bill for you." Florent was so red now that his freckles were swallowed up completely.

"A bill?" Franck frowned.

Florent pulled a piece of paper out from the back pocket of his jeans and unfolded it carefully. He sat down on one of our hand-me-down chairs from Nathanael and Jacinthe and smoothed the paper out on the table in front of him.

He cleared his throat. "Pauline and I calculated the amount of gas, electricity, water, food, and rent we paid during the time you were staying with us. We've divided those in half to figure out the amount you owe us." Florent at least had the grace to look abashed. He didn't lift his face to meet our eyes.

I looked over to Pauline, whose face was ablaze with rapacious triumph.

This is the true Pauline.

Franck, for once, was at a loss for words. I couldn't even fathom the shock he was feeling. Cousins in his family bunked at each other's apartments in Paris all the time as they were finding their feet. It was unheard of to *charge* anyone for that favor.

It was such a cheap shot. Life in Paris was expensive, but I was certain that Florent and Pauline were doing far better on the financial front than us. They both had full-time jobs, after all.

I was quite sure their bill didn't take into account the groceries we had been buying for weeks and all the days where we couldn't shower because they had left us no hot water.

My usual inclination was to smooth over conflict, but then I thought of Jacinthe and Madame Renier-Bernadotte. Fury consumed me. Their lack of generosity would devastate Franck. Franck deserved better. I took the bill from Florent's hand. No, none of the financial contributions we had made were taken into consideration.

"Didn't you forget to charge us for our share of toilet paper?" I finally said.

Florent looked up, finally. "Toilet paper was included under groceries." Yet again, Franck's cousin showed himself incapable of reading the atmosphere in a room.

Franck remained speechless, eyes wide with shock.

Florent turned from Franck to me, the mood finally penetrating his thick skull. "There's no need to pay right away."

"By the end of the month, though," Pauline chimed in.

"We'll pay now," I said, and took their bill into the bedroom with me.

Luckily, I had a wad of cash that I had taken out of my bank account but hadn't spent yet. I had it on hand because, apparently in France, it takes several months to receive an actual checkbook and ATM card after opening an account.

I counted out the money and rounded it up by two francs. My hands were shaking. I came out and thrust the money at Pauline. Florent was as much to blame, but I was pretty sure she was the one really pushing for this. "Here you go. Count it."

Pauline smiled with sickly sweetness and passed the money off to Florent.

"I don't think I need to count it," he said, in a tone that led me to believe he wasn't one hundred percent certain on this point.

"You know what?" I announced. "I don't feel like Häagen-Dazs anymore. I think Franck and I will stay here."

"But...but we were going to celebrate your new apartment," Florent said.

"Why don't you two go and celebrate settling your accounts? Franck and I will celebrate another time." *With real friends.*

"If you're sure," Pauline said, and then tried to place a small moist hand on my arm.

I jerked it out of her reach. "I'm sure."

"Well then, we'll be off," she said, tucking the wad of francs in the back pocket of her jeans.

"Yes," I said. "*Salut.*" I wasn't going to use *au revoir*, which literally means "until we meet again." I had no desire for that.

"*Bon...au revoir,*" Florent said and gave me and Franck mechanical *bises*. This was one of those situations where the French tradition was most unwelcome. I kissed the air about two inches from his face.

Pauline plunged in before I could take a step backwards. I shuddered at the violation of her hot breath near my face.

When I heard the door shut behind them, I grabbed Franck's hand. "Come on," I said. "We're going out."

"Where?" he asked, his voice hollow.

"Anywhere," I said. "We need to walk and talk, or at least to walk."

I pushed the button for the elevator to increase the chances of Florent and Pauline being gone—it took far longer than the stairs. I had no desire to bump into them for a long time, if ever.

When we got to the front door of the building, I opened it a crack and peeked out, then sighed with relief when I saw their car had gone. I took Franck's arm, and we walked down the street toward the Seine, past Batifol and the wonderful-looking *boulangerie* we had yet to try.

"I can't believe that just happened," Franck said, as though coming to after being knocked out with powerful sedation.

We walked down the stairs to the banks of the Seine, where

somebody was playing the accordion and others were dancing.

"Neither can I," I said. "Then again, I don't know your cousin as well as you."

"I thought I knew him," Franck said. "But now...maybe I never did."

"Pauline was the instigator," I said. "But Florent didn't have to go along with it. For someone who has done so well academically, he is incredibly dense."

"That's a generous interpretation," Franck said. "I just never...I never believed he would charge me money. I know from my aunt that he and Pauline had been given money by Mémé and his parents to cover any extra expenses during our stay—quite a lot of money. That, combined with all we already contributed, means they actually made money on our backs."

Franck had been doing the mental calculations as well. A chilly breeze was blowing off the Seine. I shivered. For the first time, the summer felt far away.

I knew for a fact that even on the bread line it would never cross Franck's mind to do such a thing. We couldn't technically afford such things as paying for everyone's lunch at Batifol on moving day, but life was too short and friends and family too valuable to be anything but generous.

"I had Florent's older brother, Mathieu, stay with me for three months when I lived above the horrible little *poissonnerie* in Saint-Denis. That apartment was not suitable for more than one person, let me tell you."

"Was that the one with the toilet that doubled as a shower?" I asked.

"That's the one." Franck thrust his hands into his pockets.

"Mathieu is a big guy," Franck continued. "He snored. We took turns sleeping under the kitchen table. He also ate through all the groceries I bought, and I did all the cooking for both of us. Still, it never would have occurred to me in a million years... no...*ever*...to charge him for anything."

I watched the melancholy sight of leaves scuttling into the Seine. "Why is that?" I asked, curious.

"He's family!" Franck said, sounding shocked at my question. "Florent has just breached one of the unspoken rules of my family. Family do those things for each other simply because it's family. To charge for it…I still can't believe it."

I squeezed Franck's hand, and we walked up to the pont Saint-Michel, built by Napoleon. It spanned the Seine and took us over to the Île de la Cité, where Notre-Dame hulked like a living thing.

"Imagine not wanting to hear the bells of Notre-Dame," I scoffed. "Pauline is strange in more ways than one. Just watch. Now that she's gotten what she wanted, she'll be all sweetness and light the next few times she sees us, until she wants something else. If there's one thing I can't stand in a person, it's duplicity."

I hadn't decided what kind of woman I wanted to become that year, but it wasn't a two-faced cheapskate like Pauline.

"She is what she is." Franck shrugged. "But when it comes down to it, I don't care about her at all. She's not my family."

"Not *yet*," I pointed out. "They could end up getting married."

"God forbid," Franck said. "Still, it's Florent that upsets me. Has he forgotten so completely where he comes from? Why does he let her walk all over him?"

"Maybe it's the Frederick's of Hollywood lingerie."

Franck shook his head. "He didn't even notice. She has no charm. No mystery. Trussing herself up in cheap red lace just reinforces that."

"Tastes vary, you know. There must be something about her he finds appealing."

Franck fell silent for a few minutes.

"I just look at him and I think, how pathetic," he said, finally. "A submissive man is a tragic thing."

"*Or* a submissive woman," I added.

Franck didn't appear to hear me. "What is most important is freedom, and that everyone has it…that's what's most important for me."

I was destabilized by this abrupt turn in the conversation. Franck's comment struck me as odd. *We have freedom, right?* I wanted to ask. *We can still love each other and be in a relationship and be free, right?*

I reminded myself that Franck was in shock. He was merely thinking out loud, as he often did. Unlike me, he didn't have a built-in filter between his head and his mouth.

We walked the rest of the way to Notre-Dame in silence. Neither of us had suggested going there. Our feet had led the way.

I opened one of the massive, carved wooden doors of the cathedral and glanced fleetingly at the stern saints carved into the stone that flanked the doors. *Hey, don't stare in judgement at me like that. Feel free to judge Pauline, though.*

Franck dipped a finger in the stone basin of holy water near the door and made the sign of the cross on his forehead. We walked along the side aisle and paused by each small chapel. Each one had a statue—usually of the Virgin Mary—a few benches, and a metal stand for candle offerings.

We separated after a few minutes. Franck seemed to want to linger, and I didn't want to either hold him up or hurry him along. I wandered at my own pace, reasoning he probably needed some processing time alone.

At a chapel with an ancient statue of the Virgin Mary with gold spikes radiating from her, I dropped a ten-franc coin into the metal box and lit one of the red candles. The scent of lit matches and melting wax permeated the air.

I sat down on one of the benches and narrowed my eyes so all I could see between the thin crack of my eyelids was the flicker of my lit candle.

Franck's strange mood fanned my rage at Pauline and Florent. If their behavior caused problems between me and Franck, I would never forgive them.

We both loved Montreal, but I knew that sometimes Franck felt desperately homesick for France. Even I felt desperately homesick for France. Actually, on days when it was thirty below with the windchill, I felt homesick for the Tahiti part of France, even though I had never actually been there.

Franck and I had been together for well over two years by then. I knew to finish off my degree, I had to go back to Montreal for my fourth year of university. Before we arrived in Paris, I had always just assumed that Franck would come back with me. After all, we had fought so hard to be together. Still, I felt foreboding that this may have been naïve.

In the context of all that, what had Franck meant with his comment about freedom? Something? Nothing?

I rested my forehead on the pew in front of me. This church had seen centuries of war, famine, and plague...surely my worries were small change. Still, I'd always hated the feeling that something momentous was coming down the pipeline but I couldn't see its outlines yet.

All I could do was light a second candle and wait.

chapter twenty-five

Now that we were settled in our new Parisian abode, I had a couple of unpleasant things I needed to take care of. I had told myself that I needed to have a fixed address before I could tackle any of these administrative tasks, but the reality was I had been procrastinating.

First, I had to report to the local *préfecture de police* in our *quartier* so they could check over my paperwork and finalize my student visa so that I could stay legally in France until the summer.

Second, I was required to go to a distant neighborhood of Paris to undergo a medical exam, which was mandatory for all foreign students.

The French require physicals for everything: to start school, to continue school, to practice any sport (even something as benign as the local *pétanque* league)… As far as I could tell, the French administration was always looking for an excuse to put people in an ugly, cold room with green painted walls and have them take their clothes off to be looked over by an unfamiliar French doctor.

Police first.

In early November, I stood on the rue de la Montagne Sainte-Geneviève, staring up at hideous building that squatted, menacing and completely out of place, across from quaint tea shops and pharmacies on the other side of the street.

The bottom of the building looked as though it had been constructed with rusted sheets of metal. The building then contracted as if it was being squeezed in at the waist with a belt. The skinny part of the building was meter-high chain mail.

Above that there were three stories of small windows set into a concrete block. To think I had found the architecture of Paris III alienating…it was downright welcoming compared to this place.

Any hope that I was in front of the wrong building was dashed by the police cars parked out front. It was pretty much guaranteed that everybody who worked in this building was in a permanently homicidal frame of mind.

After crossing the street, I was stopped by a policeman who had been standing inside a bulletproof hut constructed on the sidewalk. He stepped out to block my entrance into the building. "Identification," he barked.

Luckily, I had come prepared with all the papers—and then some —necessary for my visa processing. I showed the policeman my Canadian passport and showed the prefect my *convocation* and my French visa papers and my school card and a photocopy I had asked Franck to make of our lease.

He fingered through them all, frowning. "Fine," he said eventually. "You can go inside."

I didn't quite understand his role. Was he actually trying to prevent people from going inside the building? It wasn't exactly the type of spot that inspired people passing by to drop in for an impromptu visit.

The inside of the building was as hideous as the outside. The reception counter—or what had probably been the reception counter in better days—was not staffed. Broken air vents filled the lobby with a deafening, clunking whir. The ceilings were low and there were no discernable directions as far as I could tell. The whole place reeked of sauerkraut.

I was supposed to report there, but *where*? I wandered the hallways until I came across a woman sitting behind another sheet of what looked like bullet proof glass.

"Excuse me," I said in my best French. "I need some assistance."

"*Quoi*?" she said to me. "Are you a lawyer?"

"No," I said.

"Then you shouldn't be here. Family aren't allowed to visit."

"I'm not visiting anyone."

"Then what are you doing here?" she demanded.

"I need to check in with the prefect to validate my student visa." I pressed my letter up against the dirty glass separating us.

"I can't help you," she snapped. "That's not my job."

"I realize that," I insisted. "But maybe you could just give me a general idea of where I need to go?"

She shrugged. "*Je ne sais pas*. Not here."

Someone tapped on my shoulder and I whirled around, half expecting it to be a blood thirsty murderer, what with all the police hiding behind bullet proof glass. Instead, it was a young policewoman with her pale blond hair pulled back into a disciplined bun. "Can I help you?" she said. "You don't look like you belong here."

"*Merci*," I said, relieved at her friendly smile. "I'm lost. I'm supposed to report here to validate my student visa, but they didn't give me any instructions on where to go inside the building. I looked for directions but—"

"There aren't any," she completed my sentence.

"Precisely."

"Come on, I'll take you. Even if I gave you directions, it would still be impossible for you to find by yourself."

"You are saving my life," I said.

She laughed. "*De rien*."

She led me through a warren of back stairs and hallways. Many of the ceiling panels were disintegrating, revealing dirty gray insulation that was probably made entirely of asbestos.

Finally, she pushed open a door to a stuffy room, equipped with some broken plastic bucket seats, a half dead plant, a French flag, and two unarmed policemen behind a melamine counter.

"Gisèle!" The older one heralded the arrival of my savior. "How is it that you look more beautiful with each day that passes?"

Apparently, they hadn't gotten around yet to creating sexual harassment guidelines in France.

"Shut up, Jerôme," she said.

He just laughed. *"Du caractère!* That is what I love about you." *Jerôme loves women who insult him?*

"What do you have here?" He pointed at me.

"A lost American," she said.

"Don't that describe all Americans?" Jerôme wiggled his bushy eyebrows and laughed heartily at his joke.

Anti-discrimination guidelines were probably not much of a thing there either, I decided.

"I'm Canadian," I corrected.

"That's better," Jerôme said. He leaned his arms on the counter and studied me. "I like Canadians. Can't say the same about Americans."

Poor Grace—the girl with the big hair bow in my Dicken's class. It dawned on me that it must not always be easy for her as an American abroad.

"I received a letter telling me to report here to finalize the paperwork for my student visa," I said.

Even though four of the plastic chairs were occupied with people radiating the ripe-for-murder aura common in people obliged to deal with French administration, Gisèle's admirer waved me up to the counter. "Let's see."

Gisèle accompanied me up to the counter and exchanged *les bises* with Jerôme. She turned to me. "He'll take care of you," she said. "I should go."

"Non!" Jerôme protested. "You and your *protegée* here transform this depressing room entirely, like sunshine. Please stay."

"I would love to, but I can't." She smiled. "Criminals to catch. Old ladies to console after their miniature poodles have been run over… However, you would be doing me a favor by helping my friend here."

I smiled as charmingly as I could at Jerôme and his colleague behind the counter.

"It will be our pleasure," Jerôme admitted and patted his impressive stomach in a gallant fashion.

"*Merci, mes amis.*" Gisèle left us with one last brilliant smile before I had the time to thank her properly.

"She's wonderful," I said.

"*Oui*, she is one of the good ones." Jerôme was still watching the door she had left through. He turned his attention to me. "Now, Mademoiselle, will you do me the honor of showing me these papers of yours?"

I pulled them out and passed them to Jerôme, who complimented me on my organizational skills. He took his time looking over everything, commenting on one of the many pieces of paper issued to me by the French government. "*Ca alors*, I've never seen one of these before."

We chatted about Canada and the West Coast and Jussieu, the ugly university building across the street from our apartment. He recommended several good bistros in the neighborhood. Brasserie Le Monge was his top pick—no surprise, as he looked like the type of man who could do justice to their cheese platter. It was a delightful exchange, considering its inauspicious beginnings.

About forty minutes after Gisèle brought me to his counter, Jerôme stamped a bunch of documents and reminded me that I still needed to get my medical exam completed. "Watch yourself when you go for that," he said. "It's not in the nicest area of town."

"I've heard," I said.

"I mean it," he said. "Don't go on your own. I would hate to think of anything happening to a lovely young woman like yourself."

"I won't," I promised.

He passed me back all my papers and my new, improved visa in my passport that had now been stamped and validated.

"I hate to see you go," he said. "I enjoyed chatting with you. Any friend of Gisèle's is a friend of mine."

"I enjoyed talking to you too," I said.

"I'm also amazed that you came in to take care of this."

"I had to."

"Technically yes, I suppose, but to be honest nobody bothers."

Franck got home from work while I was at the table in our living room-slash-dining room-slash-office. I was deep in trying to decipher a tricky portion of Érec *et* Énide without resorting to my translated text.

I couldn't put my finger on why exactly, but I was motivated to work my hardest in Madame Renier-Bernadotte's classes. I could listen to her lecture for hours. I relished the challenge of trying to understand and analyze the texts in their original medieval French.

Even though her translations were beautifully done from what I could tell, there was still something lost when translating the medieval words to modern French—a rawness, a sensibility that could just not be expressed by contemporary language. I loved the erratic spellings and the odd words that had fallen out of use over the centuries.

I discovered that my background as a native English speaker was actually an advantage if I adopted a flexible enough approach to the text. Many of the words had an English root or were bastardized versions of English ones or, even more interesting, hybrids of both the French root word and the English root word.

Studying the medieval texts was a giant treasure hunt, an exercise in trying to edge up as closely as possible to the original meaning of the person who had written it down so many centuries ago.

I was so deeply engaged in what I was doing that it was difficult to change gears when Franck appeared in the room. The world of modern Paris felt like another planet.

"How was your day?" My voice sounded strange.

"*Fantastique*." Frack dropped his messenger bag on the chair beside me and pulled out a chair. "I mean, the job is still terrible, and I wonder every day if the magazine isn't going to fold, and the editor is always on my case about the English rhythm of my writing, but I got some amazing news today."

"What?"

"They're sending me to Morocco!"

This snapped me to attention. "*Quoi*? When?"

"The day after tomorrow. The Moroccan tourist board is putting on a promotion event for French journalists. The person from *Expo News* who was supposed to go has a family wedding this weekend, so they offered it to me instead."

"That's amazing. Can I come?" I said, only half joking. We had always talked about going to Morocco together. It was a country I longed to visit.

Franck shook his head. "I'm sorry. No guests allowed. I need to take photos while I'm there and write a few articles afterward. It won't all be play."

I wasn't by nature the jealous type, but I felt strangely unsettled by Franck's news.

He had been a bit off for the past month since we received the bill from Pauline and Florent. Nothing dramatic, just slightly distant.

Was he feeling trapped? That was the impression I had from time to time, but it was so vague, I second-guessed myself. Still, something about him going to Morocco with a bunch of French journalists on an all-expenses paid trip set me on edge. Was this the freedom he was looking for? If so, would it be enough?

"Not too much play, I hope," I said, laughing. Immediately I wished I could unsay the words. I sounded like some sort of clinging female, the type my pride forbade me to be. "Joking," I added.

"Mainly work," he said. "Promise."

"You love Morocco. I'm happy for you."

"Will you be all right by yourself?"

"I have Paris. I don't need anything else," I stood, but then once I was up, I wasn't sure where I was going to go in our tiny apartment. "Besides, even if I did, Jacinthe is only a phone call away."

"You sure?" he asked.

"Absolutely," I said. "You need to do this."

"I should pack," he said, excitement written all over his features.

chapter twenty-six

Two days later, I returned to our apartment after a full day of classes. Franck had left early that morning. It felt strangely empty, knowing that by this time Franck was across the Mediterranean ocean in North Africa.

It was just Paris and me. A glorious prospect, I reminded myself.

I made myself a mug of orange pekoe tea and a little plate of *biscuits pur beurre* from Brittany and settled down with *Great Expectations*, the riveting part when Pip finds out that his benefactor is in fact Magwitch, not the cobwebby Miss Havisham, as he had hoped.

I had only been reading for about five minutes when I was rocked by an enormous boom.

I dropped to my knees under the table. The windows rattled. I curled into the "duck and cover" position, with my head bowed and my arms and hands wrapped around the back of my neck to protect my spine.

I cowered like this while the vibrations died down. At last, my logic kicked in. *Wait a second. They don't have earthquakes in Paris.*

I crawled out from under the table, glad that I was alone and no one had seen that. I sniffed. There was an acrid smell in the air that hadn't been there before.

I cautiously opened the front door to the apartment and peeked into the corridor, half expecting to see licking flames. Instead, I found my elderly neighbor from across the hall slumped against the wall like a rag doll. Smoke billowed from the open door of his apartment—clearly the source of the toxic mix that reeked of sulfur and gunpowder.

"Monsieur." I knelt and took his hand in mine. I didn't know, or couldn't remember his name, if in fact Jacinthe had told me. I did remember that he was the elderly man who Monsieur Arseneau wanted to die because he lived in a rent-controlled apartment. He was still wearing a ratty, old dressing robe and a threadbare pair of plaid pajamas. One of his slippers had slipped off his pale, narrow, and surprisingly elegant foot. "Are you all right? What happened?"

"*Le gaz*," he murmured. "*Explosion*."

Could I leave him long enough to call the fire station? Firemen dealt with gas explosions in France, didn't they?

His eyelids fluttered.

I squeezed his hand a little harder. "Monsieur, you must try to open your eyes."

 Fox Lady emerged from the elevator just then, pulling her market caddy behind her. I noticed the familiar Louis Vuitton logo. *Louis Vuitton makes market caddies?* Embarrassment made my face burn. Our last interaction had been when Jacinthe and I were stuck in the elevator on moving day.

I cudgeled my brain to be practical. Now that she was there, I could run into our apartment and phone the firemen. Maybe, I thought, observing Monsieur's extreme paleness, I should call for an ambulance too.

Fox Lady caught sight of our neighbor. Panic flashed in her eyes. She dropped her caddy handle and rushed over to us. "Monsieur Pierrepont! What are you doing on the floor? What is that smell?" Her equine nostrils flared. "*Le gaz!*"

She reached down and took his free hand in hers. "Was there an explosion, Monsieur Pierrepont?" I never thought someone who could scowl like her was capable of such a tender tone. She did not kneel, but she bent over him, her other hand primly on her knee over her royal blue Chanel wool skirt. "Can you tell me what happened?"

She rigorously adhered to the formal "*vous*" pronoun, which was the first thing, I realized now, that had abandoned me. Addressing my elderly neighbor using the casual "tu," as I had done, was a social solecism, even in an emergency.

Monsieur Pierrepont opened his eyes and kept them open this time. He seemed steadied by Fox Lady's excessive formality.

She turned to me. "I suppose you have already called the fire department."

"N-No...," I stuttered. "I got out into the hall just seconds before you arrived."

"*Alors*, what are you waiting for now that I'm here?" She did not use the gentle tone with me. "It could endanger the entire building if there is a gas leak. More importantly, Monsieur Pierrepont needs medical help."

I had a brief thought of Franck returning from Morocco to find the building burnt to ashes. "Should I call the ambulance too?"

"*Bien sûr que non*! The firemen will look after the first aid."

In France, there isn't a 9-1-1 service like there is in Canada, where one number connects you to all the emergency services. What was the number for the fire department again? Was it 1-5 or 1-7 or....?

"What is the number for *les pompiers* again?" I asked.

Fox Lady looked at me as if I was an imbecile, and said, "It's 1-8, *bien sûr*! Never mind, I will go call them, although I don't like to leave Monsieur Pierrepont alone with just you."

I was offended, but this wasn't the time to indulge my ego. "We'll be fine," I said. "I'll try to keep him awake."

"We are old friends, *vous voyez*, Monsieur Pierrepont and me," she said, more for my neighbor's benefit than mine. He mustered a smile for her.

I knelt beside Monsieur Pierrepont and patted his hand, a gesture that Fox Lady looked at with distaste before marching back to her apartment.

She returned quickly. "*Les pompiers* are on their way," she said to me. "You can stand up now."

I didn't. "Do you think we should try to stand Monsieur Pierrepont up?" I asked her. He had kept his eyes open but still appeared dazed.

"Certainly not!" Madame Fox snapped. "The firemen will be here shortly, and Monsieur Pierrepont is quite comfortable where he is. He had a nasty shock. Besides, he suffers from low blood pressure. Am I not right, Monsieur?" she asked him formally, and he looked up at her and smiled almost a roguish smile.

"A shock? I did indeed," he agreed, seeming to gain his wits with each word that came out of Madame Fox's prim lips.

"You know who I blame?" Fox Lady declared.

"Who?" I asked.

"That horrible Monsieur Arseneau. His father always made sure all the gas lines into the building were properly maintained and he had the gas board come by once a year to check everyone's appliances and make sure they were safe. *He* was a large-minded man. That son of his though…" She made a sound of disgust. "A money scrounging, ill-bred bully. You can bet that he came in and tampered with Monsieur Pierrepont's gas. He wants to get rid of him, of course, even if it means murder—"

"Now, now," Monsieur Pierrepont rebuked from his position on the carpet. "Madame Rol-Tanguy, there is no need to cast such aspersions on the man, even though I know as well as anyone that he will not shed a tear on the day of my funeral."

So that was Fox Lady's real name: Madame Rol-Tanguy.

"Of course not!" Fox Lady snorted. "He will be dancing on your grave when he rents out your apartment for full rent."

"No person can be all bad, even Monsieur Arseneau. We cannot accuse him of attempted murder," said Monsieur Pierrepont.

"Speak for yourself," Madame Fox muttered.

"Now, now Madame Rol-Tanguy," Monsieur Pierrepont remonstrated.

"You always were too kind-hearted," she said. "Far more tender-hearted than I."

"Ah, but you have *du caractère*," Monsieur Pierrepont said, looking up at Madame Fox with a gleam in his eye. "Who knows better than I how strongly you hold your convictions?"

Were they *flirting*?

In any case, his repartee with Fox Lady had put a bit of color into Monsieur Pierrepont's cheeks.

I strained my ears to listen for the sound of French firetruck sirens. They were higher pitched than those back home. I couldn't hear anything, but then I guessed we might not, tucked behind two courtyards as we were.

"We have been through much, you and I, haven't we?" Monsieur Pierrepont was gazing up at Fox Lady with a certain sadness in his eyes and…was that…longing? "This is nothing. Remember the war?"

"Your brain must have been scrambled if you're asking me if I remember. How could I forget those years? Never. The most terrible time."

"Yet there were some sublime moments," Monsieur Pierrepont's eyes met hers with a charged look.

"Yes, but…" The stinging air caught in my throat and I coughed. Madame Fox snapped her head in my direction and blinked. "Perhaps the less said about that the better."

Damn that cough. I was dying for them to continue.

Male voices and the thump of numerous footsteps echoed up from the lobby below.

Soon after, two glorious Parisian *pompiers* appeared in their uniforms—black leather flack boots, fitted navy shirts with a red stripe across the chest, and equally snug navy utility pants with a red stripe down the side. *Oh là* là.

"Bonjour, Messieurs Dames." They nodded at the three of us. What do we have here?"

"A gas explosion!" Fox Lady declared. "It's the fault of our landlord!"

"And you?" The taller of the two firemen caught my eye and smiled at me. "What do you think, Mademoiselle?" He was using the "*vous*" form as well, and it hit me like a lightning bolt how the formality could be ridiculously seductive.

My face must have blazed crimson. There is so much more to the French language than meets the eye. I would have to go back in my texts and see if this was also the case in the Middle Ages.

"I'm the neighbor." I seemed to have a hard time talking, so I pointed to our door. "I heard an explosion. At first I thought it was an earthquake."

"An earthquake?" The other fireman, who had a pair of perfectly chiseled cheekbones, arched a questioning brow.

"Where I'm from earthquakes are…there are a lot of earthquakes." I couldn't help but stare up in admiration as I stumbled over my words.

"Where are you from?" the first fireman asked. "You have a charming accent, but I can't place it."

Madame Fox cleared her throat loudly. "Aren't you two *pompiers* here to take care of Monsieur Pierrepont and ensure the whole building isn't going to blow up?"

"Yes, yes, *bien sûr*," the taller fireman with almond-shaped green eyes placed his first aid bag on the floor and knelt down beside Monsieur Pierrepont. He took out a blood pressure cuff and began strapping it to my neighbor's arm. Monsieur Pierrepont looked at the young fireman with understanding in his eyes.

"Never mind Madame." He excused Madame Fox. "She forgets what it is to be young and charmed." He looked up at her, and they shared another charged glance.

"I forget nothing!" she declared. "But there is a time and place for flirting, surely? Not after you have been thrown from your apartment from a gas explosion in your pajamas and the *pompiers* have arrived to attend to *you*, not your *jolie* young neighbor."

"Madame Rol-Tanguy was always a stickler for propriety." Monsieur Pierrepont shared a complicit smile with me.

"I am not!" Madame Fox said. "How can you say such a thing? You of all people—"

He winked at her, the old rogue.

She shook her finger at him. "I don't know why on earth I stopped to help you. You're no better than a naughty boy, trying to get a rise out of me."

"And succeeding," Monsieur Pierrepont noted.

Before Madame Fox could riposte, the first *pompier* emerged from the apartment. "*Le gaz*, like you guessed," he said to Madame Fox.

"I didn't guess. I knew. I also know you can blame it on our landlord."

"Now, now, Berengère, don't go throwing accusations around like that. She is impulsive, you see," Monsieur Pierrepont explained to me and the firemen.

Berengère? Madame Fox had a first name, and it was Berengère?

"Your blood pressure is quite good." The fireman said to Monsieur Pierrepont. He unstrapped the cuff, then took out a stethoscope and listened to Monsieur Pierrepont's heart. "You've suffered a nasty shock though. I think we should take you in to the hospital for a quick check. How do you feel about going for a ride in our firetruck?"

"*Vraiment*?" Monsieur Pierrepont said. His face became animated like that of the young boy Madame Fox reprimanded him for being. "That would be beyond everything wonderful. I never imagined when I got up this morning that today was going to be so exciting."

"You say that as if it is a *good* thing," Fox Lady said.

"Don't try to convince me you don't like a little bit of excitement, Berengère. I know the truth." he said.

He had done what I would have thought was impossible—robbed Fox Lady of words. Her eyes shined. What exactly was their shared history? Before I could think of a diplomatic way to ask this, the second *pompier* emerged again from the apartment.

"I'm sorry to tell you there's quite a lot of damage to your apartment." He leaned down toward my neighbor to deliver the bad news.

Monsieur Pierrepont waved his hand. "I'll face that when I get back, but first I want to ride in the firetruck."

"Silly man," Madame Fox said, but with tenderness softening her features. "While you are at the hospital, I will go through your apartment and begin to set things right."

"Would you like me to help?" I asked.

"No," she said. "But...thank you. It is a kind offer."

"I will also make a call to Monsieur Arseneau immediately," she added. "Don't worry about a thing, Roland. I will fix everything."

"I know you will," he said comfortably. "You always do."

"Do you think you could walk with our help, or would you like us to bring up the stretcher?" one of the *pompiers* asked.

"Stretcher!" Fox Lady answered, but Monsieur Pierrepont waved her suggestion away with his eloquent hands.

"I'm sure I can walk with you two strapping young men to help me. Just give me a hand up from the floor here. I imagine that is going to be the most difficult part."

"With some grunts and groans and the strength of the *pompiers'* muscular arms, which I found myself gaping at as though hypnotized, Monsieur managed to stand up.

Fox Lady frowned.

"Aren't you going to come out and watch me get into the firetruck?" he asked us. "It was one of my boyhood dreams, and it just wouldn't be the same without an audience of beautiful ladies."

"You are incorrigible, Roland." Fox Lady shook her head at him.

He twinkled a smile at us as he began to make his way slowly into the elevator, obediently following the *pompiers* instructions. Madame Fox and I followed down the stairs.

There were so many things I wanted to ask her. What was Paris like during the war? What happened in this building during those terrible years of Occupation? Most of all, what were Monsieur Pierrepont and Fox Lady to each other?

I opened my mouth to formulate a question and then saw Madame Fox had assumed her habitual forbidding countenance. It was not an expression that welcomed intimacy.

We walked in silence out to the courtyard, following our neighbor flanked by the firemen. The sun had come out from behind the clouds and shined down on their glorious uniforms.

I took a moment to appreciate how their snug shirts highlighted their biceps, then I felt a spasm of worry. Was Franck likewise admiring the women in Morocco? If so, was there any harm to it?

The *gardienne* of the building, a small Northern African woman, of whom I had caught a few fleeting glances but whom I had never heard talk, was waiting in front of her lodgings right inside the front door to the building. She had beautiful black eyes fringed with thick, long lashes. She did not ask any questions but watched inscrutably as our procession passed her by. I tried to catch her eyes and smile, but with no success.

She buzzed open the large metal door for the *pompiers*. They had managed to park their fire truck right in front of the front doors to the building. Its glossy red and yellow paint reflected the sunshine like a mirror. The firetruck sported an impressive ladder, which was now folded over its entire length. It was the perfect vehicle to fulfill a child's, or in this case—an elderly man's—fantasies.

La gardienne followed us out onto the sidewalk. How had the fireman managed to move the other cars that were always parked where their truck now was? I decided they must have been some sort of demi-gods.

The guardian, Madame Fox, and I stood on the sidewalk and watched Monsieur Pierrepont as he was helped into the firetruck. They even let him stand up, so his head, with its wispy strands of white hair, peeked out the top. A huge grin was plastered across his face, and he waved at us as if he was fit to burst.

Even the taciturn *gardienne* chuckled, and Madame Fox was positively beaming. She waved back at him. "He will always have the soul of a naughty boy, Monsieur Pierrepont," she said, her voice full of affection.

"Find me a man that doesn't," *la gardienne* remarked.

"That's true, Madame Maachi." Madame Fox looked at *la gardienne* with respect.

The firetruck eased away from the curb. Its sirens began blaring, echoing down to the Seine. Monsieur grinned even wider and pointed up at the sky and laughed. "I asked them to do that!" he shouted at us.

Once the sirens faded in the distance, we three women looked at each other.

"I must get back to work," said the guardian.

"I have been meaning to tell you that, since you started the job here, the lobby has never been so *impeccable*." Madame Fox said. "We have often talked about it among ourselves, we old-timers."

Madame *la gardienne* didn't look particularly gratified by the comment, but she raised her chin. "I was raised to take pride in my work."

"It shows," said Fox Lady. "And it is much appreciated." With a brief pause, then a nod, *la gardienne* opened the large metal door for us and then slipped inside her *loge*—her private apartment.

Fox Lady and I headed back upstairs, sharing the elevator again. I usually took the stairs, but it seemed impolite to do so when she held the metal door open for me.

"I wouldn't have missed seeing Monsieur Pierrepont leave in the *voiture de pompiers* for all the world," I said as the elevator reached the fourth floor with a bounce.

"Me neither," she said, smiling as though enjoying a private joke.

I opened the door and held it open for her. "I'm busy this afternoon," she said as she passed by me. "But perhaps you would like to come over at some time for a *thé*?"

"I would like that very much," I said. "*Merci*." I was surprised to discover I meant it. There were so many questions still unanswered about my two neighbors.

"*A bientôt*," she said, shutting her door behind her.

chapter twenty-seven

The next morning was Saturday—market day on the place Monge and the rue Mouffetard. I couldn't wait to explore.

The previous evening, Franck had called from Ourzazate. The connection scratched and hissed. All I could make out was something about a bright blue sky and rose petals being thrown at his feet when he got off the plane.

I hung up the phone feeling happy for Franck, but also a tad jealous that he was having a wonderful adventure without me. I gave myself a mental shake. Where was I? Paris!

The morning dawned drizzly and gray. Perfect weather for hiding in a café reading Victor Hugo or maybe finally delving into the Dumas I had been assigned on my reading list. Maybe I would bring along one of my medieval texts and not bring the translation, just to test how much I understood. That was a suitably intellectual pursuit for a rainy day in a Parisian café.

I slid out my suitcase, which was hidden under the bed, and dug around for my winter jacket. It was a sort of blanket jacket that had been all the rage in Montreal about two years earlier, and was striped burgundy, brown, and green.

Now, I found it not only ugly but also terribly un-Parisian. I was trying to suck up the style of Parisian women by osmosis; I knew that this jacket was not going to cut it there.

I glanced down at my Eastpak backpack. The French girls at school carried their few school books (how did they manage to carry so few? Did they ever study?) around with them in stylish leather satchels or Longchamp bags.

Students in Montreal used backpacks, but again, ones not chic enough for Paris.

I needed to search for a new bag that was more Parisian, and in my budget—not an easy feat. In the meantime, the backpack would have to do.

I locked the apartment door and descended the stairs, starting to feel more Parisian as my hand slid down the polished wood banister.

I made sure to close the big metal door of the building behind me when I stepped out onto la rue des Fossés Saint-Bernard. I had already learned that *la gardienne* and my fellow tenants did not like having it left open even the tiniest crack. Most of the conversations I had overhead in the lobby concerned *la sécurité*, a foreign preoccupation to my trusting Canadian mindset.

I strolled up the rue Monge, wondering which café I should stop at for breakfast. This had been the stuff of my Parisian daydreams before I left Canada.

I chose one right on the corner of rue Monge and boulevard Saint-Germain.

I took a seat by the window. The café was warm, and its window was fogged up from all the conversations, warm food, and drinks being served up inside.

The *garçon* came by to take my order. I decided it was still early enough for the proper café breakfast of a basket of pastries and a big bowl of *café au lait*, which Franck had taught me to order as a *café crème*—only tourists ordered *cafés au lait*.

I could have cracked open my book, but I was contented to gaze out the window. The comfortable sounds of dishes and glasses being clinked together wrapped around me like a cashmere sweater.

Paris felt like home.

The *garçon* brought me my *café crème* in a large, white ceramic bowl with a dark green stripe around its rim, and a basket full of croissants and sliced baguette. On a little ceramic dish sat three miniature jars of Bonne Maman jam—apricot, strawberry, and black currant, as well as a generous pat of butter.

I sighed with pleasure.

First, I cracked open the croissant with my fingers and added a little bit of butter and some apricot jam. I closed it again and then dipped it in my *café crème* for just the perfect number of seconds—around five—and pulled it out at the critical moment, when the croissant had soaked up the milky coffee but not so much that it had started to disintegrate. I took a bite of the coffee-soaked croissant and sat back to better enjoy the milky, coffee-flavored, buttery, jammy, flaky concoction melting on my tongue.

I ate slowly, my thoughts sliding from the Paris morning to the blue skies of Morocco. *What is Franck doing right now? Are women still throwing flowers at his feet?* I hoped not, because I had no plans to become a rose petal-throwing girlfriend.

I thought back to the distance I had felt between us since that evening with Pauline and Florent. Had Franck somehow drawn a parallel between us and them? Was he worried that if we stayed together he would wake up one day and find himself subjugated like Florent? Anger crept up the back of my neck. Couldn't he see how ridiculous that was?

Ever since I had first met Florent, I couldn't get over how two cousins who were the same age and had been brought up together could be so fundamentally different.

Most importantly, I was nothing like Pauline. To worry that we would become like them was to cast me in a role that felt as irritating as a pair of ill-fitting tights.

With this thought still in my mind, I bit into my croissant like a lion ripping the leg off an antelope. I was not Pauline. I loved Franck, but I had no desire to control him. I was an independent woman who needed no man.

My fantasies of meandering the market on place Monge were vaporized by this surge of defiance. I remembered the medical clinic I had been procrastinating visiting for the final hoop to jump through for my visa requirements. It was open on Saturdays. The clinic was still located in the dodgy area of Paris that I had been warned away from by Jerôme the policeman.

Jerôme had warned me not to go alone. Yet, wouldn't a self-sufficient woman defy that? An independent woman wouldn't need an escort to go anywhere. She would go and get her medical checkup done by herself. What's more, she would do it at that very moment.

I ate the last crumbs of my croissant, drank back my last gulp of *café crème*, and took out my Metro map to plot my route.

Forty minutes later, I emerged from the Barbès - Rochechouart Metro station with my chin raised, prepared to take on this so-called notorious quartier of Paris.

I was in the 18th arrondissement, according to my map. My hands shook a bit as I folded it back up and slid it into the back pocket of my jeans again.

The neighborhood might have had a questionable reputation, but I was a girl born in Canada who had grown up hiking forests rife with bears, I told myself. I was from a town where cougars routinely strayed into parks and backyards. Paris dangerous? *Please.*

The Metro station smelled of rancid oil and stale urine, but that was no different from the other Metro stations in the posher areas.

People pushed and walked past in all directions. The crowd was more multi-ethic than in the 5th arrondissement, but all of Paris was such a huge improvement on the stultifying whiteness of my colonial hometown that it was just a matter of degrees.

Anyway, the people there in the 18th were in just as much of a hurry as all other Parisians. So far, nobody was remotely interested in bothering me.

I managed, after a few false starts, to find a series of escalators, most of them broken, that led to an exit. As always, when coming out of a Paris Metro stop, I felt as if I was emerging from miles under the earth.

I popped out on street level, where several people had set up brightly covered blankets on the sidewalk and were selling all kinds of wares, from beaded bracelets to mini plastic cars. They called out to me and all the other passersby, but they were no more aggressive—probably less so—than the guys hocking stuff at the foot of the Eiffel Tower.

I took the papers sent to me by the immigration department out of my backpack and looked at the address. The medical office was on the boulevard de Rochechouart. I had no idea where that was. I considered pulling out my map but knew that in any big European city that would be a bullseye, broadcasting that I was an easy target.

I leaned down to a man dressed head to toe in African garb, who was set up closest to where I was standing. He was overseeing his blanket full of underwear and bras that looked like they were made for elderly French farmwomen. They were a variety of shades of beige and highly reinforced with extra panels and industrial-strength elastic.

"*Bonjour*," I said.

"Are you interested in a bra?" he asked in a French that was even more accented than mine.

"Not today, thanks. Could you tell me how to find boulevard de Rochechouart?"

He stood up and smoothed out the brightly patterned robes he was wearing and straightened the small hat perched on his head.

I was about to compliment him on his outfit but then had a last moment doubt. Did I call it a dress? A robe? Something else? Instead, I merely waved in the direction of his outfit and said, "I like that. It's got so many beautiful colors."

"*Merci*, Mademoiselle," he said. "Are you going to Tati? You can tell me. I won't be jealous."

"Tati?" I said. "No, that's not where I'm going. What's Tati?"

"You don't know what Tati is?"

"No."

"It's only the best store in all of Paris." He waved his hands to encompass the whole city. They have everything, and better yet, everything is cheap. Not as good a bargain as my things, *bien sûr*, but second best after that. Everybody goes to Tati. It is on the boulevard de Rochechouart too."

This was sounding better and better. "I have to go somewhere else on that road, but I'll check out Tati afterward."

"You should," he said. "My wife goes every day."

"Promise."

He provided me with directions, which were easy, as in fact, the boulevard I was looking for ran alongside the street I stood on.

I walked along the boulevard de Rochechouart and looked for the address of the medical clinic. Luckily the clinic ran seven days a week, according to my paperwork.

When I found the place after a few minutes, I was surprised to see its run-down, ordinary doorway. The only thing telling me I was indeed in the right place was a little bronze plaque that read Clinique Médicale.

I rang a buzzer and was buzzed inside by a mysterious person who remained hidden, sort of like the Wizard of Oz.

I walked down a long and ill-lit hallway that ended in a room furnished exactly like the préfecture de police of the 5th arrondissement and the cafeteria of Paris III. They must have gotten a group deal on the ugly, plastic bucket seats, half-dead plants, and disintegrating ceiling tiles.

The ugliness punctured the balloon of my defiance. I wished, for the first time since arriving in the 18th arrondissement, that I had waited to come with Franck.

Who was I kidding? I was terrified of this medical visit. I was confident I could handle anything I met with on a Parisian street, but I didn't feel prepared to fend for myself, in French no less, with some strange doctor who was going to want me to take off all my clothes in this salubrious setting. I feared doctors at the best of times.

I reminded myself that I am a strong, independent woman. I am Laura, not Pauline. Besides, I was there already.

chapter twenty-eight

I lined up at a crowded desk shoved in a far corner of the room. Manning it was an exasperated woman with flushed cheeks and sweat pearling on her forehead, who was chewing her lip as she rifled through the paperwork of a woman wearing a burqa. That woman's two children were playing hide and seek underneath the billowing folds of her burqa.

After fifteen minutes, it was finally my turn. I passed the woman behind the desk my forms and my passport, and explained why I was there.

She didn't even bother trying to hide the look of surprise on her face. "Most people don't bother doing this," she said. "Are you sure you want to?"

"I have to for all my papers to be in order. It says so there." I pointed to the paragraph that stated this in no uncertain terms. "Isn't that correct?"

"Well…yes…but is it really so important that your paperwork be completely in order?"

I shook my head in disbelief at this question. That was the

law. Those were the rules. Was someone who worked for the French government advising me to disregard them?

"That was my impression," I said, confused now. "But now you've confused me...maybe I should just—"

She sighed as though I was subjecting her to relentless harassment, pressed a button on an antiquated machine beside her that spat out a number on a ticket, and passed the ticket to me.

"Take a seat," she said. "Try to find one that's not broken. You'll be there for a while."

I turned to take a seat but realized they were all taken. Like several other people, I just leaned against the nearest bit of grubby wall. I took my book out of my backpack, but discovered that at that juncture, I didn't have the concentration span or inclination to dive into the world of medieval French literature.

Should I just leave? The police in Paris were known for stopping people for random ID verifications. Would they be satisfied if I told them that I didn't complete my visa paperwork because the clerk discouraged me? Doubtful.

Doctors had always scared me. I had done enough self-analysis about my doctor phobia to determine my fear stemmed from two things—fear of dying, and fear of not controlling situations.

Neither of these was, unfortunately, easily resolved. I come from a long line of control freaks and—nature or nurture debate aside—the need for control and the consequent pathological fear of pain, illness, or death has been ingrained deeply in my body and brain.

My heart began pounding and my head swam, and everything took on a warped, distant quality, as though I was a fish swimming in an aquarium and looking out at the world through a swampy window. Anything remotely medical never failed to trigger these horrible sensations.

Almost an hour later, I was still debating whether I should stay or go. If I were even halfway sane, I would have just left and never went back. I picked up my backpack and slung it over my shoulder. I was out of there. I turned toward the exit, when a white-coated doctor called my name.

Merde. A Man. I had been hoping for the female doctor I had seen pop out of one of the examination rooms a few times, calling new patients. Both doctors looked exhausted and fed up.

I followed the doctor, nausea sweeping through me. My pounding heart would make my blood pressure score off the charts. This thought made it pound even harder. Being a self-sufficient woman sucked.

When the doctor ushered me into a grubby, white exam room, I was sure I was going to faint before making it to the examination table.

He used the pen in his hand and pointed to the table. "Up," he said. He sat down on the stool at the foot of the bed. I was leery of what he was planning on doing down there. Just how involved was this exam, exactly?

"What country are you from?" he asked, not even looking at me.

"Canada."

"How old are you?"

"Twenty-one."

"Are you fully vaccinated?"

"Of course..."

"Ever been sick?"

I wasn't sure how to answer this question. It was a pretty wide net he was casting. "Well, colds and stuff..."

"No, I mean *sick*. Cancer. Aids. Heart disease..."

"God no. Nothing like that."

He glanced up at me, then. "Any health concerns at the moment?"

"No."

"Then why are you here?" He lowered his reading glasses.

"They made me come!" I protested. Why did the immigration department tell us we needed to do this if it wasn't true? "I have a letter that says I need to come here and get a medical exam to validate my student visa."

"Give me the form I need to sign."

I handed it over to him and watched in surprise as he scribbled his signature. He passed it back to me. "You're healthy," he said. "There you go."

"But...you didn't examine me..." I stuttered. He hadn't even bothered to take my blood pressure, which I had been so worried about.

"Do you *want* me to examine you?" he asked, arching an eyebrow.

"*Non!* Nothing against you, I just don't like medical exams."

"Look, *mademoiselle*. I have a waiting room full of people out there. Some of them, unlike you, have big health issues. You look perfectly healthy to me and you are lucky enough to come from a country with world-class health care. However, if you insist..." He rolled his stool closer to the table I was sitting on.

I hopped off with alacrity, holding my now-signed paperwork against my chest. "*Non...non...*that's great. I'm great. Perfectly healthy. Nothing to see here. *Merci. Au revoir.*"

I left the room quickly and hurried out of the building to the street, taking a deep breath of exhaust-filled Parisian street air. It had never smelled so beautiful—like freedom.

I had done it. Even if it had ended up being anti-climactic, I had managed to tick that one dreaded task off my list with nobody's help.

To celebrate, I was determined to find this intriguing Tati store before heading back to the 5th arrondissement. A store full of discounted merchandise? There is nothing I love better than treasure hunting.

As I walked along the boulevard, I noticed people walking by me with huge pink and white checked plastic bags with TATI emblazoned across them in bold blue letters.

On the corner of the street, I spied a large Haussmannian building with a rounded front. All its awnings and windows were the same color as the Tati bags. I lifted my gaze and read the sign perched on top of the building. It was a sign that would have made Haussmann—the legendary planner who designed modern Paris—turn over in his grave. In massive blue and pink letters, it spelled out TATI—*Les Plus Bas Prix*. The lowest prices. Promising.

I hurried across the street and didn't enter the building so much as get sucked in with the streaming crowd of people.

Inside, it was chaos. People of every race, ethnicity, and appearance were rifling through the racks. It seemed to be de rigueur to throw articles on the floor or back on the racks without putting them nicely back on the hangers, so clothes were strewn everywhere.

I ignored the shelves of knickknacks—we had no space for knickknacks in our apartment, as I'd already filled up the bookshelf with books. I made my way through the roaring river of different languages and dialects to a section where it looked as though a bomb had exploded among several large piles of handbags.

I plunged into the crowds of people rummaging through them. About halfway down a pile, I pulled out a black leather bag that was brilliant in its simplicity. It was the same rectangular shape as the Longchamp bags, with a long zipper that ran across the top. This one, though, was made from buttery soft leather. I checked the label: *Cuir véritable—Fabriqué en Italie*. The price tag said sixty francs. Sixty francs for a real leather bag that was made it Italy? Bonified treasure.

I went on to the coats and managed to unearth a black wool coat that had tortoise shell toggles and exposed, white, wool stitching detail around the edges. I checked the price tag. Fifty francs. I tried it on over my clothes. *Parfait.*

I arrived back at our apartment glowing with satisfaction over my accomplishments for the day. Maybe I hadn't meandered around the local markets as planned but I had ticked off the final immigration-related task I had to do. I also found the perfect bag and coat for my new *parisienne* look, as well as two new scarves I had grabbed on the way to the cash register at Tati.

Better yet, I was able to tell my new friend at the Barbès - Rochechouart Metro station that I had followed his advice and found some serious bargains. When I showed him my Tati bag, he gifted me a pair of reinforced granny underpants.

I decided I might wear them too, simply because that was another thing that Pauline would never do.

chapter twenty-nine

Franck's flight was due to arrive while I was in my Dickens class. There was a flutter in my stomach that hadn't been there the day before.

Would the temporary geographical distance between Paris and Marrakesh lessen the emotional distance I had been feeling between us lately? Or make it worse?

I was in the habit of walking along the boulevard Saint-Germain when I went to my classes at the old Sorbonne. There was always something to see. I paused at the open construction site on the corner of the boulevard Saint-Germain and the boulevard Saint-Michel. Beyond the wrought iron fence, there was a sunken area where boulders, large stones, and piled bricks stood, some half embedded in the compact dirt. The rectangle was fenced in, but I had never seen any construction equipment.

That day, a boy about my age appeared at my side as I peered into the pit, contemplating its mysteries.

"*Bonjour.* If I may ask, what are you looking at?"

I looked over at him. His accent had the Parisian sound as if words were formed in his nostrils rather than his mouth. His ironed jeans, leather loafers, button-down shirt, wool sweater, and casual scarf draped around his neck confirmed his Parisian status. He was carrying a beat-up leather cartable. That clinched it.

He was not just a Parisian, but a fellow student—quite a handsome one with his light brown hair, black eyes, and dramatic bone structure. It took me a few moments to remember his question.

"This pit," I explained, gesturing at it. "Were they trying to build something and stopped?"

"They aren't building. They're digging."

"Digging what?"

"Roman ruins. That's what they found here. See that arch?" He pointed to a pile of rocks that, I could see now that I looked closer, did form three-quarters of an arch. His arm was touching mine.

Was he just being French as far as the smaller personal space requirement, or was he flirting? Part of me felt flattered, but the other part felt flustered. I had a long way to go before I took daily flirting in stride like a true *Parisienne*.

"I think I recognize you from the Amphitryon and Satan class at Paris IV," he said.

"That's right," I said, before I even had the chance to think the better of answering with such enthusiasm.

He smiled a lazy, charming smile. "What do you think of it so far?"

"The prof is boring, but I love the amphitheater."

"Really?" He quirked his head, still smiling at me as though I was the most the entrancing woman in the world. That, I supposed, was a big part of French charm. "What is so special about it?"

I laughed. "You're joking, right? It's stunning. It's like learning in a museum."

"I never noticed."

My words dried up on my tongue. How could he so lack a sense of wonder or appreciation of the beauty around him? Franck was the first one to show me that amphitheater. He understood.

I checked my watch. "I better get to my Dickens class. I'm already late." In fact, I was still twenty minutes early, but I was no longer interested in making small talk.

"Can I buy you a coffee after your class?"

"Sorry. I have another class after Dickens."

"Another day?" he asked. "I believe I need to teach you more about Roman ruins."

I wondered for a split second if I was interested. Then I remembered the feel of resting my head on Franck's shoulder. Franck was going through a weird phase right now, but he was my home.

"I have a boyfriend."

"So?" He reached out and pushed back a strand of hair that had fallen out of my clip. "I may have a girlfriend. That doesn't stop us from enjoying each other's company."

"I'll take a pass," I said. "*Salut.*"

Just as I had with Pauline, I had been careful to say "bye" rather than "*au revoir.*"

The week before, I had handed in the first essay of the year of my Dickens class. The topic was "Discuss the role of guilt in *Great Expectations.*" I knew I'd aced it. My conviction wasn't based on conceit, but on the fact that I'd written the same essay in my first year of English literature at McGill and received ninety-eight percent.

We waited in the ancient desks for a few minutes before Professor Gabrielle—I couldn't figure out if Gabrielle was her first name or her last name—walked in and greeted us in her stiff way.

"I will hand back your essays at the end of the class because I don't want you to be distracted. Overall, I was disappointed with your work, with only a few exceptions."

I enjoyed a smug certainty that I was one of those exceptions.

The class seemed to progress like treacle. The professor had a pedantic manner of lecturing and a monotone voice. I studied the particles of chalk dust that were always floating in the air in the classroom.

Finally, she finished up her droning lecture and opened her briefcase—*what twenty-something-year-old woman carries a briefcase?*—and removed a stack of papers.

She handed them back one by one, taking the time to criticize them loudly and publicly, except for the essays of two sycophantic girls who wore their hair in the identical style of chignon as Professeur Gabrielle and Grace.

Mine was at the very end of the pile, so I had to wait through everyone else's public humiliation. Apprehension began to trickle through my anticipation, but I reasoned it away. My essay was insightful and well-written. McGill professors, especially the one who taught my Dickens class, were known to be exceptionally hard markers. They had deemed literally the same essay as a slam dunk...I had nothing to worry about.

"Mademoiselle Bradbury," she said, butchering the pronunciation of my last name. "I expected better. Much better." She dropped my essay on the desk in front of me. A six out of twenty was marked in vivid red marker. That wasn't even a passing grade.

I looked up at her in shock. She met my gaze with a malicious gleam in her eyes, similar to Pauline's when we'd handed over the cash for their invoice.

"This can't be right—" I began.

"You may stay after class if you wish to discuss this further."

I flipped through the pages of my essay while the other students filed out, most of them dejected and a few crying. The pages were bright red from slashes of her pen and comments such as "not logical" and "poor choice of words."

That was bullshit.

I stood up and marched over to the podium where she was putting things away in her briefcase.

"This was a good essay." I waved it to underline my point. "I don't understand your grading criteria. Can you explain why it received such a low mark?"

"It was poorly argued and lacked logical progression."

"What does that mean?"

"It means it was a weak essay."

"Then can I see an example of a strong essay, because in Canada, this would have received top marks."

"I doubt that." She let out a disbelieving titter

"As it happens, I wrote an almost identical essay for a class back at McGill and I received ninety-eight percent on it."

"Then you just confessed to plagiarism," she said, as if that clinched it.

"I can't plagiarize *myself.*"

She looked down her nose at me and then sniffed the air. "Then I can only assume they are much less academically rigorous than we are here at the Sorbonne."

"That's not it," I said. The words coming out of her prim mouth were just…ludicrous.

"Besides," she added, "while it may not be technically termed as plagiarism, it's not fair to your fellow students if you have already written the same essay. It would have been more honest of you to inform me, and I would have assigned you a different topic. I should make you rewrite a new essay, but it's hardly as though you are a threat to your classmates in the end." She arched her brows at me and gave a little shrug.

I could feel myself begin to tremble, not with anxiety but with fury. The injustice of the mark and her treatment of me was just…despicable.

"Do you have something against me?" I said, in English this time. Up until then, we had been conversing in French, but I wanted this conversation to be on my turf. "A grudge?"

"A grudge?" She made a sound of disgust. "What kind of word is that? Some sort of slang?"

I narrowed my eyes. "No, 'grudge' is a proper English word. One that I would think an English teacher should know. Look it up." I was beyond being polite.

This woman was probably not far from my age and had never done anything to earn my respect. I didn't care if she was in a position of authority if she abused it.

Her eyes widened. "That is not the way students talk to teachers in France. I should give you a formal reprimand."

"I should take this essay into the head of the English Department here and ask for their opinion on your grading," I countered.

"You won't do that," she said, doubt in her eyes now.

"I would," I said. "But I think the easiest thing is for me to just find another class and transfer out of yours because obviously this dynamic is not conducive to learning."

"I am here to teach, not make friends," she said. Funny, I had no issue with Madame Renier-Bernadotte saying essentially the same thing to the boy in our class on the first day. Somehow, though, I just knew she would apply that rule equally. She was too busy being brilliant to play favorites with students.

"You're not here to make enemies, either," I said, slipping my backpack over my shoulder and walking out, shaking with rage.

chapter thirty

I walked fast back to the apartment, fueled by anger. I opened the door and found Franck dressed in an ankle-length, royal blue embroidered djellaba—a nightgown-like Moroccan garment worn by the men. I had seen a few of them in the 18th arrondissement, as a matter of fact.

He was in the kitchen stirring a saucepan of Poulain—the French brand of cocoa he had been drinking since he was a child. The whole apartment smelled of warm milk and chocolate.

"*Marhaban!*" He claimed a kiss.

"What does that mean?" I threw my leather Tati bag on the floor with more force than necessary.

"Greetings."

"In Arabic?" I leaned against the kitchen wall.

"But of course." He bowed.

He looked so absurd, I burst out laughing.

"Do you want a cup of hot cocoa too?" he asked.

I nodded. He plucked a Duralex glass bowl off the shelf and poured one for me. "It's so cold I needed something to warm me up. How do you like my djellaba?"

"It looks comfortable. Are you planning on wearing it around town, or is it just for my edification?"

"Once you've started wearing a djellaba, I'm not sure you can go back to Western clothes." Franck shimmied his shoulders. "*So* confining."

I went into the bedroom to take off my jacket and shoes and, more importantly, to compose myself. Now that the first rush of anger with Professor Gabrielle had subsided, I prickled with irritation and vulnerability. I couldn't let that show to Franck, at least not right away.

I found Franck again in the living room, where he was putting our hot chocolate on the table. I pulled out a chair, but Franck pulled me onto his lap as I was sitting down.

I yelped.

"I missed you." He gave me a lingering kiss. I felt better—anchored. "Did you miss me?"

Relief filled my pores. It felt as if I had my old Franck back. *Hopefully he left the cagey one somewhere in the deserts of Morocco.*

"I did miss you." I ruffled his hair, which was still damp and scented with the Le Petit Marseillais *fleur d'oranger* shampoo I always bought.

Rain started tapping against the window, and dark clouds had filled the sky. We didn't even bother to taste our hot chocolates, but instead moved to the bedroom to celebrate our *retrouvailles* in the most Parisian way possible.

Lying in bed afterward, my head nestled in that perfect crook above Franck's collarbone, I murmured, "Tell me about your trip."

The rain began to beat down harder, and everything felt cozy and right with us snuggled together under the duvet. I didn't feel like mentioning the Dickens class yet—the moment was too pleasant to be interrupted with that.

"Morocco is beautiful," he said, caressing my back. "Just as beautiful as I remembered. Ourzazate looked like a painting under the blue sky. I could have spent weeks exploring the alleyways of Casablanca, not to mention the souk. You would love the souk. Everything is just so completely different from France or Canada. The smells, the calls to prayer, the sounds of Arabic…

"What was that you said about rose petals on the phone?" I inhaled his familiar scent. "Or did I hear that wrong?"

"Oh no. You heard that right. When we got off the plane in Ourzazate, there were local women dressed up in traditional clothing throwing petals at our feet."

I nipped the side of his neck. "To think I didn't welcome you back to Paris like that."

"I have no complaints with the way you welcomed me back." He dropped a kiss on my ear. "Still, next time you might consider adding rose petals into your repertoire."

I gave his arm a light pinch. "So could you."

"One evening, the organizers set up a tent in the desert for us and put on a *méchoui*—"

"Am I supposed to know what that is?"

"What? A *méchoui*?"

"Yeah." The duvet felt heavy on my body, as was Franck's leg that was draped over mine underneath it.

"A *méchoui* is a traditional lamb barbeque in a sort of pit dug into the earth."

"Oh." I had to force myself not to drift off to sleep.

"There were beautiful cushions and carpets all over the ground, just like in *Arabian Nights*." As if on cue, a pigeon cooed outside our window.

"I'm surprised you came back," I said, only half joking.

"I could enjoy life there, I think." Franck rubbed his foot against mine. "I always felt a bit Arab in my soul."

I lazily lifted up Franck's arm from the duvet and examined his dark Mediterranean skin tone. "It's possible you have some in your blood from a few generations back."

"That's what my Pépé Georges always believed about his side of the family."

I couldn't claim any such thing. My pale complexion is a direct inheritance from my Gaelic forbearers.

"Anyway, they played us traditional music, and the rose petal ladies sang Berber songs for us," Franck continued. "They kept coming around with the most delectable food while we lounged on the cushions drinking mint tea. *Magique.*"

"Sounds like it." I could tell that Franck was still on a high from his trip.

"I could do that for a job, you know," he said, after a while. He was still holding me tight.

"What?" I was suddenly wide awake. I pulled away so I could look into his face.

"Travelling around the world as a journalist. Writing stories about different places. Taking photos...I think it would suit me perfectly."

"Would you never feel the urge to settle down?" I asked. "Live in one place?"

"*Non.*" He shook his head. "This trip confirmed for me that I am a vagabond at heart."

I rolled away from him and propped my head up on my bent arm. I felt my tendrils of vulnerability and anger ignite. "Where would that leave me, then?"

"You could come with me. We could do it together. You could write and I could take photos."

"Maybe in a few years once I'm done school."

"We could do it now. There's no time like the present."

"And what? I would drop out of university? What about kids? We may want some of those one day."

"You don't always need to think so far ahead. Just think of the freedom..."

Freedom. That word again.

I wasn't convinced it would truly be a liberating lifestyle, trying to scrounge up work from cash-strapped travel magazines and never knowing where the next paycheck was coming from.

"I love traveling," I said. "You know I do. It's just that I also like having a base I can return to. I happen to think a sense of security is not a completely bad thing. That's how I'm wired. I can't help it."

"For me, freedom is the most important thing."

My heart sank. We were back there. I stood up and awkwardly began putting on my jeans, stumbling and bumping into the wall that the bed was jammed up against.

"Where are you going?"

"I need a walk."

"What do you mean? Wait. Are you angry?"

Are you blind? His confusion was infuriating.

I took a deep breath. "We're living here together in Paris—we've been dreaming about this year. Instead of being happy with where we are and what we're doing, all you can think of is moving on to the next thing. Is it so hard to be happy here with me? All this talk about freedom is making me think that what you really want is freedom from *me*, but that you just don't have the courage to say it."

Franck sat up. "That's not what I meant."

"I thought Paris was an adventure in itself—that it would be enough."

"It is…but still…being here has me thinking…can't Paris be a step to other things for us?"

"Like what? Me dropping out of school when I'm almost finished? Us both being unemployed?

Franck didn't answer.

"You've been weird for weeks." My voice filled up the empty space. "I had hoped your trip would snap you back to normal, but—"

"What are you talking about?"

"Ever since that thing with Pauline and Florent. Just in case you hadn't noticed, you are not Florent and I am definitely not Pauline. Do you want to break up? Is that it?"

Was it the confrontation with Professeur Gabrielle that made me overreact, or did this conversation have to happen? The words made me scared, but I had to say them. Anything was better than the uncertainty.

"*Non! Pourquoi?* Do *you* want to break up?"

"No. But I certainly don't ever want to trap you. I would rather be without you than that. I would rather be *anything* than that."

Franck pulled me back onto the bed beside him. "I don't want to break up."

I sat down but stayed as stiff as the marble sculptures at the Rodin Museum. I didn't turn my head to look at Franck or lean into him, even though he was pulling me against him.

"You're angry," he said, finally. "I'm sorry. You know how I talk when I get carried away. Most of it will probably never come to pass."

I didn't answer for a moment. "I'm not just going to continue pretending like things haven't been weird between us. I can't stand things being buried under the surface and not spoken about."

"I haven't been acting differently."

I fixed him with a stare.

"Maybe *un petit peu*," he conceded.

"If you don't want to break up, then what maggot has buried itself into your brain?"

It took Franck several minutes to answer. I had to restrain myself from tapping my foot.

"I guess I was shaken to see how much Florent was under Pauline's thumb. It got me thinking…what have I been doing for the last two, going on three, years?"

"We were in Montreal," I answered. "Then we moved here to Paris."

"So, basically, I've been following you."

"That's one way of looking at it," I said. "But not the only way. All those moves were things you chose at the time."

"That's true. But still, here I am back in France, where I'm comfortable with the culture, with the language, with everything. I find myself wondering…maybe I'm becoming like Florent. Maybe I should figure out my own thing."

"Your own thing? Like living by yourself?"

"That's not what I mean. I mean my own thing, like a job, a social life, travel…something that means that I am with you but still independent."

Being in a relationship but retaining one's independence. I mulled this over. How did a person achieve that? Was it even possible?

"Independent?" I needed clarity on this point. Did Franck mean self-sufficient in the same way I had when I decided to be the anti-Pauline and go by myself to get my medical exam?

"*Oui.* I've been thinking maybe we could stay here longer than a year."

"But then I couldn't finish my degree in Montreal," I said. "I only have one year left. I won't just throw away three years of hard work."

"Could there be a way of transferring the degree to France?"

I shook my head. "Remember what it was like to register at the school here and get my courses recognized just for the exchange program? I'll never be able to transfer two years of my degree over here. Besides, my degree is in English literature, and the one class I am taking of that here isn't exactly going well. We only need to go back to Montreal for one more year."

Franck's forehead crinkled.

"At least *I* need to go back for one year." I lifted a questioning brow at Franck.

He sighed. "I just don't want to feel like everything has been decided for me already."

"What are you suggesting exactly?" I asked, wanting to clarify this once and for all. "If I went back to McGill and you stayed here, we would break up, right?"

He grabbed my hand. "We could manage for a year apart, couldn't we?"

I thought back to the four months apart during my first year of university, before Franck joined me in Montreal. It had been hell. "But we fought so hard to be together." I tried to pull my hand away.

"I love you, Laura," Franck said, not letting my hand go. "I'm just trying to figure all this stuff out, but never doubt that I love you and want us to stay together."

I couldn't reconcile the things Franck was saying. "You need to start acting that way, then," I said. "Because you have to consider how it makes me feel to see you acting so skittish. You must know that I would never trap you. Ever. You are always free to go."

"That's a bit harsh." Franck frowned.

"It's the truth."

"I'm just trying to figure out a way to feel free in our relationship." Franck sighed.

Wasn't that wanting to have something *and* its opposite?

"You don't want to turn into Florent," I said.

"Exactly."

"Trust me, I have zero desire for you to turn into Florent, either."

"I know that." He squeezed my hands again. "When I saw how he had changed so fundamentally, I began to worry that maybe I could change in the same way."

"But I'm far too lazy to ever want to control other people like Pauline does. I have enough problems with managing myself."

Franck pulled me close to him and held me tight. "Do you want to see your presents now?" he asked, after several minutes.

"Presents?" Had we reached some form of truce? I didn't feel like storming out anymore, but this still didn't feel resolved.

"Yes, for you."

Franck instructed me to stay put and went into the living room. When he came back, he stood in front of me with his hands behind his back.

"I did find you some things." He nodded down at his hidden hands. "Pick one."

I pointed to his right hand. He withdrew it from behind his back and passed me a perfectly square, intricately carved wooden box. The smell of freshly carved rosewood and foreign spices drifted up. I opened it. The wood was sanded smooth inside, and the scent there was even stronger.

I closed it again and ran my finger over the surface. "It's beautiful. You may be improving at this present thing."

"That's not all."

"Really?"

"Choose a hand again. Quickly, it's getting heavy."

I chose the left hand.

Franck brought out a large urn-type vessel that was made of brightly colored ceramic and intricately twirled silver. It was gorgeous, not to mention completely unique.

"Open it up," he said.

I did. The lid stuck a bit, but when I finally opened it, I was hit by the fragrance of dried dates. It was filled to the brim with them.

"They have the most delicious dates in Morocco," Franck said. "Figs too."

He picked one up and motioned at me to open my mouth. He popped one in and I chewed. It was delicious and tasted like it came from a place of sunshine and ancient mosaics and sky blue water.

"Mmmmmm," I said, my mouth still full.

"Are you still mad at me?" Franck asked.

"A bit," I admitted. "But probably not as much as ten minutes ago." I admired the ceramic container again. "But don't cast me in a role that I have zero interest in playing," I added.

"I'm sorry."

I stepped out into the main room and put the ceramic container on our black bookshelf so that it propped up my original medieval textbooks. It looked fantastic. The will to fight drained out of me. Our questions were too big and too confusing, and I had already done battle in my Dickens class that day. My stomach grumbled.

"I want chocolate mousse," I called to Franck, who was still in the bedroom.

"Batifol?" Franck read my mind.

"We can't really afford it."

"No," Franck agreed, coming out of the bedroom with his djellaba back on.

"You're going to change, right?"

"For you?" Franck took my hand and squeezed it. "For you, anything."

chapter **thirty-one**

When we had emerged from Batifol, my stomach replete with chocolate mousse and a delicious dinner, the sun had emerged from behind the clouds and the evening was turning warm and golden after the rain—a complete anomaly for that late in the fall. The sounds of accordion music and laughter swept along on the soft night air.

"Let's go see where that's coming from," Franck said.

"Let's." It was too gorgeous an evening to go back inside, and besides, there we were living in the center of Paris—it would be crazy not to be experiencing the unique moments it offered. I also wanted to obliterate any traces of the unfinished argument from my mind.

We walked down the ramp across the street and reached the banks of the Seine. The music was coming in the opposite direction from Notre-Dame.

About five minutes later, as we rounded a bend in the river, we came across a massive group of people dancing on a raised cobbled area on the banks of the Seine. The accordions—at least four or five of them, from what I could count—all squeezed and pumped the notes of the same melody, and a woman dressed in a flowered housecoat and slippers was behind the microphone, crooning a vintage-sounding ballad.

"It's a *guingette!*" Franck cried.

"What's a *guingette?*"

"This." Franck swept his hand at the dancers, singer, and accordionist. "It's like an impromptu dance."

"You forgot the accordions."

"*Pardon.* A dance with accordions. Come on."

Franck swept me up, and we spun to the accordion music in the orange-pink dusk of the early Parisian night. Nobody seemed to mind us joining in.

Franck held me close, I enjoyed the mix of chocolate mousse and the espressos we had drank to finish off our dinner on his breath. His arms stayed wrapped around me as we did an impromptu waltz around the cobblestones. There was still enough of a chill in the air, so I soaked up his warmth.

The people spinning around us were completely caught up in the music. There was no small talk, I noticed, and anyone without a dance partner danced alone without embarrassment. Some of the dancers sang along to the words.

"Is this sort of thing a planned event?" I asked, thinking that if it was, I should keep my eye out for flyers or advertising in our *quartier* so we could come again.

"Usually not," Franck said, then nodded over to the singer in her housecoat and slippers. "It doesn't look she planned to be here. She probably heard the accordions while she was whipping up her *purée* and *jambon blanc* for dinner in her apartment and ran out here to take part."

"Who knows?" I said. "Maybe that's her performance outfit."

"She does wear it with a certain sublime confidence."

"She does." If I had a songbird voice like hers I would probably run out in the streets completely naked to sing.

The sky became darker, and Franck swung me around faster. The lights from the buildings twinkled on and the bright beams from the *bateaux-mouches* swept over us at regular intervals, illuminating the scene in an otherworldly blue light. It gave me the oddest impression that the light was freeze-framing that moment in time—the dancers, the smell of wet leaves, the singer, the accordionist with a trickle of sweat running down his temple.

Franck and I locked in a kiss, our mutual relief palpable that our earlier argument felt shelved for the time being.

"Do you remember Bastille Day the night before you left for Canada that first year?" Franck whispered in my ear. The caress of his breath created a trail of goosebumps down my arms.

That was a night I would never forget. Franck and I were going to be separated the next day, maybe forever for all we knew, when I flew back to Canada at the end of my exchange year in Burgundy. We'd spent the whole night of Bastille Day going from one fire station to the next in Paris. It is tradition that each of the fires stations hosts a traditional ball that goes until the sun comes up.

I had been so devastated about leaving Franck the next day, but at the same time I was hungry to grasp on to every single moment we still had together. That night, even more so than the many others with Franck, anchored itself in meticulous detail in my memory.

"I will never forget that," I said, and kissed him again. "Or this."

We kissed until dancing became a distraction. After that we just stood there, interlaced, our lips joining as desperately and tirelessly as three years before.

After that last, incongruous gasp of warm weather, Paris was plunged into winter. Bare tree branches rattled underneath leaden skies.

I had one of Madame Renier-Bernadotte's classes at eleven o'clock, but I left early and walked along the boulevard Saint-Germain. I was going to transfer out of Mademoiselle Gabrielle's Dickens class, and I needed to go to the old Sorbonne to do it.

For no reason that I could determine, Professeur Gabrielle hated me. To be fair, I hated her too now, but she had hated me first. As I walked, I pondered why she was so spiteful toward me. My mark on the *Great Expectations* essay had been wrong—it was that simple. I knew the French graded hard, but my essay was excellent. In no universe did it deserve a six out of twenty.

Was she threatened by me? I found this hard to believe. There was such a hierarchy in academia in France that it seemed ridiculous to think any professor would even be aware of an individual student, let alone bother developing an insecurity about them. Still, I did speak and write perfect English. Did she resent teaching someone more fluent than herself?

I arrived at the old Sorbonne, where I flashed my student card at the security guards posted at the door. Inside, I began the adventure of locating the administrators who took care of course changes. The flagstones in the grand entrance hall echoed against the soles of my leather boots.

Parisians didn't ask for directions among themselves, I knew, but I went full throttle Canuck and accosted every person I could find in my vicinity until I received a plausible answer.

I climbed three flights of stone stairs, so trod upon by intellectuals over the centuries that each stair dipped in the middle. Finally, I found the room number and knocked gently on the door. Nobody answered. I waited about a minute and then knocked again. Still nothing.

I twisted the door handle, fully expecting it to be locked, but to my surprise the door swung open and three shocked faces behind ugly industrial-style desks stared at me.

"*Désolée*," I said. "I knocked."

"We heard," A frizzy-haired blond answered. "We just didn't answer."

Nobody said anything for several uncomfortable beats after that (at least they were uncomfortable for me; the Parisian trio appeared nonplussed).

"I need to change a course. I was told to come here to do it. Am I in the right place?"

The three women exchanged questioning glances with each other. Didn't they know the answer to the question?

"Maybe," the frizzy one said, cautious. "Which course, and why?"

"It's the course on Dickens' novels taught by Professeur Gabrielle."

"Why?"

Why didn't I prepare a diplomatic answer to this question? Dammit. "Um…I took basically the same course last year at university in Montreal. I'm an exchange student, you see. I'd like to transfer out of the Dickens class and into a new class that teaches me something I don't already know."

I silently applauded my quick thinking.

"You can drop the class," one of the other women said. "But you can't start a new class now. Once you start your classes at the beginning of term, that's it. *Fini!*"

"But it's for my degree back home in Canada. I need to take an English class—any English class—or I'm booted out of my university program at McGill. I'm not picky. I know I could catch up fast."

"Not possible," the woman said, "but I will remove you from the Dickens class. What is your name?"

"Uh…" I absolutely needed an English course or my degree would be invalidated by McGill.

"You don't know your name?" The frizzy woman asked, sharing a mocking look with her colleagues.

"I do," I said bitterly.

"It doesn't look that way."

"The problem is that I need an English class. I'm going to be completely honest with you." The women's eyes became instantly more intrigued. "Professor Gabrielle hates me," I confessed. "I have no idea why, but she does."

"Wait." The frizzy-haired woman said to the brown-haired woman. "Professor Gabrielle? Isn't she that young one who came in here and acted like she farted higher than her bum?"

Fortuitously, I was already familiar with this popular French expression for someone pretentious. "That's her," I said. "I'm certain of it."

The frizzy-haired woman looked at me—her face quite transformed with sympathy. "Now I truly do wish I could help you. *Quelle pétasse celle-là.*"

I nodded. "That's it *exactly*. So—"

"The problem is that there exists nothing in the system which allows me to enroll you in a new class," she said. "Even if I was able, any new teacher would refuse to take you into their class this late in the year. I'm so sorry, but it is impossible. That's the truth."

The other women nodded with sympathy.

I looked up at the ceiling in frustration and was stunned to see there the most exquisite fresco of cherubs encircled by elaborate molding that was glowing gold—maybe embellished with real gold leaf. Its presence in the room was an incongruous contrast with the office furniture.

I was so busy admiring it that I forgot why I was standing there in the first place.

"Don't cry," the frizzy woman broke my reverie. "Just let Professor Gabrielle know you won't take any grief from her. Women like her are bullies, but I'm sure if you refuse to bend to her, she will back down."

I wasn't crying, but I blinked my eyes a few times to reinforce their compassion.

"No submitting to the bitches!" The brown-haired woman shook her fist in the air. "Never!"

The other two women cheered.

"But what am I going to say? She'll take such satisfaction from knowing I'm trapped with her for the year."

"Go in with your head held high, your chin up." The woman who had been silent up until that point piped up. "Let her know that you may be trapped by university rules, but that you remain as ever *insoumise*! You will rebelliously and passionately oppose her oppression."

"*Oui!*" I said, swept up in the spirit of their cry for rebellion. "I will! *Merci*."

"You go and fight against Mademoiselle Gabrielle and the system, then come back and update us."

"I will! *Promis*! Forward!"

With this rallying cry, I let myself out of the office and ran back down the stone steps. I checked my watch. I was going to be late for Madame Renier-Bernadotte's class, and that simply could not happen.

I might be feeling stronger, but I knew I wasn't that invincible. Yet.

After Professor Renier-Bernadotte's absorbing class, I walked all the way back to the old Sorbonne with my head held high and my chin jutted out, as advised by the office ladies, just for the practice.

When Mademoiselle Gabrielle arrived, she scanned the class behind her podium and caught sight of me. I raised my chin even higher. She grimaced.

For the rest of the class, she pretended I was invisible. I wasn't interested in answering any of her questions anyway. I needed all my energy to combat the rage brewing in my chest. She ran out of the class, in a rush for a meeting, she said.

I had planned on talking to her just to inform her I would not be dropping Dickens, and that we would just have to endure each other. Frustratingly, that would have to wait another day.

I was packing up my things, somewhat ferociously, when a soft, southern-accented voice came from behind me. "Hi, Laura. How y'all doing today?"

I turned to see Grace, distracted by yet another preposterous bow in her hair—this time black with white polka dots like Minnie Mouse's.

"I've been better," I said. "I found out this morning that I can't drop this class," I said.

"Darn it," she said. "You don't have time for a coffee, do you?" she asked hesitantly.

I checked my watch, but I already knew the answer. I had ample time for a coffee before Franck got home from work. Besides, I was in a mood where I was dying to talk to another anglophone, maybe even touch on my confusion about Franck in vague terms.

"Let's go," I said. "I know a place."

Ten minutes later, we were ensconced in one of the window seats of the café on the rectangle leading to the old Sorbonne that Franck and I had been to several times.

"This place is fantastic," Grace raved. "*So* Parisian. I haven't dared going to cafés on my own much so far."

"Why?"

She blushed right to the roots of her blond hair. "It's weird to go places alone."

"What? Haven't you noticed that Parisians sit down and enjoy cafés and restaurants on their own all the time? Look around us." As if to prove my point, more than half of the people nursing glasses of wine, Champagne, or espressos were flying solo.

"See? It is one of the most Parisian things to do, being alone. You came to Paris alone, didn't you? And moved into the family's home where you are an *au pair*? You did that by yourself."

"I wish I didn't have to, though." Grace fiddled with her ponytail. "I wish my beau had come with me, like yours did."

I stifled a smile at the notion of Franck being labeled a "beau" in any universe. He was just about as far as you could get from a Southern gentleman.

"Since I arrived, it's like nothing I've done seems real when I'm by myself."

"Do you think if you had your…beau…with you, it would be different?"

She nodded with enthusiasm. "I'm sure it would. Everything would be a hundred times more fun."

"Huh," I said, thinking of my experience with Franck in Paris so far. There had been amazing moments, and I hadn't felt alone so far. Still, despite our evening at the *guinguette*, it still felt complicated. I felt a twinge of envy for Grace. It almost seemed easier to be alone like her than to be so deeply in love like me yet not be sure if that love had an expiry date.

"I think life is always messier than it appears on the surface," I said. "Don't you?"

"Not necessarily. Everything was so simple when Charlie and I were together."

"Charlie? That's your boyfriend's name?"

Grace nodded, blushing again. "It must be so simple with you and your beau, right?"

"With Franck?" I thought back to the argument we had just left hanging the night before. "I wouldn't call life with Franck simple, and I doubt life with me is simple either. We're both pretty fiery."

"You're not in love?"

"Oh no. I didn't mean that. We're very much in love. We're just in the middle of figuring out where we want to go as individuals and as a couple. I'm not sure if those paths go in the same direction."

"You fight?" Grace gasped.

"Of course."

"Charlie and I never fought. None of the couples I know fight."

"Really?" I was skeptical. "How is that even possible? Didn't you fight when you said you were coming to Paris for the year?"

Grace frowned. The expression looked unnatural on her sweet face. "No. I mean, I think maybe we were both upset, but he just gave me his ultimatum, him or Paris, and I chose Paris. He said good-bye, wished me well, kissed my hand, and left."

"Didn't that make you angry that he didn't discuss it more with you? That he just made you choose like that?"

She reached back and tugged at her bow. "It made sense. He comes from an established, wealthy Southern family, you see. He's a catch. Me, not so much."

"How can you say that?"

"I know it."

"I don't believe it, and if he makes you feel that way about yourself, he deserves to be kicked to the curb. You need to find yourself a French lover while you're here. That's what you need to do."

"I couldn't," she demurred, but with a mischievous tilt to her lips.

"Hmmmmmm," I said. "We'll see about that."

"But if being with Franck makes you feel confused, then how long do you want to live like that?" Grace asked, displaying an unwelcome flash of perception.

I frowned into my espresso cup and answered her with a French shrug.

chapter **thirty-two**

It was mid-December and things were settling into a routine, although a routine in Paris could never feel hum-drum to me.

Monsieur Pierrepont was letting himself back into his apartment with his morning baguette under his arm when I came out of ours.

"Bonjour, Monsieur Pierrepont," I said. "How are you this morning?" I made sure I rigorously stuck to the formal form of address.

"Ah! Mademoiselle! What a pleasure. I'm feeling spry."

"I'm glad to hear it."

Monsieur Pierrepont seemed ten years younger since the gas explosion. Madame Fox had somehow managed to have his apartment completely remediated and renovated by the time he returned from the hospital. He confided in me in the manner one would reveal a state secret that his newly styled abode even contained a microwave.

"*Au revoir.*" I waved good-bye with a smile, and he touched his beret.

As I walked to school up the rue Monge, I thought of how I wanted Madame Fox to renew her invitation for coffee. So far,

I had caught the occasional glimpse of her in the building and always greeted her politely, but she remained far more elusive than Monsieur Pierrepont.

I was almost at the school when I was lured in by my favorite *pâtisserie.* The two women who worked the front of the boutique knew me now. I couldn't decide whether I was satisfied or embarrassed about this fact.

"*Torsade suisse?*" the one behind the counter asked after saying a polite *bonjour.* It was a confirmation rather than a question.

"*Oui, s'il vous plaît.*" I rarely strayed from the perfection of their Swiss twist.

"You came at the perfect time." She peered toward the back of the bakery where I could hear the strains of Europe 1 station on the radio and could see glimpses of the baker's fleshy arms. "He just took a batch out of the oven. I'll go back and get you a warm one, *d'accord?*"

"*Oui. Merci,*" I said.

She wrapped it up, and I did the extremely North American thing of walking along the sidewalk eating my piping hot pastry. These are irresistible at any temperature, but fresh out of the oven…the pastry cream was warm and mixed with the melting chocolate nuggets on my tongue. The flaked pastry itself melted in my mouth. If true artists created such things, who was I to resist them?

I finished off the last bit of *torsade* just before I took my seat in the lecture theatre, with five minutes still to spare.

 I was beginning to feel like I knew what to expect in my classes. The volume of reading assigned wasn't as onerous as I had feared. Luckily, I found most of it—especially that of Madame Renier-Bernadotte's classes—interesting.

My only exception was, of course, the Dickens class, where Professor Gabrielle and I had wordlessly agreed to ignore each other. It bothered me that she hated me so much, but so far, she hadn't assigned a second essay, so I was content to coast for a while. I did feel a nagging guilt, though, that I was letting down the administrative ladies with my lack of confrontation.

It was sort of the same with Franck, I thought ruefully. We had been coasting...happily so... But I felt the argument we had not finished after Morocco was still hanging in the background, biding its time.

All in all, though, I was feeling pleased with myself. I had adapted to yet another new place, one that was unexpectedly hostile in some ways: Pauline, Monsieur Arseneau, even Madame Renier Bernadotte at the beginning.

Madame Renier-Bernadotte swept in just then, dressed head to toe in flowing, black knits, with stunning amber jewelry. She took her time setting up her lecture notes, as was her custom.

"*Bonjour*," she said when she was done. She surveyed the class. "There are fewer of you now. This is excellent. We're almost down to the *real* students."

Who was I kidding? Madame Renier-Bernadotte still terrified me as much as she impressed me. I surveyed the auditorium. Now that she had mentioned it, there were a lot fewer students now than during the first two weeks of classes. The boy who she had ejected from that first class never showed his face again.

"I bear excellent news," she said.

I waited, eager to hear the details.

"It is time for me to assign you the first of two oral presentations you will be giving this year. You will be presenting it at the end of January."

A shared groan rumbled through the auditorium as this news sank in.

"*Bah alors*." She tutted. "I have no idea why students always make such a drama out of an oral presentation. Not only is it crucial that you all gain experience speaking about our subject matter in front of others, but it will oblige you to exert a rigor to your translations and analysis that you might otherwise lack. There is no better cure for intellectual indolence than the idea of standing up in front of a room of your classmates and *moi*.

As far as I knew, I was the only non-French-speaking student in Madame's class. I could manage speaking in public in English, but in French, I inevitably became tongue-tied. How would I be in *medieval* French?

I went to the bibliotèque Sainte-Geneviève after class with significantly less spring in my step.

Madame Renier-Bernadotte had assigned us the subject "Compare the medieval models of courtly love in *Les Quinze Joies du Mariage* and *Érec et Énide*." That was a massive topic. I had no idea what constituted a quality oral presentation in France…or what Madame Renier-Bernadotte considered intellectual laziness for that matter.

I paused in front of the golden stone columns of the Panthéon. What was I going to do? Where was I going to start? I transmitted calls for help to Victor Hugo, Rousseau, Voltaire, Zola, and the other illustrious intellectuals buried within. That, however, didn't feel like enough. I felt to be taken seriously, I had to go inside and ask for their help in person.

I went inside, dipping into my leather bag from Tati for the entrance fee.

The interior of the Panthéon was certainly glorious. Neoclassical domes soared above, and the central oculus let in a piercing ray of light. The intricately patterned marble floors shined with polish.

I went down into the crypt, looking for Victor Hugo's tomb. *He is the one I needed to talk to.* I had read *Les Misérables* when I was about fourteen, mainly for the sheer pretention factor of being able to tell people that I had read it. But in fact, that book changed my life. It was then I started dreaming of coming to France one day, specifically Paris. It also showed me how a gifted storyteller could transport me to a completely different time and place.

How was it that I had neglected to pay him a visit until now? He was practically my neighbor there in Paris. That was neglectful of me.

His tomb was easy to find in the crypt. At first, I was surprised by its lack of adornment, considering his literary glory. On further reflection, though, I realized that I had never imagined him as a fussy sort of person.

I ran my fingertips across the fine bumps of rough stone that encased Hugo's resting place. Carved on the side, so simply, was XXIV, Victor Hugo, 1808-1885. The tomb was stoic, a bit brutal, unforgiving...a bit as I imagined Hugo himself to be.

I pressed both of my hands flat against the stone. The cold seeped into the tender skin on my palms. They grew so chilled a burning sensation kindled there.

There were a few other people in the crypt, but they talked in hushed voices. The dank odor of unrelenting damp and the haunting echo of footsteps was enough to quell even the unruliest temperaments.

I decided that I would talk to Hugo in my head. He was dead; if anyone could hear unspoken things, it was the deceased.

Please let me figure out a way to do this oral report for Professeur Renier-Bernadotte, I transmitted silently to him a few minutes into my confessions. *I respect this teacher, even though she probably doesn't know I even exist. I don't want to be a laughingstock. I want to do a good job because I love this material and, even more than disappointing her, I don't want to do a disservice to the medieval texts I'll be analyzing. You understand that. I know you do.*

I continued in the same vein for quite some time until my feet began to ache. They really needed to put chairs down there just as they did in the chapels at Notre-Dame. But then, maybe people didn't come to chat with him that often?

If you could help Franck decide to come back to Montreal with me at the end of this year and not be all weird about the whole freedom thing, that would be great too. I'll just leave that with you.

I patted the stone under my hand and bid him good-bye. I suspected that this would not be the only time I would come to talk to Victor.

I walked out and found myself contemplating one of my favorite quotes of his on the walk home—"To love or have loved. That is enough. Ask nothing further. There is no other pearl to be found in the dark folds of life."

I didn't agree. If my future was simply to "have love," I knew I could never settle for that.

chapter **thirty-three**

Christmas, or rather Noël, had arrived in Paris.

On a Saturday morning, we were wandering down la rue Mouffetard, which was in full swing for market day. Fresh oysters were appearing everywhere, as well as fattened geese and all sorts of exotic-sounding poultry that I had never seen before in Canada.

We wandered aimlessly, having already bought two baguettes, some interesting cheeses, a nice slice of *pâté de foie*, two heads of *frisée* lettuce, a bag of pale green endives, and a package of freshly sliced *jambon blanc*.

I was munching on fresh-roasted chestnuts. Several vendors selling them had popped up on the street corners in the past few weeks. My package, wrapped up with newsprint, warmed my hands, and the piping-hot, mealy insides of the chestnuts heated me up from the inside.

Franck was entertaining me with stories of the dramas at his workplace.

Apparently two of the four journalists were driving the boss crazy. He would tell them to their faces that he wanted to get rid of them, but because of French labor laws, it was…complicated.

At first, I felt sorry for Franck's poor colleagues, but he quickly disabused me of my displaced sympathy. Their general ineptitude was startling, Franck assured me.

"One of them barely ever comes into work," he said. "Whereas the other one doesn't appear to know how to write or read French and spends all his time trying to get the female secretary to sleep with him."

"What about sexual harassment?" I asked Franck. "He can't be allowed to be talking to the secretary like that. It's an abuse of power."

"She's above him in the chain of command," Franck said. "He's just too stupid to recognize that. She told us that she wants to deal with it herself."

"Still...," I said.

"I know," Franck said. "We've all called him out on his behavior to his face and to our boss... Lately, the *patron* has started talking about folding the magazine completely."

I stopped in the middle of the cobblestones, my hand still buried in my toasty bag of chestnuts. "What?"

"The magazine is not meeting its financial targets and, more importantly I think, it's the only way the *patron* can think of to get those two morons out of his life."

"Does that worry you?" I knew it worried me. "How would you feel about being out of work again?"

Franck shrugged. "I'll find something else."

We never seemed to have quite enough money between us. Paris was expensive, yet it was so sublimely beautiful that even running constantly short of francs had a certain allure. Still, we needed to eat. Chestnuts were cheap and filling, but... "Have you thought about where you would find something else if the magazine folds?"

Franck shrugged. "What would the point be in that? It may not fold in the end."

"It doesn't sound like it's on very firm foundations."

"It's not." Franck stopped for a few seconds to inhale the scent of smoke from one of the chimneys far above the sidewalk. "Still. You never know."

"I guess if you're not worried about it…"

"I'm not." Franck reached over and took my hand. "Now. Come back to the present, Laura. Look around you."

Indeed, we had arrived in the middle of one of the oldest Parisian markets. The bump of an ancient cobblestone poked up under the sole of my boot. The smells of rotisserie chickens and ripe cheeses frolicked in the wintry air.

Franck squeezed my hand. "There you are! Welcome back. Are you excited to be leaving for Vienna tomorrow?"

"*Oui.*"

My friend Tanya was studying in Vienna for a term on an exchange program with her university back in Canada. She had gone with a bunch of her friends from her Bachelor of Commerce program, but she had a distinct advantage—her mother was German and Tanya spoke German fluently.

I, on the other hand, spoke no German whatsoever. She told me the city was already filled with Christmas markets, called *Christkindlmarkts*, and she had already signed us up for several brewery tours. I could certainly get behind that program.

Franck, in the meantime, was staying in Paris alone, as I had when he was in Morocco. He, on the other hand, was an old hand at the solo life in Paris from his days as a student at the Sorbonne.

Part of me felt relieved that the possibility of losing his magazine job meant that he wouldn't have much to stay there for, but of course I worried about the inevitable cash-flow crisis.

I hated leaving for Vienna with what I felt were major questions unresolved between Franck and me, but I didn't quite have the courage to bring them up again. I dreaded the thought of having to leave for Vienna in the wake of a fresh fight. The longer I waited, it seemed, the more scared I became to find out Franck's answers.

The next day, Franck accompanied me to the gare de l'Est on his way to work. My train left at the ungodly hour of six o'clock in the morning. I had downed a bowl of coffee before leaving the apartment and hopping on the bus with Franck—I was proud of myself for finding a bus route that was theoretically quicker than the Metro.

Besides, the route was stunning. The bus went up the Champs-Élysées, which was still bright with white Christmas lights looped in all the trees. I wondered if they stayed on for the entire month of December?

We passed many of the *grands magasins*, all of which all had luxurious Christmas displays in their windows.

My favorites, I had decided during one of our evening walks, were the windows of the Printemps store, which were filled with vistas of arctic high fashion. We passed them now, and they—just like the Champs-Élysées—were still lit up in the dark morning.

Polar bears wore sequins and carried Prada handbags. Two white foxes dressed in leather clothes with lots of buckles and straps, which I suspected were designed by Jean-Pierre Gaultier, sat at a table enjoying a bottle of Champagne. Fake snow was everywhere, as was magical blue lighting and rotating, haute couture ice skaters. It was the most incongruous representation of the Far North that I had ever seen—its quirkiness and devotion to style was *très* Parisian.

I thought back to the afternoon Franck and I had spent in the Galleries Lafayette. We couldn't, *bien sûr*, afford to do any of our present shopping there, but we spent hours soaking up the Christmas atmosphere of the store. In the middle of the galleries rose a humungous Christmas tree, bedecked with tiny silvery lights and huge fluffy flowers. On the top perched a white snowy owl.

Franck and I had so much fun together. Unplanned, spontaneous fun. I didn't want that to end.

Both of us shared a fantasy of long, overland train travel in the old style, à la Orient Express. When we arrived on my platform at the station, my train to Vienna didn't disappoint. It stood, gleaming black, with a thin red line painted across its glossy carriage. Curtains hung on all the windows, and a properly uniformed conductor was checking people's tickets and ushering them into the correct carriages.

It was a far cry from the clackety and graffiti-covered regional trains we took in Burgundy. I felt like asking Franck if he could play hooky from work and hop on with me. I was sure that all our future decisions would be left behind us on such a conveyance.

Still, Franck had been to Morocco, and this was my turn to travel solo. As an independent woman, I should have been over-joyed, right? Besides, Franck had been nothing but encouraging. *I am self-sufficient*, I reminded myself. *The anti-Pauline.*

"We need to do a long train trip together," Franck said as we walked down the platform to reach my designated carriage.

It relieved me that our thoughts were running in similar lines for once. When we reached my carriage, I gave him a long kiss and took the smaller of my bags, while he heaved up the larger one.

"We will," I said. "In the meantime, I'll test it out."

Franck took my face between his hands and we kissed again until the whistle of the train sounded. "Nothing like saying good-bye on the train platform," he said with a smile when we broke apart.

He held my hand while I climbed up into the train like a pas-senger in a 1920s film. I hoped he didn't feel that my hand was shaking slightly.

I waved at him through the closest window as the train pulled away from the platform. I watched him wave at me until he van-ished into the blur of distant things.

The whistle sounded; we were on our way.

My train burst from the obscurity of the station and was bathed in winter sunshine. I sighed, then checked my ticket. Cabin number eleven.

I walked along the plush, carpeted corridor, bumping into the walls with the sway of the train. About two-thirds of the way down the carriage, I found my cabin. I slid open the glass-and-polished wood door and admired the benches upholstered in a vibrant crimson fabric inside. Wooden luggage racks lined both sides of the cabin above the seats. The impression I was in an old film strengthened.

Even better, for the moment, I had the cabin all to myself. I chose the seat nearest the window—we would be going through Germany for the better part of the day, and I didn't want to miss a thing.

The outskirts of Paris gave way to fields, glowing orange-yellow in the dawn. In the distance, I could make out the outlines of an occasional crumbling château.

Just on the French side of the border, in Strasbourg, a large couple speaking German bustled into the cabin and settled themselves down on the bench opposite me. They looked like jolly cabin-mates, as well as people who enjoyed the merits of schnitzel and bratwurst.

"*Guten Morgen*," I said, employing just about the only German words I knew.

They nodded kindly at me. I smiled and nodded back.

"*Française?*" she asked me with a German accent. Was my German pronunciation so bad that she could tell I wasn't German from one word? Before I could answer, the woman nodded her head as if I had just confirmed her hunch without saying a word. She said something to me in rapid German, still in a kindly manner. I could only shrug apologetically.

She shrugged as well, and we shared a laugh. I checked my watch. Seven thirty in the morning. My stomach had been rumbling for a while.

Franck had told me that there is always a diner carriage on these old trains and that I shouldn't pass up the opportunity to eat there.

I waited a few more minutes so my new neighbors didn't think I was leaving because of their arrival. I left my sweater on my seat so nobody else would nab my view. It was going to be a long day, and I liked my spot.

I followed the signs and moved through several carriages toward the front of the train until I opened the door to a carriage that took my breath away.

Tiny tables were set with starched, white tablecloths, and traditional lights swung in unison from the ceiling. Formally dressed waiters wore all black with only a white shirt, bow tie, and white gloves. I was still taking it all in when one of the waiters approached me. "Would you like to take breakfast?" he asked me in French.

How did he know to speak to me in French?

"*Oui, s'il vous plaît*," I said.

With an elegant wave of his arm, he ushered me to a table tucked up alongside the window. A field of cows whipped by—surely German cows, as we had crossed the border.

I sat down, feeling like I should pull a silver-plated cigarette holder from my make-believe beaded purse. I picked up the menu that lay on the table. It was a thick menu, not because the selection of food was extensive but because it was translated into English, French, German, Italian, and Spanish, and something that must have been, by process of elimination, Flemish.

There were some strange offerings, to be sure. Pâté and crackers? Cold meat? Ugh. I went the French route and ordered two croissants in a basket accompanied by about half a baguette, butter, and jam, and a *café au lait*.

The waiter moved fluently in sync with the train from my table to the next table, where he took my neighbor's order in German.

I had brought a book with me, *La Reine Margot* by Dumas, which I needed to read for my eighteenth-century French literature class. It lay, unopened, beside my white china plate as I gazed out the window.

A train ride was the perfect suspension of reality. A space where there was nothing to do but rest, daydream, take stock... and eat.

The houses changed dramatically somewhere between France and Germany. There were more and more houses with exposed beams on the outside, usually stained a dark brown. Many houses in Germany are painted a bright color such as lime green, sunshine yellow, orange, or, my favorite, cornflower blue. They looked freshly sprouted from the pages of a fairy tale—the kind of abode conjured up by magic elves at night.

The waiter brought me a basket of pastries and served me my

steaming *café au lait* in a pure white china bowl. A white ceramic pot held strawberry jam and another butter almost as white as the china.

Franck would love this. I felt a stab of regret that he wasn't there to enjoy it with me. I thought back to Grace saying that nothing felt real without her beau around. I had thought that ridiculous at the time, but now...

I didn't want to become the kind of person who was so used to being in a couple that I no longer enjoyed being on my own. That was pathetic. Franck enjoyed his adventures in Morocco by himself.

What did the future hold for us? I wondered for the hundredth or so time. Franck was my first true love. Could a person's first love also be their last love? And, if so, was that what I wanted?

Sometimes I had a hard time believing that I had been with him for three years. None of my romantic daydreams in high school (of which there were many, although few actual real-life boyfriends) involved a long-term relationship this early in my life.

In Grade 12, I had imagined France as being my springboard into an existence of adventure for many years before settling down.

Meeting Franck and us being together still felt like a miracle in many ways, but it also required a radical readjustment of how I imagined my future. The single student life I thought I would be living was no longer a possibility.

Now, plucked out of my day-to-day Parisian life, I realized I had been so concerned about Franck's yearning for freedom that I forgot to consider that I might have yearnings of my own.

chapter **thirty-four**

A relaxing twelve and a bit hours later, my train chugged into the Wien Westbahnhof station in Vienna. Night had fallen long before, but even after my delectable dinner of veal cutlets with a white wine-and-mustard sauce and braised endives with tagliatelle, I found myself staring out the window into the dark.

The nighttime landscape was fascinating in a different way— the way the village lights highlighted only a few fleeting shapes before they were swallowed up by the dark once again.

Tanya was waiting on the platform. The cold was the first thing to hit me when I got off the train. It felt to me as though I had edged significantly closer to Siberia during the day.

"Welcome!" she said. "Do you want to go out beer drinking?" She gave me a big hug and I sank into her puffball of a down jacket. It was far more adapted to the frigid air of Vienna than my Parisian duffle coat.

I looked down at my suitcase and felt a wave of fatigue sweep over me. It had been an early start and a long day, yet if Tanya wanted to...

"I'm just kidding," she said. "Let's get you fed and into bed, and tomorrow we can start bright and early."

"That," I said, "sounds like a perfect plan."

The next morning, I woke up beside Tanya in the basement bedroom at her host parents' house in the outskirts of Vienna. Her host parents were a tall, austere Austrian couple. The night before, they had said a curt hello to me when I arrived after a dinner of schnitzel at a traditional schnitzelhaus on our way back from the station. I knew Austrians are experts at everything schnitzel, but it was hands down the best schnitzel I had ever tasted.

Tanya had warned me during our phone calls that her host parents spoke no English, and while they were perfectly nice, they weren't what you would call warm people.

The thin winter light coming in the window brought me back to consciousness. I stretched, stiff from a long day sitting on the train with only the occasional walk to and from the dinner carriage to stretch my legs. I could hear the shower in the bathroom running. The rest of the house was, as Tanya had promised the night before, quiet.

I closed my eyes and dozed off for a few more minutes until Tanya came into the room, fully dressed and drying her jet-black hair with a towel.

"We can't be too long," she said. "If we're going to go to the brewery tours today, we need to catch a trolley into town in less than an hour."

I hopped up, gathered my things quickly, and headed into the bathroom. After a speedy shower, I pulled on my warmest sweater. On the way back from the train station the night before, the air possessed a dagger-like quality that was completely different from the dampness of Paris.

Everything about the house struck me in its non-Frenchness. The antiques were built on a massive scale, as well as ornately carved and crafted from wood so dark it was almost black. The décor was a utilitarian mix of brown and green tweed. There was little ornamentation—certainly none of the silk flowers or upholstered Louis XV chairs or collections of miniature perfume bottles that adorned many French houses. It even *smelled* different. A mix of something utilitarian—meat and rye bread?

The kitchen table was set with what Tanya informed me was a typical Austrian breakfast.

On offer was some sort of solid-looking pâté; cut-up, cold sausages; a few dense-looking rolls of bread (dark brown and full of seeds); and thickly sliced, pale white cheese. There was also a funny, cured-looking meat and a bowl of eggs, which I hoped were hard boiled.

"That's *Schinkenspeck*," Tanya said, nodding down at the sinewy-looking meat. "It tastes like really cold, chewy bacon."

There was no jam, butter, or pastries of any kind. For people who loved savory breakfasts, they would be in heaven, but I always liked to start my day off gently with something sweet—not something called *Schinkenspeck*.

I picked up a roll that proved to be as rock hard as it looked. I struggled to tear it open so I could tuck some of the cheese inside.

"Do you like Austrian breakfasts?" I asked Tanya.

Tanya shrugged. "I'm used to all this stuff. It's what I grew up eating because of my mom. My dad always fried up his own kippers."

"Kippers?" I made a gagging sound.

"Yup. British. So, you can see why I don't mind a bit of *Schinkenspeck*."

"Definitely."

"It wasn't until I started high school that I convinced my mom to stop serving German breakfasts when friends came to stay overnight. I just wanted Pop Tarts for once."

I cautiously selected the least sinewy-looking piece of *Schinkenspeck* and placed it in my mouth. It took me a long time to chew and swallow it—it was more the type of thing that required gnawing.

Deciding that one piece had fulfilled my obligation for culinary experimentation, I filled up on cheese, which was edible.

God, am I becoming as hard to please as the French? Instead of filling with me dismay, that thought suffused me with pride.

When I got up from the table to grab my coat, I realized there was a newly acquired lead ball in my stomach.

Tanya locked up the house and led me to a nearby trolley stop. "Do you have any Austrian money?" she asked.

"Yup." I pulled out a few Austrian coins so I could see how much they were worth.

It was several degrees below zero, and the air had the same unforgiving quality as the *Schinkenspeck*. I hadn't brought a pair of mitts. Actually, I didn't *own* a pair of mitts in Paris. I thought longingly of my Québec winter gear—silk long johns, huge woolen gloves, a toque like a bank robber's that covered my head and most of my face except for my mouth and eyes—packed in a storage container in the suburbs of Montreal. My hands already ached from the cold. I buried them deep in my pockets.

"Where exactly are we going?" I asked.

"A beer tour!"

It felt a wee bit early in the morning to be drinking beer, but *when in Vienna*... Little flecks of snow began to fall from the sky.

"I've discovered they're *very* generous with their beer in Austria," Tanya added.

"That sounds promising."

"But first we have to go meet my friend Julie and a bunch of other students at the UN. They're working there."

On the way, I stared out the trolley window, wondering at the juxtaposition of buildings that were so intricate that they looked like giant wedding cakes, side by side with concrete cubes straight out of the Communist architecture textbooks.

We hopped out, and Tanya snapped a few obligatory photos of me in front of the half circle of flags of all the UN countries.

"Tanya!" A smiling person about our age and wearing glasses was walking toward us and waving.

"Laura, this is Julie. She's in my year at UBC. Julie, this is Laura."

About eight other students joined us on our way to the trolley stop and hopped on the next trolley with us.

Standing next to me was a lanky blond guy in a tweed overcoat. I was perched on one of the old wooden benches installed along both sides of the trolley car. My hands began to thaw, and the swirl of German around me wrapped me in a comfortable daze.

After we had been riding a minute or two, the blond guy leaned down and began talking to me in German. His eyes were a startling blue.

"I'm sorry." I said. "I don't speak German."

He smiled at me. "It's not my first language either," he said in almost accent-less English.

"You could have fooled me."

"That's flattering to hear, but how would you know the difference?"

"I wouldn't," I admitted. "But I could probably tell if you spoke terrible French."

"*Tu parles français?*" he asked with an accent that I hated to admit was better than mine.

"*Oui,*" I said. "*J'habite à Paris en ce moment.*"

"What other languages do you speak?" he continued in English.

That was an odd question. Coming from British Columbia and speaking two languages—English and French—was already doing rather well. Most people I knew back home only spoke English.

"English and French. That's it. Wait…I took Spanish in high school, but I forget most of it."

"Laura was terrible at languages in school," Tanya who had been following the conversation chimed in. "She was always in the bottom of the class."

"Thank you for that." I rolled my eyes at Tanya, who laughed. "But it's true. Why? How many languages do you speak?" I asked him.

"Let's see." He began to count on his fingers. "English, French, German, Danish, Swedish, Norwegian, Spanish, and Italian—although my written Italian still needs some work."

I was speechless for a minute or so. "Eight languages? Isn't that some sort of record?"

"I'm from Denmark. It's not uncommon there."

I wondered what we were doing wrong back in Canada that none of us had the multi-lingual capacity of.... wait...I didn't even know his name yet.

"How is that even possible? How old are you?"

"Twenty-three."

"Do they teach all of those languages to you in school in Denmark?"

"Some. The rest I just picked up here and there. The more languages I learn, the easier it gets. "

"Doesn't it just become more confusing?"

The trolley screeched to a stop in front of a large, sprawling brick building, but we continued our conversation seamlessly as we got off.

"More confusing? Not at all."

"How is your accent so good?" Indeed, I could barely tell that English wasn't his mother tongue. "And why is your accent more North American than British?

"Ah, so you want me to reveal our language-learning trick in Scandinavia?"

"Indubitably."

"Our populations are too small for movie companies to bother translating films for us, so if we want to watch anything other than Danish movies and TV shows, we have to watch them in their original, non-dubbed version. We have an excellent language program at schools, but honestly, I am convinced that is the real trick."

"Did you know what 'indubitably' meant just now?"

"Of course. It is a synonym to 'certainly.'"

"Damn."

He smiled. "But enough about me. What about you?" he said. "I know you are Tanya's friend from Canada. What are you doing in Paris?"

"I'm doing the third year of my BA at the Sorbonne. My degree is in English literature, but with this year, I'm getting a minor in French literature."

Small potatoes to him, perhaps, but considering my general inaptitude at foreign languages in high school, having a bilingual university degree was a major accomplishment for me.

"Dumas, Camus…all those writers?"

"Yes, and lots of medieval literature. I'm not going as modern as Camus—French literature becomes seriously depressing once the nihilists and the absurdists make their appearance."

We reached the door to the brewery, and when he opened it for me, the heady smell of malt tickled my nose.

"My name is Anton." He put out his hand and I shook it. He kept holding it and, to be honest, I didn't want him to let go. It felt pleasingly toasty. "It's a pleasure to meet you. Truly."

Tanya and Julie came up behind us, and I let go of his grip. "We can't get separated now if we want to be in the same tour group," Tanya said to me

"If you *want* to be in the same tour group as us," Julie added with a meaningful look at Anton.

What a strange thing to say. Wait a minute…was she suspecting Anton and me…

A heavy-set woman dressed from head to toe in moss-green tweed came and indicated in a way that did not broker argument for Tanya and Julie and me to stand to the left of her.

Anton tried to sidle alongside our group but, being tall and fair, he was nothing if not noticeable. The guide said something harsh-sounding in German that made Anton's shoulders drop. He walked over to the other group.

"That's strange," Julie said as we were led into a massive room with copper kettles that reached from the floor almost to the ceiling. "We've done a lot of beer tours with Anton, but he has never been so keen to be in our group before."

"Can you believe he speaks eight languages?" I said. Diversion was always a good tactic.

"Most of the Scandinavian students can," Tanya said.

"He seems quite keen on *you*." Julie was not easily shaken from her line of thought. "I've had my eye on him for a while, but he doesn't even look my way. Would you be interested?"

"What?" I said. Honestly, the idea hadn't even crossed my mind. Anton was nice-looking and interesting, but I'd had just one conversation with the guy.

"Didn't Tanya tell you I have a serious boyfriend?" I said. "We live together in Paris."

"She may have mentioned it. Did you tell Anton that?"

"Don't be ludicrous. I just met him."

Julie crossed her arms and gave me a complicitous smile. "Hmmmm. Curious."

"He was just being friendly," I insisted.

"*Shhhhhht.*" We were hushed by the green tweed woman, who launched into an exegesis of something—probably beer making, but it could have been building a nuclear bomb for all I understood—in German.

chapter thirty-five

The tour was rambunctious, with a lot of laughing and joking and much being called to order in annoyed-sounding German by the green tweed lady.

It had been a long time since I'd been with a bunch of students around my age on a social occasion. Even back at McGill, Franck and I only had a small circle of friends. I had forgotten how much fun it was to goof off in a group.

Finally, we were led to a tasting room and told that this was the end of the tour but that we could stay as long as we liked. Sawdust was scattered on the gravel floor, and the room smelled refreshingly woodsy. Long wooden tables were scrubbed ruthlessly clean, but even that Austrian spit and polish couldn't disguise the many layers of beer stains that had soaked into the wood.

A buxom but bored-looking waitress, wearing a full-on Bavarian maid outfit that must have been chilly despite her fuzzy, white tights, brought us two fistfuls of beer steins to the table. They sloshed when she set them down, but nobody seemed surprised or bothered by this. It explained the stains.

258   MY GRAPE PARIS

I took a sip. The beer was light and pure tasting, making me think of crystal-clear mountain streams running through the High Alps, with goats frolicking on the adjacent pastures. I was still contemplating this when Anton slipped onto the bench beside Julie and me.

"What did you think?" he asked me. "Were you impressed?"

"Definitely." I nodded. I tried to sound cool but felt a blush rising like a high tide up my face. Was it because I was maybe a bit flattered by Anton's attention, or was it because Julie had gone and made me feel self-conscious?

"I believe it is the oldest brewery in Vienna."

I couldn't deny that I was sharply aware of Anton's leg pressed against mine on the crowded bench. "The beer tastes so pure." Staying on the subject of beer felt safe.

"It should," he said. "This brewery has always followed the *Reinheitsgebot*."

"The what?" I asked. How could anyone keep a straight face speaking a language that included words such as *"Ausfarht"* and *"Schinkenspeck"* and *"Reinheit"* and whatever Anton had just said? At least he had distracted me from the inch of charged air that separated his hand from mine on the table.

"Reinheitsgebot."

"What does that hilarious word mean?"

"It means...hmmmm...I suppose it directly translates to English as the "German Purity Law.""

I recoiled. "That doesn't sound good."

"No. No." He waved his hand. "Nothing to do with the atrocities of World War II. It refers to the German Purity Law for beer. It means using clear spring water taken from a well that is more than one hundred metres deep and brewing with only the finest sorts of malt and hops, carefully selected by the master brewer."

"I guess that's acceptable then." I took another sip. "Quite acceptable."

"You're very funny." Anton clanked his Bernstein gently against mine. It would have been innocuous, except that Tanya, across the table, shot me a we-told-you-so look.

"Danke schön." I thought I was doing a decent job of acting unaffected, but I felt the rising heat in my face once again. "So, you like beer too?" It was a feeble but conscious attempt to change the topic.

"Of course. We drink a lot of beer in Denmark. At Julefrokost, we drink special Christmas beer to wash down the shots of akvavit we must drink each time someone says *"skål!"*

Which question should I start with? This at least opened many innocent topics.

"We get extremely drunk," Anton continued. "We don't work much that time of year. Do Canadians have drinking traditions?"

"Um." I thought about this. "After our team wins a hockey game. When else guys?" I waved at Tanya and Julie to help me.

"Bush parties," Julie said.

"Bush parties?" Anton sounded confused.

"When you're a teenager and nobody can have a party in their house, you take the festivities into the forest," Tanya explained.

"I've never heard that term before."

"It's common in Canada," Tanya said. "Laura and I went to at least one bush party most weekends in high school."

"Until the police shut us down," I added.

"Why would they do that?" Anton asked.

"Puritanism," Julie said.

"That doesn't sound like fun," Anton said.

I thought of the more relaxed attitudes toward drinking I had experienced in France, especially in Burgundy where people live among some of the world's most famed vineyards. "It's not."

One of the guys Anton was riding the trolley with called him over. Anton gave a little jump and checked his watch.

"Oh no. We're already late. I must go." He squeezed my arm. "You are coming to the next brewery, aren't you?"

I glanced over at Tanya and she nodded. She did a poor job of biting back a grin.

"Seems so."

"Excellent," he squeezed my shoulder as he got up off the bench. I felt a conspicuous lack of his warmth. He pulled on his tweed coat just as waiters with plates of what looked like schnitzel began to emerge from the back of the brewery. "I look forward to seeing you later," he said to me.

Would this be a good time to mention Franck? No. I wasn't even sure he was being anything beyond friendly.

"Yes," I said, looking down at the plate of schnitzel that had appeared in front of me and feeling flustered.

"Right then." He paused. I glanced up, and he was looking down at me, hesitating over something. *"Auf Wiedersehen."*

"Auf Wiedersehen," I attempted to use one of the few words I knew, gleaned from repeat viewings of *The Sound of Music* when I was in Grade 5. Yet Anton didn't budge, and our eyes remained locked. I waited for him to leave, or to say something else.

Finally, his friend game over and gave him a light tap at the back of his head. "Come on!" he said in English. "What are you dawdling for?"

Anton wrapped his scarf around his neck. "Nothing," he said. "Nothing." He gave me a final nod, then hurried off.

Tanya and Julie were giving me the side-eye.

"Shut up," I said pre-emptively. I dug into my plate before the food got any colder.

"Why didn't you tell him about Franck?" Tanya said after she'd had a few bites.

"When did I get the chance?" I demanded. "He was asking me questions."

"Still—" she said.

"At the first opportunity, I'll set him straight *if* I think it's necessary and *not* in front of you two. He probably doesn't even like me that way at all."

Every time I looked up from my plate of schnitzel, I caught Tanya watching me, a troubled crease between her eyebrows.

"Stop looking at me like that. You're taking something that's completely innocent—"

Julie snorted. "Sorry," she said. "I couldn't help it. It's just that even if you aren't interested, Anton clearly is. I have no doubts about that. Are you...interested?"

"No!"

"Not even the tiniest bit?" Julie asked. "You're only twenty-one. You're not seriously ready to settle down, are you?"

"Sarah, it's none of our business," Tanya reminded her.

I should have just agreed and left it at that, but Julie's comment niggled me.

"We can't choose the age we are when we meet the right person," I said. "I met Franck when I was eighteen…so what? I'm not going to bail on what we have just because of that. Honestly, the dating world doesn't seem all that fun."

Tanya nodded. I could see that I had scored a point. "It's not," she confirmed.

I cut a few pieces of my tender, crunchy Weiner schnitzel—pounded scallops of veal, breaded in crumbs and then fried. I squeezed two fresh lemon slices garnishing my plate over top of the meat and enjoyed the foreign, savory yet tart crunch. There were no greens to be found, but the schnitzel came covered with a creamy sauce rich in lemon and accompanied by a potato salad that boasted sprigs of freshly cut parsley. I couldn't think of a more perfect accompaniment for the beer.

As I savored my schnitzel, I couldn't help wondering if my intentions were truly as innocent as I had claimed. A flush still warmed my cheeks. I was—if I was totally honest with myself—flattered.

Guilt overtook me. Not only was enjoying Anton's attention a betrayal of Franck but it was also likely a betrayal of my feminist principles. What would Madame Renier-Bernadotte say to a man who hit on her out of the blue? I wondered if she would send him packing because she had no valuable brain cells to waste on men or if she would she act like many Parisian woman and take him to bed, enjoy him, and then not think about him afterward. How would a liberated French woman act? But then, was I a liberated French woman?

"Sorry," Julie said, fiddling the pieces of cut-up schnitzel left on her plate with her fork. "My Mom became accidentally pregnant when she was eighteen. She always drove it into my head that it was a huge tragedy to miss her twenties. I've always been determined not to settle down until well into my thirties. I guess I harp on it a bit too much."

"You do," I said. "But I get it."

The fact of the matter was that Julie's confession bothered me even more than her prodding.

I *was* young—only twenty-one—and, besides Franck, inexperienced in long-term relationships. Was I forgoing all kinds of experiences and adventures by settling down too young? Maybe this was the time in my life when I was supposed to grow as an individual, not as half of a couple.

Even another pint of beer couldn't chase these troubling thoughts out of my head.

As we rode the trolley for the next beer tour, my mind whirred with questions.

Perhaps I understood Franck a bit better now that I was experiencing doubts of my own. Still, none of this changed the fact that I couldn't bear the thought of Franck with any other woman. Neither of us could have both—each other and the single life. We both had a choice to make.

At the second brewery tour, Anton did not, thankfully, reappear as expected.

Sarah, Tanya, and I got slotted in with a group of prodigiously parched Belgians. Afterward, Tanya and I went back to her hosts' house for a bit of a rest.

I lay on the bed writing postcards. My first one was for Franck. It was a photo of the Wiener Staatsoper, which was the amusing name for the Vienna State Opera house.

The picture had been taken at night and highlighted the building's intricate two-tiered wedding cake structure. Franck loved opera and, thanks to living with him, I now knew the difference between *Carmen* and *La Traviata*.

A pulse of anger ran through me. If he hadn't expressed doubts himself, would I have even entertained any thoughts of Anton? I wished Franck was with me. Things would have never become weird with Anton if he were. But then again, in a committed relationship, I shouldn't need the safeguard of the other person's physical presence.

"What do you think of going to the opera tonight?" Tanya asked, as though she was a mind reader.

"I was just writing a postcard to Franck with a photo of the opera house on the front."

Tanya lay on her bed, reading a massive economics textbook entirely in German. "What did you write?"

"Actually, I haven't written anything yet. I was just thinking about that."

"So, interested? Not everyone is into opera."

"How could anyone pass up the opportunity to see an opera in the Vienna Opera House?" I said. "It's world famous."

"Great," Tanya said, closing her book.

"Wait though," I said. "It must be expensive. Franck and I are on a limited budget."

"They sell standing spots for students—cut rate. You're okay with standing, right?"

"Of course."

"Don't worry. The view is good from the standing spots. It's center stage and just at the back of the first floor."

Tanya was at least five inches taller than I was. "I have no problem standing, but you do remember that I'm short, right?

"We'll get there early," she assured me. "You can't buy the standing tickets ahead of time anyway."

Through the ceiling, we heard the front door to the house opening and shutting.

"Ah," Tanya said. "They're home from work."

"Should we go up and say hello?" I asked.

Tanya shook her head. "They don't like having to make small talk. They'll call when it's dinner. In the meantime, I'm going to call Julie and a few of the others. Do you want me to invite Anton?"

"Don't be stupid," I grumbled.

"Is that your answer?"

"Yes."

chapter **thirty-six**

When we sat down at the table, there was something that resembled stew that had already been served onto the plate set for me.

I smiled. *"Danke schön."*

Tanya said the same thing, but with a vastly better pronunciation than me.

The host mother was talking to Tanya. It sounded more like she was giving Tanya orders rather than conducting a dinnertime conversation, but what did I know?

Tanya nodded several times, then turned to me. "She wants me to explain to you that this dish is called *Tafelspitz* and is a traditional Austrian dish of beef boiled in broth and served with a chive sauce...and these." She pointed to a lump of something white and then another brownish-orange lump on her plate. "Applesauce and horseradish."

"Oh...right. The other things are potatoes, aren't they?"

"They are," Tanya said. "Boiled. Germans and Austrians boil everything." I slid her a look. "Do they speak any English at all?"

"No," she said. "None."

I met their eyes and took a large bite of *Tafelspitz.* "Mmmmmm," I nodded. "Delicious. Thank you very much. I love it. Can you translate that for me, Tanya?"

Tanya turned and did this, and that's pretty much how the dinner went. I had never been much of a stew person, but it was certainly replete with the meaty flavor which the Viennese seemed to use as a criterion for good food.

Tanya and I cleaned up the dishes. Tanya consulted her watch. "We've got to hurry up if we want to get seats...er...I mean, spots. Julie will hold us a place in line, but Austrians don't like it when people do that. They think it's unfair."

We lucked out and caught a trolley that was just pulling away from the curb a block from the house.

Within twenty minutes, we were trying to spot Julie in the line in front of the opera house. The second floor of the building was lit up to showcase a different statue in each of its five curved stone arcades. It created a sense of magic, and we hadn't even entered yet.

We found Julie with the group of her and Tanya's fellow students, including, I was flustered to see, Anton.

I didn't know why I felt so unsettled—did he have an effect on me or was it because I was so self-conscious now in front of Tanya and Julie? I wasn't sure. Anton smiled at me.

"I didn't know you were planning on coming tonight, Tanya said to him.

"In the end, I couldn't make it to the second brewery tour, so I thought I'd join you here for a bit of culture."

"So *that's* why you came?" Julie nudged him. "Culture?"

Couldn't Julie just let it rest? None of this would have taken on the proportions it had now if it wasn't for her.

If I wasn't mistaken, Anton was the one blushing now. "I haven't been to the opera nearly enough since coming to Vienna," he said.

I avoided eye contact with everyone and pretended to be engrossed in reading the posters on the bulletin board posted beside the box office. What was I supposed to do anyway? I couldn't just blurt out to Anton that I had a boyfriend in Paris.

"I can't believe I forgot to ask," I said to Tanya after a while. "What opera are we going to see?"

"*Don Giovanni*," Anton answered.

We bought our tickets and entered the lobby. The surroundings made me feel as though I was entering a palace. Gold leaf, frescoes, marble statues, and red velvet were everywhere. The people lingering in groups inside were dressed for the dazzling surroundings. Many men were in black tie, and the women wore exquisite gowns and glittering jewels.

Tanya hurried us along so that we could claim our spots. Being inside the opera house itself was like being inside an elaborate wedding cake. Besides the row upon row of plush, red velvet seats on the floor level, the balconies rose one, two, three, four... five levels. The front of each section of balcony was carved in a beautiful shape that was repeated again and again. I pinched myself. *I am inside the Vienna State Opera.*

Anton found both Julie and me a spot in the front, without which we wouldn't have been able to see. I took note of his gallantry.

I opened my program, which was, of course, all in German. As I tried to decipher it, I enjoyed the heady smell around me. It was like a mix of expensive perfume and polished wood and... was that Anton's cologne?

Anton, who had a spot behind us and beside Tanya, leaned forward and whispered, "You're in luck. We're getting the A cast tonight—they are the best singers. We never know which cast we're going to get until we get here."

I could feel the warmth of his breath on the back of my neck and something flipped in my stomach. I dug my fingers deep in the plush of my velvet armrest. Suddenly, this place felt dangerous—a place where reality was suspended and the outside world didn't exist.

Was this the right moment to tell him I had a boyfriend in Paris?

Before I could decide, the lights went dark.

The heavy curtains parted and the first notes of Mozart's

composition made the hair on my arms stand up. From that moment, not to mention the murder of the Commendatore on stage, I was transported to Italy and the parlous deeds of the legendary Don Giovanni—libertine and seducer.

During intermission, we went into the opulent lobby and collapsed on velvet Louis-something-or-other chairs. The other stately operagoers were busy stretching their legs, while the standing audience members did the exact opposite. Anton had disappeared somewhere. He was just being friendly, I told myself. If his intentions were what Julie imagined, he wouldn't have gone off.

I was glad I hadn't said anything about Franck earlier. Relief poured through me, but I felt a confusing prickle of disappointment too. Was I tempted to see what else was out there? Anger flashed through my chest. If Franck hadn't been so cagey, I wouldn't have even been entertaining the possibility of Anton.

Tanya and Julie and I got into a deep discussion about the opera, and just when I was wondering when we were supposed to go back in, Anton materialized with a flute of Champagne.

"Champagne!" I laughed, looking up at him. "Aren't you clever."

He held it out to me. "It's for you. I wanted to make your Wiener Staatsoper experience complete, but the line took much longer than I bargained for."

I took it, conscious of Tanya and Julie's eyes on me. "Thank you," I said. "That was thoughtful." I took a sip so I could take a moment to gather my thoughts.

Just then the chime rang, telling us to reclaim our spots.

"I'm sorry." Anton said. "You enjoy. I'll go and save our places."

I gulped down the Champagne, and we hurried in a minute or so after Anton.

Julie opened her mouth to say something as the lights began to dim, but I interrupted. "I don't need to hear it," I said.

The second act was even better than the first, if that was possible. Luckily, as I was so transported by Don Giovanni's evildoings and the powerful, exquisite voices of the singers that I was distracted from Anton and the Champagne. The pure emotion they expressed vibrated through me until the final scene of Don Giovanni's ultimate retribution involving demons and the Commendatore's statue.

When it was over, we clapped until our palms ached.

"Thank you for bringing me, Tanya," I said as we walked back out into the frigid reality of an Austrian street in December. I didn't know what I was going to say to Anton, so I purposely didn't look to see if he was following us. "Truly. It was a once-in-a-life-time experience." Cold pinpricks of snow stung my face.

Just at that moment, Anton materialized by my side. He smiled down at me and pulled the loose hood of my wool coat up over my hair.

"There," he said. "That will be warmer."

I looked up at him, the blush back again. "It is. Thank you."

What should I do? What should I do? What should I do?

"Who's up for a Viennese coffee and a slice of *Sachertorte*?" Julie asked. We all said yes, except Anton.

"I can't," Anton said, with a rueful glance down at me. "My host parents are strict about me getting back by a certain time."

"Why?" Julie asked.

"It's that they live in an apartment, and they're both light sleepers. They say that when I come in, it wakes them up."

"Haven't they ever heard of earplugs?" I asked.

He laughed. "Maybe I will buy them a pair for an early Christmas gift. But I am happy you are disappointed I can't come with you." He said this directly to me, his eyes eager.

I was just joining in the conversation. I didn't mean—

"I can't see you tomorrow, either," he said. "I am working at the translation booth in the UN. But...what are you two up to tomorrow night?"

Tanya said, "I was thinking of taking Laura to the *Christkindl-markt*."

"Which one?" Anton asked.

"The one in front of city hall, of course."

"I'll meet you there, by the entrance?" Anton said to us.

"What time?" Julie asked. "I'll come too."

"Seven o'clock?" Anton pulled his scarf tighter around his neck.

"Great. See you then," Julie said. They waved him good-bye, and I joined in. He flashed one last smile to me before leaving.

"Who else wants to come tomorrow night?" Tanya asked our group after Anton left and, just as we had about the *Sachertorte*, everyone agreed.

I couldn't pretend now that I wasn't aware he was interested in me, could I?

Had I not clarified things with Anton already because there really hadn't been the opportunity or because deep down I didn't really want to clear it up?

At a high-ceilinged, baroque café, I enjoyed a Viennese coffee sprinkled with cinnamon and a delicious slice of the deep chocolate-and-apricot cake the Viennese revere as *Sachertorte*. The chocolate cake layer was dark and dense and the apricot jam full of the taste of summer, without being too sweet.

Afterward though, I couldn't fall asleep. I wanted to blame the rich chocolate, but in truth, I couldn't stop mulling over Anton. I tossed and turned on my mattress as Tanya and her host parents slept soundly in the silent house that smelled of pâté.

chapter **thirty-seven**

I tried to phone Franck the next morning, but I couldn't connect to Paris. An automated message in German kept coming on, but I had no idea what it was saying.

What was he doing? Was he out with one of his friends from *Expo News* or Nathanael? I hoped those two weren't reliving their university years, gallivanting around in the seedy *quartiers* of Paris.

What would Franck think of Anton's interest in me? Would he be jealous? Would he be amused? I reminded myself that I hadn't done anything wrong...yet. *Wait a second...yet?*

Tanya and I took a long time to leave the house that morning for downtown. I'd barely slept. Snow fell outside and frost covered the windows.

I bought a pair of gloves from a stand on the side of the road. My hands were, for a refreshing change, toasty warm, and I had doubled up on my socks and sweaters and had pulled up the hood on my wool duffle coat and anchored it with a warm scarf.

The freshly fallen snow created sparkling angel wings of crystals from the trolley wheels. We spent our time at two museums and a fantastic high-ceilinged café, where we had a wonderful schnitzel lunch.

In the afternoon, the snowflakes became fatter, and the entire town started to resemble a fairy tale.

Finally, it grew dark. Tanya took me to another wonderful restaurant that smelled of cheese and cinnamon. We feasted on a goulash and then apple strudel for dessert, and then she announced it was time for the *Christkindlmarkt*.

I hadn't decided exactly what do to about Anton, and I was supposed to have figured that out by then. If only I had been able to talk with Franck in the morning.

My mind spun with rejected plans and possibilities on our walk there. Tanya dutifully pointed out landmarks, and I made noises of amazement, but my mind was elsewhere.

Tanya checked her watch. "We're here a little early. Just in time to get ourselves a *Glühwein*."

"A *Glühwein*? What's a *Glühwein*?" I asked. I was grateful that something finally distracted me. The word was almost as promising as *Ausfahrt*.

"It's the traditional drink at Christmastime in Germanic countries. It's mulled wine with spices. It's delicious. You'll see."

Tanya led me over to a wooden stand festooned with fairy lights, fresh boughs that smelt like a forest, and little stars cut out of paper. She said something in German, and the man behind the stand opened the metal lid on a huge vat behind the counter.

I was spell-bound by the aroma of red wine, cinnamon, and cloves. If there was a smell that encapsulated Christmas, I was pretty certain I had just found it.

We were each given a large, ceramic mug of steaming goodness that was kitted out with an adorable knit belt around the cup so we wouldn't burn our hands.

"I can't believe they serve it in nice mugs like this," I said.

"Always. We'll take them back to the stand when we're done."

Fragrant steam—maybe there was allspice in *Glühwein* too?—rose off the heavenly brew I held in my gloved hands. Its heat warmed my fingers, and my first sip was full of earthy, spicy goodness. "It tastes like Christmas!"

"I know!" Tanya said. "Doesn't it?"

We wandered through the stands that were selling tiny wooden Christmas ornaments, beautifully hand-crafted snow globes, and all manner of tree baubles. The *Glühwein* went perfectly with the festive atmosphere.

"I wonder why we don't have *Glühwein* in Canada?' I mused.

"I know," Tanya said. "Of all places that need *Glühwein*..."

I wasn't keeping track of where we were within the market, so when we found ourselves back at the entrance, it was an unpleasant snap back to reality. Anton was waiting for us, eating a large, doughy pretzel studded with chunks of salt. Julie was talking to him.

When he glanced over and saw Tanya and me, his mouth curved into a grin.

"Ah! There you are!" Anton leaned over and kissed me on the cheek and then, after a moment's hesitation, did the same to Tanya. Neither Tanya nor I said anything.

"I got hungry while I was waiting." Anton sounded a bit flustered. He held up his pretzel. "I see that I'm falling behind you two though. I need a *Glühwein*."

The four of us turned back to the *Glühwein* stand, and Anton fell into step beside me. Tanya and Julie dropped back a few steps.

Far from acting amorous, Anton acted like a tour guide. He kept up a constant stream of chatter, pointing out the wooden toys that were locally handcrafted and the intricate cut paper ornaments. I began to question everything all over again.

When Anton was waiting in line to buy his *Glühwein*, Tanya pulled me aside. "Julie and I feel like third and fourth wheels. She thinks we should leave you two alone for a while. Is that what you want? It's clearly what Anton wants."

"No!" I said. Then I realized that this was going to happen at some point. It may as well happen now. It was just that...I was unsure of myself. I was unsure what I wanted to do. Damn Franck. Why did he have to put his yearnings for freedom in my head?

I took a deep breath. "Actually…it might be for the best…but don't stay away for long. Just go to the bathroom or something."

"Ok." Tanya patted my back. "Good luck."

She and Julie disappeared quickly into the crowd.

Anton turned to me with his fresh mug of *Glühwein*. Before I knew what was happening he leaned down and kissed me. His lips were warm and intriguing, and his cologne was spicy and pleasant. For a moment I was unsure, but…

I pushed away, breathing hard.

His lips hadn't felt right. His kiss didn't feel like home, the way Franck's had from the first.

"I can't believe you just did that," I said. I would have been interested in Anton, I thought, if there was no Franck. But there was a Franck. In Paris. Hopefully waiting for me.

"I'm so sorry." Anton's face was bright red under his pale hair. I've been wanting to do that ever since I caught sight of you on that bus. I never do things like that, but I thought—"

"You thought wrong," I said, gently.

"Look." He reached for my hand, but I pulled it away. "I like you. I'm sorry about the kiss. Truly. I think I misread…um…we can take this slow if you want. Will you forgive me? Could I maybe come and visit you in Paris?"

I felt a pulse of affection for him. He was trying to be romantic. In any case, he was being brave.

Things were clear now, at least. If I had been single, I would have been interested in Anton—decidedly interested. But his kiss showed me that I would chose Franck over him, and always would for as long as I had that choice.

"Visit me in Paris?" I said. "I'm not sure how my boyfriend would feel about that."

"Boyfriend? What boyfriend?" He brushed hair out of his eyes. "How have I not heard of this?"

"We just met two days ago," I reminded him.

"It feels like so much longer than that."

"It isn't."

"Is it serious with your boyfriend?"

"He's from France. We live together. We've been going out for three years now."

"That's serious." He stared down at his feet. "You're not planning on breaking up with him?"

"No." I owed him the complete truth. "I love him." My body felt hollow with vulnerability. It was scary to commit myself so fully to Franck while I was still unsure what he was going to choose for the end of that year.

"I feel like such an idiot," Anton said, still not looking up.

"Don't," I said. "I would have mentioned Franck to you before now, but there just never seemed like the right time, and I wasn't sure—"

"If I was falling in love with you?"

I was struck to silence by this declaration.

"Franck? Is that your boyfriend's name?"

"Yes."

"It's not a very French name," he muttered.

"That's a popular misconception," I said.

Anton threw up his hands. "A Frenchman...who can be expected to compete with that? Does he realize he's lucky to have you?"

I laughed, thinking about the strangeness of the year so far. "I believe so. Most of the time."

Anton raised his eyes to mine and watched me, perhaps waiting for a cue from me as to how to proceed.

"There must be so many girls who would love to go out with you," I said. "I mean, look at all the girls in your program here. I think Julie—"

Anton shook his head. "There was something different about you from the start."

Is it the fact that I am already in a relationship? I wondered if I gave out the signal that I wasn't looking for a boyfriend, which in turn make me irresistible to men. Given human nature, this was entirely within the realm of possibility.

"I've enjoyed your company and our conversations. As a friend," I clarified.

"Me too," he said. "But *not* just as a friend. I was hoping for more."

"I'm flattered, but—"

"Look who we found!" shouted Julie, bearing down on us with Tanya and three other people I recognized from the opera and the brewery tour.

"Yes...well...," Anton said. "I should be getting back home now. I have lots of homework."

"No!" one of the guys protested. "It's far too early." Tanya and Julie didn't add their voices to the general protest about Anton leaving.

Anton just blinked, shook his head, and strode off.

"What's wrong with him?" one his friends asked.

Tanya shrugged. "Who knows? Come on, let's go get pretzels."

I stood, watching Anton disappear. I felt terrible about leaving things like that. Tanya tugged my arm to make me come.

As we made our way toward the pretzel stand, Julie and Tanya and I walked a few steps behind the main group.

"You told him?" Julie said.

I nodded. "I think he was embarrassed." I was just about to mention his kiss when I thought the better of it. That wouldn't be doing Anton any favors. Or me. In fact, the fewer people that knew about that, the better.

chapter **thirty-eight**

The train ride from Vienna to Paris was long, although not quite long enough. As we neared the gare de l'Est, I worried about how it would be when I stepped down from the train and met Franck on the platform.

I thought a lot about Anton and Franck on the way back to Paris. Should I tell Franck about that kiss? I couldn't decide if honesty was always the best policy or whether it would just complicate things unnecessarily. Also, telling him might necessitate confessing that I had been tempted for a moment. Yet, did that even matter when, ultimately, I'd chosen Franck?

I had always believed when I was in high school that if I found the right person, everything would be incredibly simple. In a way, it was. Falling in love with Franck had been effortless and living with him felt natural…at least most of the time. Still, I was discovering that long-term relationships could be a whole different kind of complicated.

I wasn't sure anymore where Franck ended and I began, or vice versa. We had been together for three years and had been living together for most of that time. For the first time, I felt that our years of carefree coupledom could be numbered.

By the end of the year, we would have to truly commit or break up. No matter how long I wracked my brain, I couldn't see any middle ground.

The shining train pulled in with a chug and whistle. I searched for Franck's shape on the poorly lit platform.

It was a dark, damp night—almost eleven o'clock. I took my suitcase and stepped down the extendable stairs onto the platform. The yellow pools of light were misty, like something out of Dickens. The air against my face was cold, but softer than in Vienna, without the sharp edge of ice.

I peered down one end of the platform, then turned and peered down the other. I could make out some people milling around. Others walked briskly toward their destination. A few were waiting, as I was.

I turned and began walking slowly toward the station. Franck was going to come and meet me, wasn't he? That hollow vulnerability I felt when I turned down Anton surged back. By choosing Franck, I had left our future in his hands.

The image of what life would be like without Franck made me shiver. An ache started in my chest and radiated through every limb and joint.

Yes, I would be fine on my own, and perhaps even living that student life I imagined for myself when I was a teenager, but... *thank god I hadn't done anything stupid with Anton.*

I walked on a little farther, feeling increasingly forsaken as the platform emptied of passengers.

Just as tears began to prick my eyes, I heard my name. I turned around and saw Franck emerging from the shadows, striding down the platform toward me.

"I've been calling you!" he said as he drew closer. "It's so misty, it's hard to see anything."

I soaked in the familiar sight of him. He came closer and swept me in his arms. Our lips met, and my entire body eased, as though I had reached a safe harbor after sailing rough seas. He swung me around. The familiar scent of him, the overwhelming rightness of his body against mine, the way the nape of my neck tingled... I would have been such a fool to give this up. When the kiss finally broke after a long while, I immediately longed for more. More Franck. More commitment. More future together.

Then came the flash of fear. Franck still had to decide.

He took my duffel bag from my grasp and heaved it over his shoulder. He grunted at its surprising weight. I had bought a few things.

"What did you bring back from Vienna?" He laughed. "A cello?"

"Presents," I said, taking his other arm in mine and strolling down the platform to the stairs. "Some of them are even for you."

"The best one is here beside me," he said. He leaned over and drew me into another kiss.

I was back on another train soon after, but this time with Franck.

The TGV from the gare de Lyon in Paris swept past a frozen winter landscape of frost-covered fields. The breath of white Charolais cattle created puffs of condensation in the frigid air, and frost-topped stone villages whipped by on the way to Beaune.

It was wonderful to leave my courses and school work behind me. I would have to prepare for my medieval presentation in Professor Renier-Bernadotte's class, of course, but I would do that when we returned to Paris after Christmas.

Inside the train, Franck and I were cozy in our seats. He had bought us both *cafés au lait* and *pains au chocolat*, which were way better than train food had any right to be. I loved how good food is found everywhere in France. The French live by the belief that nothing, including travel, should warrant a compromise in gustative pleasure.

I can't believe we haven't been down to Burgundy since September," I said.

"I know. I guess we underestimated the time and cost it takes to get settled in Paris," Franck said. "TGV tickets aren't exactly cheap."

"Neither is our rent," I said.

The time had whipped by since those crazy first weeks in Paris. Half our year was finished already. Since returning from Vienna a few days before, I had listened hard for any indication from Franck, but he had not once hinted at his thoughts about the future. I hadn't mentioned Anton, yet debated whether I should or not on an hourly basis.

"It'll be nice to see everyone again," I said, redirecting my train of thought. "Is la Mémé already in Villers?"

My head was rested against Franck's shoulder, and I could feel rather than see him nod. "She got there yesterday."

"To see her favorite grandson." I chuckled.

Mémé of course insisted she didn't have any favorites among her numerous grandchildren and now great-grandchildren. When chided for doting on Franck, she would always say, "As my mother always said about the nine of us children, 'You all have your qualities; you all have your faults; and you all have something that makes you loveable.'"

Franck didn't bother denying that he was her favorite. He smiled. "She'd never admit it."

"Doesn't mean it's not true." I brushed a few croissant flakes from the front of his green wool sweater.

He caught my hand and turned it over. He laid a gentle kiss in the center of my palm, which resonated through every nerve in my body.

Oh God. I couldn't give this up. "Who's picking us up from the train?" I asked, my voice unsteady.

"Olivier, Martial, Isabelle, and Sandrine. Papa is still at work, so Maman was relieved when they offered. We'll see Papa at lunch."

The train we were on had left Paris early—seven o'clock—and was scheduled to get into Beaune shortly after nine in the morning. Before I knew it, we were pulling into the small *gare*.

We hopped off the train. The cold took my breath away. It wasn't quite as frigid as Vienna, but not far off.

"It's always several degrees colder here than in Paris," Franck said, observing me shiver. "I was always surprised by that when I came back during university."

Cheers and whoops were coming from the far end of the platform. There, in the distance, I could make out our four best friends in Burgundy—the ones who had been there the night Franck and I first met.

Olivier—small and wiry, with a beaked nose and kind brown eyes—walked fast in our direction. Martial—tall, blond, and game for anything—loped behind him. Isabelle—a *petite garçon-manqué*—and Sandrine—my pugnacious best friend during my year of high school in Beaune—followed. They all sucked on cigarettes, as usual. Smoke wreathed the grins on their faces.

"*Alors! Les Parisiens!*" Martial called out.

He bent down to give me *les bises*, and then kissed Franck as well. "Too *Parisien* to come and visit your Burgundian friends until now, *n'est-ce pas?*"

Martial and Oliver took all my bags. When I tried to carry one small bag, my attempts were met with a chorus of protests.

"That's it exactly," Franck said as he kissed his friends on both cheeks, including Martial and Olivier. "Laura and I are far too sophisticated now for anywhere outside of *la capitale*."

"Why didn't you guys come and visit us?" I demanded. "We issued you all an open invitation once we got our apartment."

"Paris." Martial gave a faux shudder. "*Quelle horreur.*"

I noticed that Olivier was looking even more jumpy than usual. "Stop your dawdling," he said to all of us. "I'm badly parked."

We turned to walk down the platform and then underneath the tunnel that lay below the tracks. Olivier and I pulled up front, and Franck and the rest of them seemed to be dawdling on purpose just to drive Olivier around the bend.

I walked faster so I could keep up with Olivier. "They're naughty. Don't mind them."

"I try not to." Olivier took a drag of his cigarette. "At least now that I have one other sane person here with me. How do you like Paris so far?"

"It was hard at first," I admitted. "Getting an apartment and figuring out the school stuff, plus coming to terms with how expensive everything is… honestly, it was way more complicated than we had anticipated."

"I could never live in Paris." Olivier shook his head. "My uncles live there, and I used to go visit them, but honestly, it scared me. All those crowds."

"I didn't know you had uncles in Paris."

"Actually, it's my uncle and his partner. I've just always called them my uncles. They seem to love it there. Of course, when you were gay twenty years ago, I think anywhere was better than the small villages of Burgundy."

"It's crowded," I said, thinking of telling Olivier about my thwarted attempt to go Christmas shopping on the rue de Rivoli, where it was so thick with people that often I was lifted by the mob so that my feet were no longer touching the ground.

I decided against it. "Paris is beautiful, though," I said. "Not to mention fascinating."

"You mean all the churches and museums and things?" Olivier said.

I nodded.

"I've never been interested in that stuff. Besides, they're not worth having to put up with *les Parisiens* all day long."

This was not the first time I'd heard our friends and family in Burgundy disparaging *les Parisiens*, just as I had often heard Parisians deride anyone from outside of Paris.

We arrived in the parking lot in front of the train station, and I immediately saw what Olivier meant about not being properly parked. Olivier's car was parked half on the sidewalk in front of the station, with its rear hanging out into the lot, not remotely fitting into anything that resembled a parking space.

"Nice work." I patted Olivier's thin shoulder.

"I'm not going to say I'm proud of it," Olivier said. "But thanks to Sandrine, we were late, and we didn't want you and Franck to think that we had abandoned you on the train platform."

"That's sweet," I said, and went up to the windshield of the car. "*Régarde!* You haven't even got a ticket yet."

"It's too cold for the parking police to be outdoors," Olivier said. "They're all in their staff room drinking espresso, I'm sure."

"La Goutte, more likely," said Martial. La Goutte is a type of cirrhosis-inducing, home-distilled alcohol Burgundians adore.

I looked at the car and then at my two duffel bags and Franck's duffle bags. Olivier was carrying one, and Franck and Martial were bringing up the rear carrying the rest. There were six of us, not to mention all that luggage. Olivier's car was not a large one by any stretch of the imagination.

"We're never going to fit." I announced the obvious.

"What do you have in here?" Martial dropped both duffle bags with a grunt. "Corpses?"

"Yes," I replied sweetly. "You're always so perceptive, Martial."

Olivier opened the trunk. "I told Sandrine and Isabelle not to come, that we wouldn't have room for them, but they wouldn't hear of it."

Just then, Sandrine and Isabelle arrived beside us. "Don't be ridiculous. Laura and Franck are our friends too," Sandrine said. "After all, I introduced the two of them. That gives me all the rights. For life."

"Then why didn't you exercise your right to drive?" asked Olivier.

"Because you're the only one of us who has a car," Sandrine said. "Don't ask useless questions."

"We'll just have to cozy up," said Isabelle, always the optimist.

It took several minutes and a good deal of giggles to jam us all into the car. Olivier and Sandrine got the front seats. In the back, I sat on Franck's lap, and Isabelle wedged in between one of my upended duffle bags, half-sitting on Martial, squishing him against the door.

My other duffel bag also stood up in the foot well, and I held on to it with both hands like a giant sausage.

"This is so comfortable," Martial observed as Olivier fiddled around with his radio. "Please take all the time you want, Monsieur le Chauffeur."

Olivier was obviously taking pleasure in his revenge. After several minutes of pointed dilly-dallying, he put the key in the ignition, and the familiar sounds of Téléphone, the French rock group that had been a long favorite with Franck and his friends, blasted out of the speakers.

"New speakers!" Olivier yelled over the song *"Cendrillon."* "What do you think?"

"Loud!" I yelled back. Normal talking was impossible, so we all began to sing along to the words we knew so well.

chapter **thirty-nine**

Olivier took crazy back alleys and roads through the vineyards for the best (according to him anyway) route out of Beaune.

He took the corners so fast I wondered if he didn't in fact think he was on a Formula 1 racetrack rather than the winding medieval streets of a French town. We were all thrown against one another, and the luggage became dislodged and toppled onto us. We joined in a chorus of recriminations to Olivier, but he ignored us and turned up the music.

Just when we crossed the road that led to the vineyards running up to the famed hill called le Corton (short for Corton-Charlemagne and so named because Charlemagne's favorite wines were grown there—yes, *that* Charlemagne), Olivier turned a sharp left.

"What—" I said. "I thought we were going to Villers-la-Faye."

"You have time for a *petit café* before lunch, *n'est-ce pas?*" Isabelle asked. "We're kidnapping you for a bit before dropping you off *chez* the Germains. We all know how it is with Christmas— our families want to see us non-stop." She groaned. "We need a decent visit first."

Olivier pulled into one of the parking spots in the center of the village of Savigny-les-Beaune. It was an absurdly scenic locale, beside the huge, turreted château and the village fountain, which was currently frozen solid. An ice sculptor could spend weeks working and not create something as beautiful as the layer upon layer of tiered icicles decorating the three fountains levels.

I knew exactly where we were headed, *bien sûr*. This café held precious memories of my first few months with Franck. It was where Olivier had gotten so drunk one night on calvados that Franck, Martial, and I had to drive him back up to Villers-la-Faye at five kilometers an hour with his head hanging out the car door so that he could throw up.

The sense of belonging I felt with this group warmed me from the inside out. When I stepped out of the car, I was welcomed by that particular smell of Burgundy—macerating grapes, the tang of limestone, and the odor of freshly turned soil.

The café owner behind the bar greeted us warmly. He shook hands with Franck, Martial, Olivier, and Franck, and they chatted for a while.

A few locals leaned against the counter, sipping chilled glasses of white wine. It was not what I would have chosen to warm myself up, but I knew in France, especially in Burgundy, it was common.

We took a table, and for the first several minutes, Isabelle, Sandrine, and I caught up on all the latest gossip.

Stéphanie and Sandrine had begun to train as nurses in Beaune, and Stéph was doing her first practicum in a geriatric home just behind the Beaune hospital.

"Do you like nursing so far?" I asked Sandrine.

She shrugged. "It's not bad. It's better than university. Neither Stéph nor I really knew what we were doing there. We'll be sure to get jobs with a nursing degree in our pockets. Stéph, though...Stéph's good at it. Way better than me."

"I guess I won't see her until tonight," I said.

"I think you'll see her for lunch," Sandrine said. "André usually drives her up and down to Villers with him.

For a second, I had forgotten about the two-and-a-bit-hour lunch break in France that would give Franck's father and sister ample time to make the ten-minute drive from Beaune to Villers and still enjoy a leisurely home-cooked lunch with us. My stomach began to rumble, especially when I contemplated that Mémé must have been baking and cooking in the kitchen since before dawn, as was her habit.

"So, what do you think of Paris?" Sandrine asked me.

"Now that we've got an apartment, it's much better," I said. "The beginning though…*dur, dur.*"

Sandrine took a drag of her cigarette. "I don't know how you do it. Moving all the time. Having to settle in new places, meet new people. I couldn't."

"Sure, you could," I said.

Sandrine shook her head. "Even if I could, I wouldn't want to. I would hate it."

"So would I," agreed Isabelle. "I wonder if it's easier for you because you're Canadian. Maybe it's in your genes."

A genetic explanation wasn't beyond the realm of possibility. All my grandparents had left their families in Scotland or England to immigrate to Canada. Maybe the vagabond trait could, in fact, be passed down in DNA.

"How would you explain Franck then?" I said.

"Mutation," quipped Isabelle.

Sandrine hooted with laughter. "That's exactly it—a Burgundian mutation. It's not our way to travel far. We like to stay near our vineyards. I mean, we might go and visit Paris—"

"Not me," chimed in Martial, who was listening in on our conversation. "I have no desire to visit, whatsoever. Burgundy has everything I need. Besides, this is the only place to find good wine."

"The only place in all of France?" I winked at him. "That's not biased at all."

"Not just in France, in all the *world*," he said.

"Like I said"—Sandrine nodded—"it's in the Burgundian genes to stay put."

I suspected she was right. All our friends there had been born in Burgundy and had grown up in Burgundy, and had no desire or plans to move away.

People often moved into their family homes and lived their entire lives in "their" tiny village such as Villers-la-Faye. Franck and his love of travel was the exception.

Yet...with Franck's recent desire to move back to France longer term...maybe his Burgundian genes were declaring themselves now that we were getting more serious and he was hitting the second half of his twenties? If that was true, what did it mean for me?

I glanced over at Franck, who was at the other end of the table. He threw his head back to laugh at something Martial had just said. He happened to look over at me just then. He gave me a private smile and wink before resuming his conversation.

I pushed down the fear that trickled down my spine and tried to concentrate instead on the comfort in finding myself among old friends.

We lost track of time, catching up in the warmth of the café, and the guys ordered a round of calvados for themselves, while Isabelle and Sandrine and I ordered more espressos.

Olivier checked his watch. "We need to get you back up to Villers or la Mémé will be furious with me. I can't have that now that I'm living across the street from your family."

"Could you have her angry with you if you still lived with your parents?" Franck downed the rest of his apple brandy from Normandy.

"Of course not," Olivier said, with a puff of the lips to indicate Franck's question was nonsensical. "Nobody could stand having Mémé mad at them."

Indeed, Mémé was one of a handful of matriarchs of Villers-la-Faye, even though for several years she had lived with Franck's aunt and uncle in a town about an hour away.

"Can any of us stand to have our grandmothers mad at us?" Martial asked.

"*Non*," Olivier and Franck answered in unison.

Elderly women in Burgundy are formidable and respected. Nobody wants to find themselves on the receiving end of one of their majestic tongue lashings.

We squashed ourselves into Olivier's car again and sped up through the frost-covered vines and wound around the steep, narrow roads of the village of Pernand-Vergelesses. It looked even more like a painting than usual, with plumes of smoke coming out of the frosty stone chimneys.

We crossed Magny-les-Villers and then went down the dip toward Villers and past the chapel with the Virgin Mary statue at the bottom of the dip.

We passed Sandrine's family's wine domaine at the entrance to the village.

"You can drop me off here," Sandrine said. "My lunch is probably ready, and my grandmother will be there. I'll catch it from *her* if I'm late."

Olivier screeched to a halt and then, after Sandrine was jettisoned, drove on past the mayor's office and stopped in front of the wooden gate to Franck's house.

"Where are you going to eat lunch?" Franck asked our three remaining friends. "Mémé's cooking, so I know there's enough for everyone."

Mémé always said the happiest years of her life were working as the cook at the offices of Barton & Guestier, the reputed wine house. The people working there had serious appetites and appreciated her amazing talents, as well as tucked away prodigious amounts of her food. Now, decades later, she still cooked and baked enough for a battalion.

Olivier shook his head with regret. "I've already committed myself to my parents' house for lunch. I told my mom I'm bringing Martial and Isabelle with me."

"*Paupiettes de veau*," Martial commented, licking his lips. Like la Mémé, Olivier's mother was a prodigious cook.

"Next time," Franck said.

We all agreed to meet up the next day, and Olivier left us in front of the gate with our luggage as he sped off with a honk.

chapter **forty**

Franck rang the doorbell mounted to the stone pillar beside the gate.

Within a matter of seconds, I heard the kitchen door open and Mémé's shouts. "*Les voilà!*"

André opened the gate from the other side. He looked at us, then down at the luggage at our feet. "*Mon Dieu*," he murmured.

Mémé was doing a little jig. "*Ah! Nos Parisiens!*" Our Parisians! She launched herself at Franck and enthusiastically gave him *les bises* and a long hug. I was next.

After we had all been thoroughly kissed, André ushered us (each carrying a bag) and Franck (carrying two) inside. "Come in. Come in. *Il fait froid.*"

Franck's little brother, Emmanuel-Marie—his blond, pudding-bowl hair shining above his round brown eyes—smiled shyly when we entered the kitchen.

We had tried to schedule Franck's parents and Emmanuel-Marie for a visit *chez nous* in Paris, but Emmanuel-Marie kept coming down with sore throats and stomach flus just before their planned departures, so it never happened.

"Salut, Emmanuel-Marie!" I leaned down to give him a kiss. *"Alors, le père Noël va arriver bientôt?"* So, is Santa Claus arriving soon?

He nodded solemnly.

André divested us of our coats, and Michèle, still wearing a kitchen apron and with a ladle in her hand, hurried us into the living room, where the table was set and the room was full of Christmas decorations.

Actually, "full" was a vast understatement. The room was jammed with twinkly lights and baubles and shiny cut-outs of stars and hearts and Christmas trees. The mantle of Michèle's buffet was blanketed with fake snow and transformed into a tiny village, complete with an electric train and miniature pine trees. I didn't know where to look first.

"Wow," I said.

"I love decorating for Christmas," Michèle said, somewhat unnecessarily. "I've been collecting tiny houses for ten years now. Sit! Sit! You must be tired after taking the train so early this morning."

Stéphanie blew into the living room just as we were munching on Mémé's light-as-air *gougères* and sipping on kir royale.

"Sorry," she said. "I was just upstairs looking up a procedure I have to perform this afternoon in my textbook." She shook her glossy black hair and rushed over to give us both a kiss.

We sat back down, and once she had her glass of kir firmly in hand, I asked, "So, *l'infirmière*...how do you like being a nurse?"

"I'm not officially a nurse yet," she said. "I'm a nurse-in-training."

"Okay then, how do you like being a student nurse?"

"More than I thought I would, much to my surprise."

"Sandrine says you're good," I said. "That you're a natural."

"You know, I think I might be," Stéphanie agreed. "Things that seem to be hard for the others—taking blood, putting in IVs... It just doesn't seem hard. I enjoy talking with the patients too."

"I think you'll be an amazing nurse," I said to Stéph. I was blessed with excellent health so I didn't need to see nurses often, but if I did, I would want an energetic, positive one like Stéph.

"*Merci, ma Laura,*" Stéph said.

André placed a plate of escargot cooked in garlic, butter, and parsley and served with a salad tossed with a raspberry vinaigrette (homemade, *bien sûr*) in front of me.

"This looks scrumptious," I said. I popped a forkful of escargot with some salad into my mouth. The richness of the warm escargot was offset by the acidity of the raspberry vinaigrette. The combination was magic.

"It's delicious," I said and happily speared more with my fork. André served a mystery red that he'd found in a far corner of his cellar—his cellar seemed to have endless far corners. There is nothing that tastes like Burgundy to me more than pinot noir and escargots. I had that snug sensation of returning home, or at least to one of my homes, after a long time away.

"I was thinking I'll come and visit you in Paris in January or February." Stéph tore off the end of the baguette on the middle of the table. She always somehow managed to get her favorite piece—the crusty crouton—before anyone else. I preferred the middle part of the baguette, so, unlike the rest of the Germains, I didn't protest.

"That would be so fun," I said. "What do you want to do when you come?"

"Laura's found all the best pastry shops in the neighborhood," Franck said.

"Priorities, you know." I popped a garlic butter, parsley-infused escargot into my mouth.

Since we had climbed on the train that morning in Paris, it felt as if Franck and I had slipped back in time. I knew who we were in Villers-la-Faye, both individually and as a couple. Everybody else did too. There was a timelessness to us in Burgundy. Franck and Laura were in love—just as sure as the bare vineyards in December would sprout pale green leaves in the spring.

Things in Burgundy stayed reassuringly the same. All our friends were still there and, except for Stéphanie and Sandrine, doing the same thing for work. Michèle, Mémé, André and

Emmanuel-Marie were there. It felt cozy, especially eating a delicious lunch and watching flakes of snow falling outside the window.

Next, Mémé proudly brought her main dish out of the kitchen: roasted lamb with *herbes de Provence* and olive oil and a pot of home-seasoned and simmered white flageolet beans with an amazing combination of herbs, and, I suspected, a generous quantity of white wine in the sauce.

André served a robust Vosne-Romanée, which made my taste buds almost explode with its rich, earthy flavors.

The lamb melted in my mouth. Mémé explained this was because she had marinated it for two days (again, involving a lot of wine) and cooked it long and slowly in the oven.

"The best talent a cook can possess is patience," she said.

After some thought, she added, "The same goes for life, I suppose. Patience is truly the most useful and undervalued quality a person can possess."

Did I just need to wait for Franck to make up his mind? Patience had never been one of my qualities, but then again Mémé's wisdom was not to be taken lightly.

"What I want to see in Paris is the Barnes Exhibit at the musée d'Orsay," Michèle said. "How many times have you been, Laura?"

Shame burned up my neck. The Barnes Exhibit was a once-in-a-lifetime opportunity to see one of the finest, privately-held collections of Impressionist painters.

"We actually haven't been yet," I said. "You see—"

"Haven't been?" Michèle demanded. "But how can that be? The Renoirs! The Cézannes! The Monets! The Matisses, Laura... *les Matisses*...these painting may never be shown publicly after this. How could you not be spending time there *every* day?"

Franck's mom was not one to let stuff go.

"We'll go," Franck said to her.

"But when?" Michèle said. "The exhibit ends on January second!"

"When we go back to Paris," Franck said.

"But there's no time to properly—"

"Michèle," André said gently, "I'm sure they will go and spend many, many hours there. We don't want to ruin everyone's digestion of this wonderful meal."

"You see?" Mémé said. "Patience. André has it."

"Michèle got up from the table in a huff, but when she returned with the glorious cheese platter, she seemed determined to ignore her mother."

"We'll go," Franck said when Michèle sat back down again. "Promise, Maman."

Michèle shrugged. "It's nothing to me." She turned to me and said brightly, "Laura, you must try this Soumaintrain. It's divine."

The round of Soumaintrain cheese– the neglected big brother to its more famous sibling, Époisses—was perfection. It was splendidly ripe, with creaminess and pungency completely balanced.

After the cheese course, Mémé got up to get us dessert. "It's something I made just for you, Laura!" she said and disappeared into the kitchen. "A surprise!"

André checked his watch. "We have to go." He beckoned Stéph to get up. "Things are different now that you're part of the working class." He beckoned Stéph to come.

"Ugh," Stéph said. "The hours are one of the only things I don't like. Being a student had so much more flexibility. We're going to miss Mémé's dessert."

"Student life has flexibility, *peut-être*, but no future when you skip all of your classes and play the guitar with a bunch of fellow deadbeats in your dorm room twenty-four hours a day," Michèle added with asperity.

Stéph just laughed. "I had fun though."

"We'll save you some dessert," I promised.

"I know what it is," Stéph said. "Mémé was making it when we left this morning. I doubt there'll be any left."

I heard them say *au revoir* to Mémé in the kitchen and calm her protests about missing dessert and moving too quickly on a full stomach.

Mémé came back into the dining room with a glass bowl of chocolate mousse in her hands and an old biscuit tin from Brittany balanced on top. She tutted. "I can't believe they have to leave already. I made you chocolate mousse, Laura! I'm sure you haven't had any in Paris!"

Franck and I exchanged tiny nods. We would stay quiet about our numerous forays to Batifol.

After Mémé had served us each a generous bowl of chocolate mousse adorned with two tuiles biscuits that she had whipped up at that afternoon, Michèle went over to the window and looked out, her face tight with worry. "It's getting colder," she said without turning around. "There could be black ice forming on the roads. I hope André drives carefully. I hate them driving in this kind of weather."

Mémé went over and stood behind her daughter and rested her hands on her shoulders. "They'll be fine. André always drives carefully," she said. "You'll see. They'll be here to enjoy the quiche I'm going to finish this afternoon." The speed with which they could go from fighting to comforting each other stunned me as usual.

The chocolate mousse was delicious, as expected. The tuiles were light as air and gave away with a faint crunch under my teeth.

I got up and began to clear the dishes, but Mémé shooed me away with a dishtowel. "No, Laura. No dishes for you. You've been working so hard at school. You must rest."

I laughed. "I've been working my brain, not my body."

Actually, I walked everywhere in Paris, whereas in Montreal, it was so cold that I generally took the Metro for most of the school year. Paris was perfect for walking.

We sat at the table and tried to coax Michèle away from her post at the window, until Mémé finally brought in some coffee in a china coffee pot and a basket of praline Christmas chocolates.

We enjoyed these and managed to distract Michèle for a good three-quarters of an hour with talk of the museums we *had* been to in Paris—the Louvre, the National Museum of the Middle Ages, the Rodin museum...

When we had finished our third espresso cup of coffee, Mémé

waved us upstairs with her dishtowel. "Go upstairs and unpack. André already took your bags up there."

"Are you sure I can't rinse these cups?" I said, lifting mine up.

Franck reached out and steered me out of the dining room, through the kitchen, and toward the staircase. I had forgotten… nobody questioned Mémé's orders.

"I think a little nap is in order," he said.

I could hear Mémé laughing at something as we made our way up to the top of the house, where Franck's bedroom was a small little hideaway under the huge oak beams.

"We're going to nap?" I asked, flopping on the bed. I watched the snow fall gently on the Velux above the bed. "After three espressos, I'm not exactly tired."

"Me neither." Franck just laughed and lay down beside me. "We can just lay here and watch the snow fall."

"Or?"

"Or…"

chapter **forty-one**

When we'd reached the downstairs again, Franck and I bundled up and went for a walk in the vineyards. Big, fluffy flakes floated down on our heads. The snow was piling up, much to Michèle's chagrin, but it transformed the bare landscape of the sleeping vines into a land of velvety white.

The winemakers couldn't work their vines in the snow, of course, so no noises disrupted the calm, until the church bells in both Villers-la-Faye and Chaux rang four o'clock through the white, mushroom-like rows.

On our return, we joined Michèle and Mémé for a big bowl of afternoon *tisane*, or "herbal tea."

Emmanuel-Marie hopped around us. "Hurry up. Drink that!" he ordered us. "You have to go get ready, or we'll be late for my pageant."

He'd informed me at lunch that his school Christmas pageant was that night and that he had been granted the grand honor of playing one of the three kings.

"I need to change into my costume right now!" He pulled at Michèle's sleeve.

"No. We're not ready to leave yet. You'll just get it dirty," Michèle said.

"I won't!"

"You will," Mémé said. "You're not the first grandson I've had, you know. Children just can't help but get dirty."

"I won't! I want to put on my costume!" Emmanuel-Marie stamped the floor.

"We'll have none of that behavior!" Mémé reprimanded, to which Michèle, who, up until then had been equally annoyed at her son, sent her mother a blazing look.

"Yes, let's go put on your lovely costume right this instant," she said to Emmanuel-Marie, sending an arched look to Mémé. "Of course, you want to wear it. *C'est normal.*"

Franck grabbed my arm and hauled me up from the table where I was sitting, riveted by the exchange.

"Let's go get ready," he said, and had me up the stairs again in no time.

It took us less than five minutes to change into still warm but slightly dressier clothes. When I made a motion to go back downstairs, Franck pulled me back onto the bed.

"You in a hurry?" he asked.

"No. I just thought…you know…to be polite."

"When Mémé and my mom start arguing over Emmanuel-Marie, my advice is to steer clear for a while."

"Oh."

"Emmanuel-Marie stirs things up between the two of them."

"That must be upsetting for him," I said.

"Don't delude yourself. The little *charogne* knows exactly what he's doing."

When we got downstairs, Michèle came toward us, wringing her hands but no longer about Mémé. "André and Stéph aren't back yet. They should have been back twenty minutes ago. I hope they just stayed in Beaune and didn't try to drive. There is no way they could have made it up the road in André's car."

Franck rubbed her shoulder. "Maman, I'm sure they're fine.

Bien sûr, it's taking them longer. You know how cautious Papa is behind the wheel."

Emmanuel-Marie came into the kitchen dressed in a decorated white sheet with a hole cut in it where he could stick his head through. There were flourishes of gold glitter all over him, and he had used one of Michèle's gold belts—which looked like it dated back to the 1970s—to cinch the sheet around his middle.

In his hand, he clutched a homemade gold crown made with cardboard and colored tinfoil. Under his arm, there was yet another *biscuits au beurre* tin box from Brittany, but this one had gold stars glued over an illustration of a fisherman.

"You look fantastic," I told him.

"Franck?" Emmanuel-Marie bestowed me a patient smile and tugged at Franck's jeans. "How do I look?"

Franck peered down at him. "Kingly," he pronounced.

"Are they back?" Emmanuel-Marie squeezed Michèle's leg to divert her attention from the window. "I can't be late! There can't be only two kings!"

"This reminds me of when you danced as a swan in Swan Lake." Mémé patted Franck's shoulder. "Who knew you had such a talent for ballet?"

"You danced as a swan?" I said.

"Oh yes," Mémé answered for him.

"I need to hear more about this," I said, staring at my boyfriend, trying to imagine him in a leotard and tights.

"Not now," Franck said, gesturing toward his mother. "Later."

"Count on it," I said.

"And you can stop grinning like that," Franck added.

"Sorry. That would be impossible. It's just that I have this image in my head now—"

Emmanuel-Marie broke in. "Doesn't anyone care that I'm going to be late?"

"You won't be late." Franck sat down on a kitchen chair and patted his knee. Emmanuel-Marie hopped up and set his biscuit box carefully beside him on the table. "Now, do you have any lines?"

Emmanuel-Marie shook his head. "But it's still an important part."

Franck nodded solemnly. "I know. How can there be a manger scene without the three kings there to admire Baby Jesus?"

"There can't. And it must be *three* kings, not two."

"That goes without saying."

My heart clenched when I saw Franck with Emmanuel-Marie on his knee. He always talked to children as though they were just miniature adults. I wanted Franck to talk in the same way to our children and to tell them about the time he had danced as a swan in the village production of Swan Lake—our children who didn't exist yet and might or might not ever exist. I hoped they would, though. This was a shocking thought—a frightening thought actually—as, up until that point, I had never much considered children.

Michèle interrupted my daydreaming when she turned away from the window with tears running down her face. "Something has happened! I just know it has!"

Franck motioned at me to take over the task of distracting Emmanuel-Marie. I sat down in a chair and drew him toward me so that his back would be to his mother.

I wondered at Michèle showing her anxiety so openly in front of her young son. I know there were times when my own mother worried about things—about my father being hours late from a winter fishing expedition on the ocean or about my little sister who had gone temporarily missing in a department store—but she never showed us. She hid it like a martyr and only confessed to how she was truly feeling years later.

Michèle, and indeed most of the other French mothers I knew, didn't hide much from their children, whether it be nudity, joy, worry, or sadness.

"Can you tell me what the kings carry in their boxes?" I asked Emmanuel-Marie and opened his box to find it empty.

To solve this, we decided to go around the house and find some treasures to fill it—some used wine corks, a sprig of dried rosemary, four bay leaves, and a piece of Christmas tinsel were some of our finds.

I kept him busy treasure hunting upstairs until we heard a door opening and shutting, then a burst of shouts and crying from the kitchen.

We descended the stairs slowly, to find André and Stéphanie, red faced from the cold and snow, peeling off their layers of clothes.

Michèle had retired to a kitchen chair to weep in relief.

Franck turned to me. "Papa's car got stuck. They had to wait for someone to drive past in a tractor to help them dislodge themselves from the snowbank."

"I don't think we should go to the pageant," André said, catching sight of his royal son. "It's too dangerous."

"I agree," said Mémé. "It's just not worth the risk."

"*Quoi?*" Emmanuel-Marie said and burst into tears. "*Noooooooooooon!*"

Michèle stood, her tears miraculously gone. "We must go. Imagine how disappointed Emmanuel-Marie would be if he cannot play the king."

What? Hadn't she just been crying because the roads were so treacherous?

"Michèle"—André paused before he peeled off his sweater—"I'm almost positive the pageant will be canceled. They cannot possibly expect people to drive in this weather. There is so much snow I can barely see the roads anymore."

"We're going." Michèle took her young son's hand, and they went into the first cellar and then emerged seconds later wearing jackets, scarves, mitts, and boots.

There were six of us packed into a car made for four passengers. André crept along, but despite his caution on the way out of Villers-la-Faye, the car slipped and slid a meter to the right before he managed to get control of the steering again.

"We should turn around," Mémé said, who was terrorized by driving in a car at the best of times. "It is idiotic to be out driving in this."

Emmanuel-Marie wailed. *"Non!* We've been practicing and practicing. I'm a *Roi mage!"*

I inspected his costume. He looked more like a cross between an angel and a sparkly ghost, but he was undeniably cute, not to mention stubborn.

"But the roads are *affreux,"* Mémé protested.

"I'm driving slowly," André said, his face grim in the rearview mirror. "We'll get there." The car slid again. "I hope."

"But what if it starts to snow really hard while we're inside?" Mémé asked. "Or the temperature drops again?"

"It won't!" Emmanuel-Marie declared with certainty.

As for me, from the moment I crawled onto Franck's lap in the back seat, I decided to surrender to the situation and enjoyed being comfortably tucked up with his strong arms around me. I could stay there for hours, I figured, even if we did end up in a ditch.

The drive took three times the usual ten minutes, but we finally pulled into the *salle des f*êtes in the nearby village of Échevronne. I noticed that there were more vineyard tractors parked in the lot than actual cars. I guessed they were the vehicle of choice in that weather.

Michèle hurried Emmanuel-Marie inside to congregate with his fellow kings, Baby Jesus, Mary, Joseph, and the rest of the manger set.

The cold outside the cozy confines of the car stole my breath. Franck and I helped Mémé out of the front seat and made sure she didn't fall on the slippery ice on the way into the building. André went ahead to find seats.

As soon as we opened the door to *la salle des fêtes*, the noise and heat drew us in. André waved us over to a row of seven seats near the back of the room. Far from being canceled, the concert was very well attended, and it seemed all the parents, students, and families had soldiered their way here through the storm outside—although the use of their winemaking vehicles was a bit of a cheat, I felt.

"It's not the best, but they're the only seats left together," André said.

"They'll be fine," I said, helping Franck sit la Mémé down and wrapping her up with the requisite number of scarves and shawls and blankets so she didn't get cold. She was ever suspicious of possible drafts, or as she called them, "*les courants d'air.*" Since she turned seventy, she had said that the only times she felt a comfortable temperature were on the stifling summer days when the thermostat flirted with forty degrees Celsius and everyone else was melting.

The concert was adorable. There were the traditional songs of Noël, like "*Petit Papa Noël,*" "*Vive le vent,*" and "*Douce nuit.*" Emmanuel-Marie made an angelic king, standing without cracking a smile, clutching on to his bejeweled biscuit box.

When it was over, the crowd began to talk again. Within seconds, the noise exploded into cacophony.

Emmanuel-Marie rushed up to Franck first, his face flushed with pride. He slipped his little hand into Franck's and insisted that Franck come with him to be introduced to the other kings and Baby Jesus (a plastic doll, from the glimpses I caught during the *spectacle*).

After much chatting and giving the *bises* to people I had just met, we ventured back out into the blizzard. The weather created a definite sense of camaraderie.

Now, no vestiges of a road were left. The snow drove hard against our exposed skin. André's face had a grim set, and Michèle was doing a lot of hand-wringing and supplicating to God, even though at lunch I had heard her declare herself an atheist to her mother. I think only Emmanuel-Marie and I were unconcerned. I couldn't explain why, but I always felt safe in Burgundy.

The drive was even more treacherous than on the way there, but I stayed curled up on Franck's lap, enjoying the roller-coaster experience.

There was much gasping from Mémé and directions being issued forcefully by Michèle, all of which was met with stony silence from André.

We finally made it back to Villers-la-Faye, and Mémé whipped up some homemade quiches and a beautiful bowl of *salade frisée* with a divine, shallot-heavy vinaigrette.

After that, we had some cheese and Seville oranges, and just when I thought the meal was done, Michèle announced she had a surprise for us. She went back into the kitchen and came out with a *galette des rois*—the flaky pastry-and-marzipan concoction traditionally served after Christmas in honor of the Epiphany.

"A *galette*?" Mémé demanded, before I even had the chance to ooooh and ahhhh over one of my favorite French desserts. "But it's too early. It's not even Christmas yet."

"Isn't it wonderful?" Michèle said. "The *boulangerie* in Comblanchien is now selling them before Christmas to break from that old tradition."

"But that's *terrible!*" Mémé gasped. "What is this world coming to? We cannot afford to lose any more traditions. Burgundy *is* tradition. They should arrest that profiteering *boulanger* as well as any people who would even think of buying a *galette* before Epiphany." With this, she threw down her napkin and went upstairs, slamming the staircase door behind her.

I flicked my gaze toward Michèle, worried about what I was going to see. Of course, I hated to see anyone upset, but what worried me the most was having the *galette* disappear off the table.

Michèle, however, wore a Cheshire Cat expression. "I knew that would annoy her. Anyway, more for us rebels."

With that, we proceeded to eat the entire *galette*, and Michèle, fittingly, found the *fève* inside and was crowned queen.

chapter **forty-two**

We headed back to Paris two days after Christmas.

Our plan was to be in Paris for four days and then to grab a cheap charter flight out of Orly, where we were to meet up with a bunch of friends from Victoria who were all in Edinburgh to celebrate Hogmanay.

We had been concocting that plan for months. Franck had gone to Morocco on his own, and I had gone to Vienna on my own. The idea of the two of us taking a wee trip together was thrilling.

The minute we walked into our apartment after the quick Metro ride from the Gare de Lyon, the phone rang.

Franck picked up. *"Allô?"*

He exchanged warm seasonal wishes with whoever was on the line and kept talking while I went into the bedroom and started unpacking my bag. Franck burst into the bedroom.

"Stop what you're doing," he commanded.

I froze while hanging up a sweater in the armoire. "Why?"

"We need to drop everything and put on fancy clothes."

"Franck, we don't even *own* fancy clothes." I finished hanging my sweater.

"Still, we have to figure out something passable to wear."

"Wear to where?"

"That was Jacinthe on the phone. She just invited us to a Moët & Chandon soirée that's being held at the musée d'Orsay so that the upper crust of Paris can admire the Barnes Exhibit without the plebeians underfoot."

"And we're invited?" I clarified. "We're precisely those plebeians they don't want underfoot."

"I know we are, but yes, we're invited"

"Seriously?"

"Seriously."

I sneezed. I seemed to have caught a cold in Burgundy, despite my prodigious cassis consumption, which Mémé swore cured all ills. "I need to find something black." I started tearing through the armoire.

"They're coming to pick us up in ten minutes," Franck said. "Jacinthe kept trying to reach us in Burgundy, but she must have had the wrong number for my parents' house."

I didn't speak again—no time to—until I had assembled a rather hodgepodge outfit of black gypsy pants, black boots, and a black silk top. It was hardly high fashion, but it would have to do. I pulled my hair back into a tight, high ponytail and slapped on a coat of vivid red lipstick and big hoop earrings.

It wasn't until we were at the front door of the apartment that I paid attention to the fact that Franck had changed into a pair of black jeans, a white dress shirt, and a beige sports-jacket. Extremely handsome.

"You look fantastic," he said. "But then, you always look fantastic."

I gave him a kiss. "Same for you."

We took the stairs instead of the elevator. This was not the evening to get stuck.

Nathanael, Jacinthe, Franck, and I exchanged *les bises* when we climbed in the back seat of their tiny car. It was awkward with the car seats between us, but we managed. We whipped along the quai de la Seine. The Seine was black and glittering with the golden light of the street lamps and lit buildings.

"I've been trying to reach you for days!" Jacinthe turned around in her seat, while Nathanael drove as if he was completing a Formula 1 circuit. "I thought you might like to take the opportunity of seeing the Barnes Exhibit…but you've probably already been, right?"

Franck's eyes met with mine. "Somehow we made a gross oversight and haven't seen it yet," he said. "My mother gave us a thorough reprimand for that."

"Maybe we'll be able to meet her eyes once more after tonight," I added. "We have you to thank for that."

Jacinthe laughed. "It'll be a bunch of skinny, snotty people—I guarantee that. However, nothing prevents you from just drinking endless flutes of Champagne and admiring the Impressionist paintings. You don't have to talk to anyone. In fact, I wouldn't recommend it. Most of these people truly have nothing interesting to say."

"There will probably be some movie stars and politicians," Nathanael warned.

"Don't worry," I said. "I'm Canadian. I would never dream of accosting someone I don't know, no matter how famous they are. Besides, I doubt I would recognize most of them anyway."

I remembered with a spark of satisfaction how I had been completely unaware of Alexandrine's father when Jacinthe introduced us.

"In Canada," Franck said, "I learned, much to my surprise, that our movie stars in France are not well known outside of our hexagon."

"I don't believe it," Jacinthe said. "What about Thierry Lhermitte?"

"Nope," I said.

"Jean Rochefort?"

"*Non plus.*"

"Gérard Depardieu."

"Everyone knows Gérard Depardieu," I admitted.

"It's the nose," Franck said.

Just then, we pulled up in front of the entrance of the musée d'Orsay, which I decided when I visited it on my first trip to Paris three years previously was the most stunning museum in the world. The lights blazed, and there were ushers or some sort of uniformed person on every step and an actual red carpet leading to the main door.

"Hop out here, and I'll go and park the car," Nathanael said.

Following Jacinthe's lead, we swept up the red carpet and into the museum. The entrance was roped off, and to one side, a mob of paparazzi snapped photos. Their cameras were still going off when we walked past. Was their strategy to take constant photos in hopes of catching someone famous?

As we divested our coats, I chuckled at the idea of the photographers of *Paris Match* taking pictures of me in my quickly salvaged black outfit.

Jacinthe divested herself of her silk coat with a stylish, upturned collar at the coat check. The paparazzi might, on the other hand, hang on to their photo of her. She was wearing a short, electric blue dress and high heels. She managed to be classy but cutting-edge at the same time.

We had hardly taken two steps away from the coat check when we were offered Champagne. The uniformed waiter holding the silver tray bowed his head. "Dom Pérignon, Cuvée 1969."

"This is a wonderful vintage," Jacinthe said, handing Franck and me flutes and then taking one for herself. "They don't declare a Champagne vintage every year, you know. It's only declared in the years when the three grape varieties used to make most Champagne—Chardonnay, pinot noir, and pinot meunier—were all exceptional."

"So, if you're drinking any vintage of Dom Pérignon, you know it's good?" Franck asked.

I took a sip. The delicate effervescence and the perfect balance of acidity and sweetness made me feel as though I was drinking some sort of fairy beverage made with a heavy dose of sorcery.

"Not good," I corrected Franck. "Transcendent."

"Should we wait here for Nathanael?" Franck asked.

"*Non*," Jacinthe said. "He'll find us."

We wandered around the main part of the museum, which was as stunning as always with its white marble statues and the huge train station clock overhead. The stream of people eventually led to the Barnes Exhibit proper. We split up at this point, as we all wanted to look at the various Impressionist treasures at our own pace. Contemplating paintings, I have always felt, is ideally a solitary activity.

I spent time with *The Postman* by Van Gogh, who had made a swirling masterpiece of the stern man's beard. Then I moved on to Picasso's pre-abstract *Young Woman Holding a Cigarette* and wondered what this woman had been thinking when he painted her. Had they been lovers? Had she been to Paris?

I was standing, captivated by a breathtaking Renoir painting of a family in Normandy collecting mussels, when I heard a familiar acid voice behind me.

"I don't like this one at all." I turned and there was Alexandrine, wearing her habitual scowl. "It's so cliché. It would be a perfect fit on a generic greeting card. Look at the faces of his subjects. No mystery. Boring."

"Bonjour, Alexandrine," I said. She was wearing a bizarre puffy dress of pumpkin orange and deep purple and had stuck some sort of feathered hairpiece monstrosity in her shellacked chignon. Was she going for the Halloween peacock look? She gave me a lingering once over. "This is haute couture," she said, waving her hand down her ensemble.

"Really? I wouldn't have known."

"No...I suppose you wouldn't."

I turned back to the painting, hoping she would lose interest and disappear. Why did she even bother coming over? Couldn't we just agree to have nothing to do with one another?

Unfortunately, Alexandrine was made of intractable stuff. "I suppose you like this thing?" she said, dismissing one of Renoir's *chefs d'oeuvre* with a flick of her finger.

"I've fallen in love with it. It is so soft and evocative. When I look at it, I can smell the ocean air."

"That doesn't surprise me. So many people like *easy* things."

"Or *beautiful* things," I said.

Out of the corner of my eye, I saw Momo chatting with Caroline then making his way toward us. He looked extremely dapper in a gray suit and lilac shirt.

"Ah...admiring this one?" he said after giving us both *les bises*. "I believe it's perhaps my favorite. There's something about it that's so warm and comforting."

Alexandrine snorted. "You *would* say that. Who wants comfort? Who wants warmth?"'

"Hopefully not your future boyfriend," Momo said. I burst out laughing and Alexandrine gave us a dirty look, turned on her heel, and strutted off—her demented dress rustling like a maraca.

"Uh-oh," Momo said. "Now she'll be mad at me for months."

"Worth it," I said. "Honestly, I don't know how any of you can stand having her around."

"She serves fantastic dinners," Momo said. "And she knows all the best gossip."

"Still. She's a bitch."

"I suppose she adds a needed note of astringency to our lives." Momo shrugged.

"I can't believe she bad-mouthed this painting," I said, turning back to it. "I mean, look at it...." We both did. The hair on my forearms prickled. It was so surreal to be standing in front of one of Renoir's paintings that had been largely unknown for the many years it had been in Dr. Barnes' private collection. I could literally reach out and touch it. "It's divine."

"It is," Momo agreed, and he squeezed my arm to mark the shared moment. He clinked the side of my now-empty Champagne flute with his. "Looks like you need more Champagne," he said. "I'll be back. I'll find you."

He did in fact find me in front of a different painting—a Modigliani entitled *Jeanne Hébuterne*. I read on the description that this was a fine example of how Modigliani's style of

Impressionistic distortion achieved an entirely new and completely unique artistic harmony. Besides, I just liked it.

Momo returned and handed me a fresh flute. "Here you go. This is a pre-1965 vintage, but that's all I know."

He admired the painting for a while. "So, how's your love life?" he asked.

"Complicated. You?"

"Actually, I've met someone new. He's younger. First, I thought it was just a fling, but then he kept wanting to spend time together. I'm not sure exactly where it's going but—"

"That's wonderful. Who wouldn't want to spend time with you?"

"Do you and Franck still enjoy spending time together?"

"Definitely," I said. "But the thing is…"

"What's the thing? I must know the thing."

I sighed. "It's hard to explain—"

"Try." He gazed at me with puppy dog eyes. *"Pour moi."*

I sighed and looked to Modigliani's Jeanne for assistance. "It's just…I often feel as though I don't know where we're going. We fell head over heels in love and, as far as I can tell, we're still head over heels in love…."

"Laura, I'm not seeing a problem yet."

"Just wait." I held up my hand. "Franck isn't certain he wants to come back with me to Canada at the end of this year, and I don't think I could give up my degree to stay here. I don't think either of us wants to do the long-distance thing again. I don't know—are we too young to settle down? Do we owe it to our future selves to be single when we're young so we can figure out who we are and what we want from life?"

Momo drew his eyebrows together. "I thought you said you two were head over heels in love with each other."

"We are. It's just complicated, like I said."

Momo made an extremely Gallic sound of disgust. "No, it's not."

"What?" I said.

He looked exasperated with me. It was an expression I would have expected from Alexandrine, but not from him. "It's not at all complicated, Laura. If you are head over heels in love, why in the world would you throw that away? Tell Franck exactly how you feel. Beg him to go back to Montreal with you. Do you truly believe love is easy to find? I can tell you right now, it's not."

I thought of Anton. *Was* love that hard to find? I didn't know, because I had met Franck when I was eighteen. I had never had the chance to find that out for myself. "I guess that's one way of looking at it," I said.

"That's not 'one way of looking at it,'" Momo corrected me with the manner of a stern professor. "It's the only way. Do you think I put myself in a situation where my entire family, excepting a senile aunt, has all but disowned me for something that isn't important? I did it because one day I dream of falling in love with the right man. Love is everything."

I nodded, transfixed by what Momo was saying as much as his uncharacteristically somber manner.

"How can you even consider turning your back on that?" he asked.

"I'm not! The decision isn't only mine. Franck has to decide, too, what he wants."

"Are you truly going to be that passive? For God's sake, fight for Franck. Get over your stupid pride and fight for him. What do you think I have been doing for all these years?" His round face had flushed red.

I nodded, not daring to speak.

"Now," he said. "Come with me. You need to see this insane Champagne fountain."

chapter **forty-three**

I had plenty of time to mull over my conversation with Momo because, it turned out, I had brought an unplanned gift home from Burgundy—a doozy of a winter cold.

The day after the amazing Barnes Exhibit and Champagne soirée, the virus settled into my bronchial tubes, apparently determined to hunker down for the duration.

I had seen Gérard Depardieu, that ubiquitous French actor, at the musée d'Orsay, and he was walking around with a massive woolen scarf wrapped around his neck. I felt a tug of affinity with him—he was probably suffering from a cold too. Maybe I had caught it from him, or perhaps from Édouard Balladur, the prime minister who, with his huge jowls, always looked as though he had a cold.

Most of the doctors near us seemed to still be away in their family's country homes sourcing the freshest oysters possible to be eaten raw at their New Year's feast.

I waited two days for the bronchitis to clear, relying on the classic Canadian remedy of orange juice and aspirin, and remembering my forefathers were lumberjacks who would have had their arm cut off with a hacksaw in the morning and been back at work with it bandaged up with a dirty shirt in the afternoon.

Finally, I found a doctor open for just a few hours on the rue de la Montagne Sainte-Geneviève. Usually when I was walking up the twisty streets of la Montagne, I was never out of breath, but this time when I reached the doctor's office at the top, I was sucking air like a vacuum cleaner that needed its filter changed.

After about an hour of flipping through back issues of *Elle Decor* in the waiting room, I was ushered in to see the female doctor. My first impression was that she was tiny and sinewy and appeared to resent her job and her patients—or maybe she was just mad that she, too, wasn't sourcing fresh oysters.

She did not, unlike Canadian doctors I was used to, subscribe to my theory that I just had to give the bronchitis a bit more time and perhaps more orange juice.

She pulled a horrified face when she listened to my chest. "What you have is a bronchial infection," she told me. "An extremely bad one, too, as well as severe asthma. Who drove you here?"

"No one. I walked."

"Walked? From where?"

"Rue des Fossés Saint-Bernard."

"You Americans are *complètement fou*—"

"I'm Canadian."

She waved her hand. "It's the same thing!"

"No—"

"I cannot possibly see how you had enough oxygen in your blood to walk here. Were you not out of breath? Did you not feel light-headed—like you were going to pass out?"

I thought back. "Maybe a bit, but I just figured, you know... soldier on..."

She shook her head. "You should be in bed. Better yet, a hospital bed."

"I don't think I'm that sick," I protested.

"Do you have a medical degree?"

"No."

"Well, I do, and I say you are *extrêmement* ill." She narrowed her almond-shaped eyes at me. I was still only wearing my bra—she had made me take off my sweater to listen to my lungs. "*En plus*, you need to lose weight." She grabbed a hunk of some flesh on my upper arm. "Maybe you are Canadian, but you seem to have a bit of the *bourguignonne* in you."

Indeed, to this Parisian doctor, who looked as though she subsisted on a diet of espresso, existential angst, and maybe a few cucumbers, I probably did seem on the fleshy side, like the robust women of Burgundy. I descended from Scottish peasant stock, after all. Still, if I were pitted side by side in the Canadian wilderness with this desiccated strip of Parisian beef jerky, I was certain I would end up using her spindly little bones for toothpicks.

"There's a delicious pastry shop on my route to school," I explained. "They sell these things called *torsa—*"

"You must practice restraint."

If practicing restraint meant that I, too, had to look and act as if all the joy in life had been sucked out of me...*non merci*.

In silence, she prescribed a course of antibiotics and two cough syrups, as well as two inhalers for my breathing.

"There's one more thing," I said. "I'll be flying to Scotland in a few days."

Le docteur widened her eyes. "Scotland? Why would you want to go there?"

"We're meeting up with friends from Canada. Hogmanay is a huge celebration in Edinburgh, *vous savez*."

"Maybe...but Scotland? The food is terrible."

"Hogmanay is mostly about the drinking, I believe."

She narrowed her eyes at me. "Drinking? With those antibiotics, you perhaps could enjoy some quality French wine, but whatever muck they drink in Scotland—*non!*"

"I guess I'll just enjoy the haggis then." I hate haggis but said it for the sheer pleasure of winding her up. I was still incensed by her American comment.

"I cannot recommend taking your trip. Flying will

complicate things, and I guarantee you are going to feel worse before you feel better."

I merely shrugged.

"You must cancel your trip," she reiterated.

I nodded, having zero intention of following her advice but wanting to get out of there and to the pharmacy as quickly as possible. I was sure after twenty-four hours on the antibiotics and a fresh bottle of OJ I would be feeling like a new person.

Despite my dose of antibiotics the night before, the next morning I woke up and had to spend an hour coughing up horrible things, similar to what Jean Valjean in Victor Hugo's *Les Misérables* must have encountered in the Parisian sewer, before I could actually catch a decent breath.

"Are you sure Scotland is a good idea?" Franck asked.

"Of course it's a good idea! It's the land of my ancestors, and I've never even been there. We must take this opportunity. We're going." Besides, I wouldn't let that mean-spirited doctor be right.

Franck narrowed his eyes but held his tongue.

I was determined to be on that plane and celebrating on the Royal Mile, even though that evening my temperature spiked and I went to bed at six o'clock and shivered for at least an hour before falling into a fitful, hallucinatory sleep.

I woke up the next morning feeling wretched but with my stubbornness mostly intact, at least until I rolled over with a groan and saw Franck sitting up in bed, rubbing his left cheek.

"You're not going to want to hear this," he said.

I sat up, which triggered a coughing fit. It took me a few minutes to recover enough to ask, "What am I not going to like hearing?"

"*Regarde*." He removed his hand from where he'd been rubbing his face.

I gasped. His cheek has swollen up to at least double its normal size, all the way up to his eye, which was also puffy.

"What happened?" I said. "Did I punch you during a dream?"

He shook his head. "My tooth. Teeth, actually. They've been bothering me, but nothing too serious. I just figured that I'd have them looked at when we returned from Scotland."

"You have to go the dentist." I studied his distorted face. "That amount of swelling near your brain can't be good."

"The throbbing pain isn't exactly a carnival ride either."

I lay in bed, shivering again, as he stumbled to the living room. I heard him talking on the phone to the dentist's receptionist. He brought my medication and a glass of water to my bed, as I couldn't seem to move from my fetal position under the duvet, then he left to get his teeth fixed.

Poor Franck. He had terrible teeth and bore his frequent dental interventions with stoicism. When he was little, the local dentist in Villers-la-Faye tied his patients to a sturdy kitchen chair to perform tooth extraction and cavity filling without any freezing. Modern dentistry—even if it included root canals—could only be a breeze by comparison.

A while later—I had lost track of time and it was not beyond the realm of possibility that I had been hallucinating—Franck returned from the dentist. His cheek was just as swollen as when he had left our apartment, but now his mouth was packed with gauze.

"Oh no," I said. I was wrapped up in our duvet and shivering so violently my teeth clacked together. I was sipping a glass of cold orange juice and had just taken two aspirin, even though, as much as I hated to admit it, I was losing faith in my Canadian remedies.

"The dentist couldn't finish," Franck said, holding his cheek and collapsing beside me. "In fact, he barely got started." I unwrapped myself enough so that he could share the duvet. He wrapped himself up beside me so that we were like two peas in a pod. His warmth eased my shivers. I wondered if maybe he wasn't running a fever too.

I coughed so hard it sounded as if I was going to barf up a lung. Thankfully, it subsided before that happened. "What did he say?"

"He says I need two root canals. Once he froze me up and started drilling though, he became worried about the infection. He gave me some antibiotics to take for forty-eight hours before I go back and he continues."

"So, two days from now?"

"Yes."

"Perfect. I should have this cough kicked by then, and you can go and finish up your root canals. We'll be in great shape to hop on the plane to Edinburgh the next day. It's perfect timing, really."

Franck glanced down at me with a doubtful look.

Two days later, the miraculous turnaround I was waiting for with my illness still hadn't occurred and Franck was due to go back to the dentist.

In those two days, we had moved between the couch and the bed, popping pain killers and antibiotics all day. We had looked after each other as best we could.

"This is it," I told him bracingly as he put his coat on to leave. "You'll get your teeth fixed and I'll turn the corner, and we'll have a great night's sleep and tomorrow we'll be celebrating Hogmanay in Scotland! Can you believe it?

Franck sighed. "No."

"We just need to think positive!" I stood up on shaky legs to wrap his scarf around his neck. "You'll see."

He made a non-committal sound.

"If you have any spare time in the dentist's waiting room, say a few Ava Marias or whatever it is you Catholics do."

"You honestly think a few Ava Marias will get us to Scotland?"

"Can't hurt."

Franck tried to smile, which only resulted in a lop-sided grimace. When he left, I collapsed on the futon again, giving way to shivers that wracked my limbs.

An hour passed, then another, and then another. I was not feeling a whit better, despite working hard at convincing myself I was.

At last, I heard Franck's key in the lock.

"*Alors*?" I shot up to a sitting position that triggered a coughing jag.

He came toward me with sad eyes, and without saying a word, opened his mouth. It was still packed full of gauze—bloody this time.

Having been blessed with bulletproof teeth, I wasn't certain what to make of this. "What did the dentist do?"

"He was only able to do half of the root canal on each tooth, and the infection still isn't clearing up as fast as he would like. He wants me to wait another two days for things to calm down and for me to keep taking the antibiotics. Then I'll go back, and he should be able finish the root canals and tidy things up. Theoretically, at least."

"So, no Hogmanay." This wasn't a question.

"Not for me, in any case."

"And you have two gaping, infected holes in your mouth?"

Franck nodded.

"*Pauvre choux.*" For once, this French term for affection was accurate. With his swollen face, Franck did indeed look like a poor cabbage.

"I'm sorry," he said. "I know how much you wanted for us to go together, but there's nothing stopping you from going. You've been looking forward to this, and you won't be alone once you get there." He studied my face, and just then a huge bone-wracking shiver rattled me from head to toes. "Don't take this the wrong way, *mon amour*, but you look dreadful."

I slumped against the duvet, feeling not the disappointment I had expected but rather a wave of relief.

I coughed a long, wracking cough that left me gasping for breath. "I give up. I don't feel like going and freezing my ass off in Edinburgh. I'm too sick. *We're* too sick."

Franck dropped a kiss on my hot forehead. "All I feel like doing is going to bed."

"Me too," I said.

So that's what we did.

Two days later was New Year's Eve Day. Franck went to the dentist and had his root canals finished off. The antibiotics were finally starting to work for both of us, or maybe my antibiotics had never helped and my virus was just running its merry course.

Although we were feeling marginally better, neither of us was anywhere close to one hundred percent, or even fifty percent for that matter. But still...we were in Paris and it was New Year's Eve. Now that we weren't celebrating in Scotland, what were we going to do?

"We have to do something," I said. We were walking to the *boulangerie* around the corner to pick up a baguette. "We are in Paris, after all."

"Going to sleep at seven o'clock is something," Franck said, and shivered. The temperature had plummeted, and the entire city had been plunged into a deep freeze.

I had to admit, given how I was still running a fever in the evenings and was frequently doubled over with coughing jags, that this plan had undeniable appeal. Still, staying home felt as if we were copping out.

"There must be something going on at the Eiffel Tower," I said, opening the door to the *boulangerie* and hearing the welcome tinkling of the bell above.

"There is." Franck ordered, then waited for the *boulangère* to wrap up our baguette. We fell silent for a beat in the warm haven of the bakery, hypnotized by the scent of freshly baked bread. "There's fireworks at midnight every year, but it must be five below outside. The *météo* is predicting it's going to drop to ten below tonight. Do you really feel up to standing on the Champ de Mars in the freezing cold?"

We left the heavenly shop, and I coughed with the blast of cold air. "No," I gasped.

"Why do you feel such pressure to do something?"

"It's New Year's Eve!"

"Have you ever truly enjoyed yourself on New Year's Eve?"

"No, but this year we're in *Paris*."

"Why do you think you never enjoy yourself on New Year's Eve?" Franck asked, ignoring my Paris argument.

I shrugged.

"I can tell you—too much pressure."

I watched my feet move along the gray sidewalk as we walked back up the rue des Fossés Saint-Bernard. "Maybe..."

"And if you add the regular New Year's Eve pressure to the additional pressure of feeling like you have to mark the occasion in a way worthy of Paris, that's—"

"A lot of pressure." I pressed the code in the touchpad beside our building's front door.

Franck took my hand. "How about we make this New Year's Eve the least pressured New Year's Eve in existence?"

"How can we do that?"

"First of all, we won't stay up until midnight."

"Ok," I said, unsure.

"We'll have the simplest dinner possible."

"Pasta?"

"How about Blédina?" Blédina is a children's food that many French adults eat as comfort food. It is kind of like a dehydrated vegetable porridge you just added boiling water to.

"Ok," I agreed, with more enthusiasm as Franck opened the metal elevator door for me. I love Blédina. "How about we eat it in bed?" I said, getting into the spirit of things.

"Perfect!"

"And we can take our little TV in with us and maybe watch a movie."

Momo had bequeathed an ancient and diminutive TV set to us. It was about six inches by six inches, and channels were selected by turning a radio dial. It had extendable bunny ears, and what we captured depended on the weather. The screen always showed varying degrees of fuzzy static, but it was amazing how quickly we had become habituated to watching shows through the haze.

"*Parfait!*" Franck said, letting us into our apartment, where he put the baguette down on our small wedge of kitchen counter. "Seeing as we can't have a big Hogmanay New Year's, let's have an anti-New Year's."

I took off my coat and my boots and flopped down on the couch.

"What do you think?" Franck flopped down on the couch beside me.

I suffered a pang when I considered how I would answer people who asked how I had celebrated New Years in Paris. Still, I was twenty-one. Maybe it was time to admit that I had always found New Year's Eve an epic disappointment. But, this felt like an important New Year's in the same way our Paris year felt like an important year. I hated to think it could be my last New Year's with Franck...maybe of maybe not. Whichever, wasn't it better to celebrate with a bang, not a whimper?

Yet, I still felt terrible. Crawling into bed with my vegetable porridge was, if I was being completely honest with myself, a highly appealing option. At least this New Year's would win in originality.

"How about we get into bed right now?" I said, consulting my watch. It was six o'clock, but of course, being December, it had been dark outside for some time.

"Yes!" Franck said. "We can start by reading for a bit and then make our Blédina and then take our bowls back to bed and eat it while we watch TV.

"Perfect," I said. And the oddest thing was that for once our New Year's Eve plans felt just right. "Spending it with you will be perfect, even if we're doing nothing but being sick together."

I slipped my hand in Franck's. He picked it up, turned it over, and lay a gentle kiss on my palm. "I would rather be sick with you than anyone else. *Je t'aime.*"

Dare I hope that heralded well for the year ahead?

chapter **forty-four**

On January first, we awoke early to a pale winter sun that made our bedroom glow.

I crept out of bed, breathing slightly easier, and looked out our window. A thin layer of snow blanketed everything. The courtyard below sparkled with frost. I heard some rustling, and Franck was by my side, looking out too.

It was an entirely clean slate. *Where will I be on January first a year from now? Will I still be waking up with Franck?*

"*Bonne année*," he said softly, and leaned down to give me a kiss. His cheek, I noticed, was looking almost normal again.

"Happy New Year," I said in English.

"We should go out," Franck said. "It's so peaceful. If you dress warmly, would you feel up to it?"

"Actually, I think I do."

We bundled up and ventured out into a Paris that was as quiet and still as the remotest rural village.

We strolled up Saint-Michel past the old Sorbonne and continued until we reached the gates of the Luxembourg Garden. We went inside and, as far as we could tell, were the only ones there.

There weren't even any footprints on the snow. We had the entire enchanted place to ourselves. We held hands and wandered between the rows and past the ponds, which were all frozen over with a thick sheet of ice that no Parisian children had been able to shatter yet.

I contemplated a white swatch of untouched snow above the fountains. "We have to make snow angels."

Franck ran to the middle of the snowy expanse, flopped down, and started fanning his arms and legs back and forth. I ran to join him.

Ten minutes later, we had decorated the middle section of the field with our angels, and the bells of the Panthéon, or a church in that direction, rang out. A few bundled-up souls began making their way through the park with their tiny dogs on leashes. We decided maybe it was time to head back to our nest.

In a hidden row of the garden, flanked by two statues sparkling in the frost, Franck and I stopped walking long enough to kiss—long enough for me to want to follow Momo's advice and beg Franck to choose me and Montreal. But...still...fear and pride trapped the words in my throat.

"Here's to the New Year," Franck whispered. "May it be as perfect as last night."

"But maybe a tad more adventurous," I said.

"Ah, Laura." Franck sighed. "We don't need to wish for adventure. It has a way of finding the two of us."

I didn't sleep the night before my oral report for Professor Renier-Bernadotte.

I didn't know her standards. Was I trying to perform the impossible by satisfying her academic rigor? My nerves weren't going to help me. Maybe my French would evaporate or I would blank entirely.

Franck woke me up early that morning so I could do a last-minute review of the index cards where I'd written my speech.

When I stepped out of the shower, wet and shivering—our apartment never seemed warm enough in these cold winter months—I saw that Franck had made me breakfast. He must have even snuck out to the *boulangerie* down the block because on the table beside two jars of my favorite flavors of Bonne Maman jam—Reines-Claudes (plum) and Blackcurrant Jelly—sat a basket of piping hot croissants.

I could hear him in the kitchen preparing our *cafés au lait*. I got dressed in a hurry and then met Franck back in the living room. The *cafés au lait* now sat steaming in our glass Duralex bowls on the table. I walked over to Franck and sat down on his lap. I kissed him deeply.

"*Merci*," I murmured, holding him close.

"I couldn't let you face the dragon without a good breakfast."

I kissed him again. *Please come back to Montreal with me. Please, please, please.* Still my mouth just couldn't make the words. Especially that morning, when a "no" or an "I haven't decided yet" would most likely make me an emotional disaster before my speech.

"I love you too." Franck kissed me back. "And I'll be thinking of you all morning when I'm writing boring articles about food suppliers. I'll be sending you strength and brilliance...not that you'll need it."

"I wouldn't be so sure about that." I regretfully left his embrace and claimed my own seat.

"I'm already proud of you," Franck said. "I was terrified of oral reports when I was at the Sorbonne. If I were you right now, I wouldn't be thinking of how I could do the best possible job.

"What would you be thinking of?"

"I would be concocting a thousand excuses for how I could get out of doing the speech at all."

I dipped my freshly garnished croissant into the hot *café*. "So, I'm already one step ahead?"

"Laura," Franck said, "you're always a hundred steps ahead."

"Why don't I ever feel that way?"

Franck shrugged. "An eternal mystery to me."

I finished up my breakfast quickly, picked up my things, and went over my index cards one last time until Franck slipped my arms into my jacket sleeves and gave me a good-luck kiss before ushering me out the door.

"*Courage!*" he called after me and raised his fist in the air.

I nodded. *Courage.* I would be brave. I squared my back and went to face the firing squad of Professor Renier-Bernadotte and my fellow students.

I was relieved to see that I wasn't the only student who was freaking out. In fact, more than half the class appeared to be AWOL. The unusually high rate of absenteeism could not be explained away by the winter viruses making their rounds.

I had made a quick stop at the Panthéon to touch Victor's tomb for luck. Victor reassured me I was going to do just fine. At least in my head he did.

I took my seat and began rifling through my index cards.

Madame Renier-Bernadotte swept into the amphitheater, a rust-colored cape flowing in her wake. When she settled in at the podium, she scanned the room with a knowing look. "So, you are the tenacious ones, are you? Considering how many of your fellow students have deigned this class below their notice today, you should congratulate yourselves."

I found myself smiling.

"But not too exuberantly, however," she warned. "The fact that you are braver than many of your fellow students will not alter my academic rigor one whit."

My smile evaporated.

"Without further ado, I shall call on our first presenter of the day," Professor Renier-Bernadotte said.

Please not me. Please not me. As much as I wanted to get it over with, I wanted to hear a few other people present first so I could gauge my presentation on theirs.

"Mademoiselle Bradbury," she called and looked straight at me. She arched her eyebrow. Up until then, I wasn't even sure she knew who I was. Or maybe I had brought myself to her notice by the French errors in my assignments.

I grabbed my index cards and headed up to the podium. My hands were shaking so much I panicked about dropping them.

Professor Renier-Bernadotte took a seat in the front row. I couldn't look at her. If I did I, would completely blank.

Sweat pearled on my forehead under the hot lights. I stared out at the crowd who, frankly, looked both bored and nervous... surely anticipating their turns in the hot seat.

"Whenever you're ready," prompted Madame Renier-Bernadotte.

I cleared my throat and looked down at the index cards. If I aspired to be even half as brilliant as Madame Renier-Bernadotte, I had to do this. The words I had written looked blurry, but I opened my mouth anyway. I would rather do this and fail miserably than not try at all.

I began to explain why I had found that courtly love as depicted in the medieval texts we had studied had a strong whiff of propaganda, which served to reinforce the social obligations and traditions around marriage in the Middle Ages.

Hearing myself, my voice seemed to be coming from deep underneath water. I seemed to go into a trance-like state where time was suspended and my arguments and quotes sounded somewhat rational—at least to me.

After what appeared to be a long time, I reached the conclusion of my argument and said the second-to-last word, and then the last.

Only then could I seem to catch my breath and meet my Professor's appraising gaze. Her lips twitched a bit. Was that a smile? Or was she mocking my feeble attempts?

"*Très intéressant*, Mademoiselle Bradbury," she said, and nodded at me.

I made my way back to my seat. *Interesting?* That was, without a doubt, the most ambiguous word in both English and French.

At least the thing was done. I just needed to hold that to my chest for a time before I unleashed my mind on any further questions.

chapter **forty-five**

The day after my presentation, I was walking along the boulevard Saint-Germain to Madame Gabrielle's class, ruminating about the frustrating standstill between us. How could I not be excelling in my one English class? It made no sense, and I blamed it entirely on her prejudice against me.

I passed the domed front, or back—I was never certain which was which at the Saint-Nicolas du Chardonnet church. Just across the street, I admired the display of tulips spilling out from a tiny floral boutique and breathed in the sweet smell that always flowed out of the open door of the *fleuriste*.

I knew a lot about Dickens. I had things to contribute. Madame Renier-Bernadotte made me feel like an academic, and to my burgeoning academic self, not being able to excel was an intolerable constraint.

I thought of the disappointment the ladies in the administration office would feel if they knew I had never actually stood up to Madame Gabrielle's bullying.

Maybe the fact I had done the oral report and hadn't made a

complete wreck of it made me braver. In any case, by the time I hit the boulevard Saint-Germain, I was pulsing with indignation.

I walked into the class in a defiant mood and sat beside Grace. She smiled at me, but my smile back to her only lasted a split-second. She kept glancing at me, her face paler than usual, like a person who had just been handed a live grenade.

When Professor Gabrielle walked in and greeted the class with a simpering *bonjour*, I remained stone-faced.

"Today we are going to begin our next book, *A Tale of Two Cities*. Has anyone had the opportunity to read it over the holidays?"

A few people fanned their hands in a way that indicated maybe they had read the back blurb. I stuck my hand straight up.

"I've read it three times before, and I studied it in both high school and university," I said, knowing full well this was not going to make me any friends.

The rest of the class moaned. "You don't need to worry," I said to them in English. "That still won't earn me good marks, based on my grade on the *Great Expectations* essay."

Professor Gabrielle gasped. "You spoke out of turn."

Rage at her petty injustice consumed me. "You asked a question. I put up my hand and answered it."

"I didn't call on you."

"I knew you never would," I said. "Which is why I didn't wait to answer."

The students around me moved in their seats, making a low rumbling sound as a group. Everyone had just snapped to attention.

"We do not want to hear how eminently superior you think you are in the study of Dickens." Professor Gabrielle sniffed.

"She never said that," a boy a row ahead of me said in French. "She just answered your question. She never mentioned anything about thinking she was superior."

I shot him a grateful look.

"I was merely stating the facts," I said, my heart pounding against my sternum. "You are the one who drew a biased conclusion."

"*Oui, c'est ça!*" Several students chimed in now.

I wasn't sure how the shift had happened, and I certainly hadn't expected this impromptu support, but I was delighted to have it. Perhaps the French soul of my fellow students had caught a whiff of rebellion against The Establishment. They couldn't be left out of that, *bien sûr.*

The crowd began to get rowdy now, and Professor Gabrielle banged her fist on her podium. "Quiet! Quiet please!"

The class settled down a bit, mainly because, I believe, most of them were intrigued, like I was, to hear what she was going to say, rather than because of any desire to obey her.

"Miss Bradbury, you are a disturbance to this class. I would like you to pack up your books and leave."

The class erupted in protest. Not, I was sure, because of any love for me but rather because of their passion for resistance.

I didn't move. Eventually, silence dropped over the classroom again as everyone waited and watched to see what I would do.

"Laura, what are you doing?" Grace hissed to me in a breathless voice.

"I'm not sure," I hissed back. This wasn't what I had been planning. In fact, I hadn't been planning anything specific beyond not submitting to this teacher. I had never dreamed she would rise to the bait so quickly.

I couldn't back down now. This outrage inside me had to get out. I could put up with a lot, but once I had been pushed over the edge, there was no turning back.

"In case you are wondering," I announced in a resounding voice, "I'm not leaving."

The class erupted in a cheer.

Professor Gabrielle began to shake. She was nervous. She might even be frightened.

"I will call Security," she threatened. My fellow students boo-ed.

"Please do that," I said. "That will be an efficient way for me to get the attention of the administration of the Sorbonne and my exchange program. I could then show them my *Great Expectations* essay and how you marked it. I have made several photocopies, which are in my backpack, so I'm sure I will be able to hand out one to any interested parties for their own perusal."

Professeur Gabrielle's face turned an icky shade of green.

There was more cheering. Some students stood up and began to shake their fists at her.

"You can't do that," she said, her voice unsteady. "Administration will always side with a teacher."

"When I went to talk to the administration office about dropping this class, I got the distinct impression that you were rather disliked. I'm not scared of you, and I will not remain quiet, nor will I leave this class"

The other students were on their feet, unable to contain their glee. *A Tale of Two Cities* was a riveting book, but the drama being enacted in their own classroom was better.

I watched Professor Gabrielle's face become greener and waited for her response. My heart pounded under my wool sweater. Grace, as far as I could tell, had stopped breathing altogether. She sat as still as a mouse who had spotted a marauding cat a few feet away.

Professor Gabrielle finally opened her mouth, but instead of saying anything, she gagged, covered her mouth, and ran out of the room.

The crowd erupted into laughter, but as for me, I felt a stab of guilt, not triumph. I couldn't believe I had broken her so easily. I realized at that moment that Professor Gabrielle may have been a bitch, but she'd also been terrified.

We all waited ten minutes, then fifteen, then twenty, and there was still no sign of Professor Gabrielle. An envoy was eventually sent into the hallway, but they returned quickly, finding no trace of her.

Giving up on seeing the conclusion of our battle of the wills, at least until the next week, students began to trickle out of the class until just Grace and I were left.

She stared at me. "I can't believe you stood up to her." Her face was still ashen. "I would never have done that."

My heart was still pounding and I could hear the blood

rushing in my ears. I couldn't believe it either. I'd just been so furious. An unwelcome thought struck me—was it possible that my outrage was partly fueled by frustration that went beyond the parameters of that class? Frustration with not knowing what the future held for Franck and me?

"Do you want to get a coffee?" I asked Grace.

"Definitely," she said. "I'm supposed to be back at home to look after the kids, but I don't care."

Could it be possible that Paris's rebel soul was rubbing off on my Southern Belle friend?

In the end, I opted for a glass of wine at the café. Grace followed suit.

"Today, I need something with more sustenance," I said.

I chose a Savigny-les-Beaune Premier Cru Serprentières for us. Its familiar spiciness and velvety texture on my tongue gave me an ache of longing for my friends back in Burgundy. Somehow things had felt so much simpler when Franck and I were there at Christmas.

Grace and I thrashed out the subject of our Professor's behavior, her sudden disappearance, and the fact that the entire class had so quickly turned into a lynch mob who may have been inclined to haul her off to a guillotine if there had been one close at hand.

I reached a point when I felt if I talked any more about it I would break out in hives. I just needed to let it sit for a while before I tried to figure out what exactly had come over me, and what to do next.

"How are things with you?" I asked, to change the subject. "Is the family you're working for getting any nicer?"

Grace snorted. "If anything, they're getting worse. Now they fight all the time in front of me and call each other the most horrible names. The children are spoiled and rude, and I think one or both might actually be stealing from me."

"Are you still thinking you may leave them?"

"I have thought about it a lot, but where would I go? Where would I live?"

I couldn't come up with any brilliant ideas. I had learned the hard way that it was tantamount to a miracle to find a decent place to live in Paris.

Grace adjusted that day's hair bow—white with transparent sequins affixed. "If I couldn't find a place, I'd have to return to the States early. I can't do that. I know you must think I'm a pretty traditional person, but I have my pride."

"Of course you do."

"I can't let my beau...or I guess he's my ex-beau, think that I came back because I wasn't able to live out my dream year. I can't let him believe that I gave up."

"No," I agreed. "That would set a bad precedent."

For the first time, I considered the fact that maybe I had been far too quick to judge Grace. We had more in common than I'd first thought. Perhaps Professor Gabrielle wasn't the only one who was prejudiced. That sat like a stone behind my breastbone.

"He sent me a card at Christmas, you know." A blush bloomed on Grace's previously pale face.

"Really? Did it just say, you know, 'Season's Greetings' or something else?"

"He wrote a lot inside it...almost as much as a letter. I wasn't expecting anything like that because when I made the decision to come to Paris, we decided not to have any further contact."

"He decided, or did you decide together?"

Grace studied the incomparable cherry red hue of the wine in her glass. "I guess he decided and I agreed."

"What did the card say?"

"He didn't say he wanted to get back together, not exactly, but he said how much he has been missing me and how he would like to see me when I got back, and then asked if I had my return dates yet."

"Hmmmmmm." It wasn't exactly a declaration of love.

"You're not seeing how important this is." Grace reached over and tapped the back of my hand.

"It definitely sounds thoughtful—"

"No...not that. He broke the rules for me."

"That's a big deal?" With Franck, breaking the rules was an hourly event.

"For my beau, it's huge. He's very big on rules, you see."

I nodded. "Did you answer him?"

Grace fiddled with her tiny espresso spoon. "Not yet. I keep trying to decide what to say to him exactly. Should I let him know how much I miss him too, and how much I want to get back together with him, or should I just pretend like I'm having a great time and don't care? What do you think I should do?"

Grace's situation, I realized as she spoke, was a faint echo of my own. Did I use all my newfound bravery to simply declare how much I loved Franck and how much I wanted him to return to Montreal with me? Or did I stick with pride and being an anti-Pauline—a self-reliant woman who needed no one?

There was also my confusion about the advantages and disadvantages of being part of a committed couple at my age—though Anton (who I had still not mentioned to Franck) had settled some of that.

"I wish I knew the answer," I said, at last. "I still can't decide which is more important in life, pride or love."

"Do you think a person can have both?"

I mulled this over. "I'd like to think so, but we're always being made to choose, aren't we?"

"Do you think you could set me up with a French guy?" Grace asked.

I choked on my wine. "What? But you just said you still have feelings for your beau."

"I do, but while I'm here I want to...you know...try something else and see if I'm missing out. That way, if he does want to get back together again when I get back, I'll be sure."

"Do you think anyone is ever sure?"

Grace did a good approximation of a Gallic shrug. "I don't know, but I have to try. I've decided I owe that to myself."

I studied her. For a self-described traditional Southern Belle, she was acting...well, like a different sort of woman than I had judged her to be. More like the searching, overthinking sort. More like me.

"I'll see what I can do."

"Thanks," she said. "Now, what the heck are y'all going to do about Professor Gabrielle's class next week?"

chapter **forty-six**

It was the end of February, and I couldn't believe Franck wasn't home from work yet.

I was drinking a mug of tea and nibbling on a few *petit beurre* biscuits as I re-reading *Les Quinze Joies du Mariage* for a test Madame Renier-Bernadotte had set.

School had settled into a nice rhythm. After my impromptu insurrection, Professor Gabrielle seemed too scared of me to give me bad marks. I received an eighteen out of twenty on my *A Tale of Two Cities* essay. I still thought I deserved a twenty out of twenty, but I believed further protest on my part would send her into a nervous breakdown. I didn't need that on my conscience.

I heard Franck's key in the door.

"*Salut!*" I shouted out as I heard the door close behind him. "Ça va?"

He came into the living room, a smile on his face. "I'm good," he said. "Sorry I'm late. I went out for a drink with some people from work."

"Was it fun?" I was intent on digging out a *petit beurre* that had disintegrated in my mug before I could eat it.

"*Bah, alors...* 'Fun' isn't the word I would use. It was more along the lines of drowning our collective sorrows." Franck shed his coat and scarf.

"What?" He had my attention now. "Why?"

"*Expo News* declared bankruptcy this morning. We were informed five minutes before the end of the day today. The office will be closed and liquidated, and we've all been let go, effective immediately."

I gasped.

"I mean, we could all see that the magazine wasn't hitting its goals for subscribers, but nobody thought it would happen this fast. Can you believe they carried on for most of today like nothing was changing? I was even assigned a new article on the restaurant options around la Défense."

He shook his head in disgust. "*Saloperie de patrons.*" Villainous bosses.

I studied his face, looking for worry or stress, but couldn't find either. "How are *you*?" I asked.

He shrugged. "Relieved. The job was getting boring, and I was beginning to think it was only a matter of time before *Expo News* folded. It was a blessing that it happened fast."

Without Franck's salary, we could simply not make ends meet. "But," I sputtered, "what are you going to do now? I mean, do you qualify for unemployment? Do you have any ideas of where you'll apply?"

Franck reached forward and squeezed my hand. "I'll worry about that tomorrow," he said. "I think getting fired is enough for one day, don't you?"

"But—"

"There's no point in spinning wheels this evening. There is nothing I can do until tomorrow anyway."

"We can start making a list of potential jobs—"

"Tomorrow." Franck squeezed my hand again, more meaningfully this time.

"Tomorrow you're leaving for Russia!"

Nathaneal was going to Russia for a week to do a report on the changes from a communist to a capitalist system, particularly centering on the opening of the first McDonald's in Moscow. Franck, who had always dreamed of going to Russia, was thrilled to be joining the adventure.

Franck's face lit up. "Right! I'll worry about it when I get back from Moscow then."

"But how are we going to pay for Moscow? We're barely making our rent as it is."

"I think I can apply for a few weeks unemployment when I get back. I won't be eligible for much because I just had a CDI, but maybe a bit. Besides, Moscow can't be that expensive. It was a Communist country until just recently. I already went to the currency exchange and exchanged my francs for rubles, so I have that."

"You don't seem upset," I observed, bewildered by his sanguine reaction.

"I'm not. I'm not sure what I'm going to do next, but I'd like to find something more interesting, or at least different."

Part of me was relieved by Franck's long-term planning—or rather, his lack thereof. If he wasn't looking at jobs from a career perspective, did that mean that he had already decided to come back to Montreal with me when our Parisian year was over? I could just come out and ask him. Right now. It was the perfect opportunity…

"They did me a favor," he added.

I opened my mouth to speak.

Franck smiled at me. "You look like you've just been hit in the head with a *pétanque* ball."

"You just seem so…relaxed," I said, disappointed with my own cowardice.

"Why wouldn't I be? Besides, there's nothing I can do tonight, is there?"

"I guess not…" The opportunity slipped away.

"Right." Franck slapped his knee. "Where should we go out then?"

"What?"

"We need to go out and celebrate."

"Celebrate getting fired?"

"Celebrate new beginnings." Franck grasped both my hands.

"Huh."

"What about Batifol? Do you feel like some chocolate mousse?"

"I always feel like chocolate mousse."

"*Parfait.* I don't know how you found it walking home from school, but it's rainy and miserable out there now. If we go to Batifol, we can just roll home with our stomachs full of food."

I nodded, deciding at that moment to allow myself to be swept away by Franck's enthusiasm. *Pourquoi pas?* What could it hurt, after all, except our bank balance?

I let Franck take my jacket out of the bedroom closet and thread my arms into it. He wrapped a warm scarf around my neck while I slipped on my leather boots.

We ate steak Diane flambéed in brandy with a *gratin dauphinois* at Batifol, the meal crowned with bowls of chocolate mousse. Afterward, rather than rolling home to the warmth of our apartment with full stomachs, we were full of energy.

"Do you feel like a surprise?" Franck asked, as we were pulling on our coats and scarves.

This would be the perfect opportunity to resist my compulsion to live in the future and to always have a plan. "*Oui.*"

Franck led me to a tiny tango bar hidden under the winding streets of the Latin Quarter, where the Greek restaurants broke dish after dish in the street to try and lure in tourists.

We entered through a nondescript, dark crimson, painted wooden door set in a stone wall. Franck led me down a narrow winding staircase, poorly lit with flickering wall sconces. There were so many stairs.

"How deep underground is this place?" I asked Franck, more than a little wariness prickling my skin.

"Deep."

Finally, we arrived in a hot, muggy room with small round tables scattered in the many dark corners created by the dim yellow light. It smelled of underground dank and cigar smoke.

The place did not appear to be on the tourists' radar, but was filled with people who spoke primarily Spanish, from what I could tell.

The hostess, herself dressed in a black tango dress with a red underskirt and with a red rose in her sleek black hair, led us to a table for two in a shadowy corner. On her advice, we ordered mojitos.

When they arrived, I took a sip, and all my worries that this was an odd drink choice for a Parisian February evaporated. The crispness of the lime and fresh mint contrasted with the depth of the rum and the unctuousness of the cane syrup. My mojito was a miracle—a mini tropical vacation.

The melted wax from the thick red candle on our table and the heavy perfume in the air made me feel far removed from the Paris that bustled on the streets above us.

A couple walked onto the small dance floor set roughly in the center of the crowded tables. Their eyes were locked together with an intensity that could not have been feigned. The melancholy music swept me away—tears gathered in my eyes. Cigar and cigarette smoke lingered in the air and created swirls around the dancers as they moved.

Their bodies told a story as eloquently as any book. Love. Thwarted love. Anger. Pride. Longing. The longing is what made their dance unbearably beautiful to me. Their longing for each other and for something that was always just out of reach.

Was it truly out of reach? Franck moved his chair right up against mine, and I was acutely conscious of the weight of his arm tight around my shoulders as we watched.

Just as the man snatched the woman up from an almost parallel position from the ground and grasped her tight, I leaned my cheek against Franck's hand and gave his fingers a kiss.

Love and longing and doubt. That was exactly the mix of things I had been struggling with all that year. Somehow, in this tango club under the cobblestoned streets of the Latin Quarter, it seemed an entirely appropriate struggle for someone living in Paris.

chapter **forty-seven**

The next day, Franck got up before the sun to complete all his last-minute preparations for Moscow.

I rolled over and moaned, clutching my head. "All those mojitos...what time did we get home last night?"

Franck paused in the middle of folding a pair of jeans. "Late... and then when we got home..."

I blinked and it started to come back to me. "Oh...OH."

"Ah. You do remember."

I felt a blush creep up my throat. "I'm not about to forget *that*."

Franck went back to his folding but with a satisfied tilt to the corner of his mouth. "Happy to hear it."

"How are you feeling for your flight?"

"I woke up with a headache, but I took two acetaminophen tablets right away. There's two on the floor for you and a glass of water." Franck gestured to the base of the armoire. The room wasn't big enough for a nightstand.

I reached down and swallowed the two pills gratefully.

"My headache's not completely gone, but I figure we'll be toasting our arrival with vodka in Moscow, so...you know—"

"Hair of the dog?"

"Exactly."

"Are you going to be lonely when I'm gone?" Franck asked, zipping up his suitcase on the bed.

"Maybe," I said. "But I've got my classes and stuff planned with Grace. Oh, also Jacinthe and I are going to go out for dinner. Anyway, I have Paris at my doorstep. What more could a person need?"

Jacinthe and I did go out for dinner the next day to a cutting-edge restaurant called Le Labo near the Georges Pompidou center (known by locals simply as Beaubourg).

The first thing that struck me as we were being seated was that, unlike the Brasserie Le Monge and most other restaurants, Le Labo didn't smell like food. It smelled like…nothing in fact.

A few minutes after we sat down, I realized with dismay that we were not busy discussing our plans and aspirations as independent women but rather talking about our boyfriends.

After the slim, beautiful male waiter, dressed from head to toe in chic black, came to take our orders, Jacinthe went right back to the same topic.

"Are you worried that they'll…you know…get into trouble?" Jacinthe asked.

"You mean with the mafia there?" I'd heard that morning on France Info that a new breed of criminality had erupted in Moscow. I did entertain some concerns about Franck's prudence—or rather lack thereof—in that regard.

Jacinthe studied my face and didn't answer for a while. "No, Laura, not the mafia. I mean with Russian girls. I heard they're all angling for an occidental sugar daddy."

I laughed. "I hadn't thought about that."

But Jacinthe, I noticed, looked serious. A bit sad too. "You've seen what they dress like, haven't you?"

"Franck and Nathanael?" If I went on Franck's mish-mash of salvaged winter gear and his duct-taped, decade-old ski jacket,

I didn't think I had much to worry about. He was not exactly a prime target for gold diggers of any nationality.

"No," Jacinthe answered, still not smiling. "The Russian women. Everything they wear is tight, revealing, and made of spandex. They always wear a ton of make-up and have cleavage spilling out everywhere."

I didn't know how to answer. Honestly, despite my uncertainty about the future of our relationship, I hadn't given Russian women a single thought.

The waiter came back with our wine and tiny spoons, and set a rack holding three test tubes in front of each of us. He went on to explain with dramatic hand movements that this was *foie gras* done three ways, according to the chef's fantasy. One was a *foie gras* mousse with some iteration of figs involved. The second was minced *foie gras* and Cognac. He had lost me with his florid explanation of the third test tube.

When he whizzed away again, after wishing us *bon appétit*, I raised an eyebrow at Jacinthe.

"*Nouvelle Cuisine*." Jacinthe rolled her eyes. "Honestly, who was *stupide* enough to think that anyone wants to eat out of a test tube?"

"I never found plates had shortcomings," I said, laughing at the absurdity of the presentation. "I guess chefs feel enormous pressure to try new things all the time."

Jacinthe just nodded, that ruminating look darkening her usually bright blue eyes. "I wouldn't have picked this place, but I needed to try it out. They're considering using it for a work event."

"In that case"—I picked up a spoon and delved into the *foie gras* mousse—"it's probably perfect."

"Yeah," Jacinthe agreed, picking up her fairy-sized spoon as well. "The Champagne snobs will adore the pretension."

The *foie gras* mousse on my spoon was surprisingly delicious. It was light as air and melted on my tongue like slightly fig-infused silk.

"It's good," I reassured Jacinthe. "Even though it would be just as good served on a plate."

I took a sip of my wine. It was a red Jacinthe had chosen from the Bordeaux region—velvety and full of berry accents that went perfectly with the taste of the *foie gras*.

"So, what do you think? Would Franck be tempted by those Russian girls?"

I shook my head. "Franck wouldn't do that."

Jacinthe leaned back in her hair, strain tightening her features. "Laura, all men would do it, given the right set of circumstances."

"Do you really think so?"

"Yes."

"Do you mean all men would cheat?"

"Of course. Many women would too."

In an instant I felt that, instead of a sophisticated, almost-Parisian at home sampling test-tube cuisine in a chic restaurant that was decorated entirely in black with only a solitary blood red rose adorning every table, I was still a naïve bumpkin.

The waiter came to whisk away our test-tubes and quickly replaced them with a ball of white sorbet on top of a flared, black cylinder. "Cucumber and mint sorbet," he explained.

"Oh," I said, suitably surprised. I picked up my spoon and decided to just go with it.

"That's not…that's not how I was brought up," I tried to explain to Jacinthe after the pause. You know, to think cheating is normal."

"It's not so much normal as simply a fact of life." Jacinthe popped the first spoonful of sorbet into her mouth. "This is actually weirdly good."

"So, in France cheating is simply part of life?" I asked, disbelieving.

"In Paris, *oui*."

"How about other areas of France, outside of Paris?"

Jacinthe shrugged. "A bit, perhaps, but not as much as Paris. Nowhere, I believe, as much as Paris. Well…maybe Rome."

I pondered this. *"Non,"* I said finally. I just couldn't believe it of Franck. I knew him so well. Besides, he knew I would never tolerate that. "Why, have you caught Nathanael?"

Jacinthe shrugged.

"You *have?*" I couldn't disguise the shock in my voice. Nathanael often joked about infidelity, but I had never seen any proof of it. I also could not fathom the idea that if there was cheating, Jacinthe would put up with that.

A memory flashed in my brain. Mémé had declared shortly after meeting Nathanael for the first time that, "Nathanael is exactly like my first husband—a philanderer. Once they're like that, you know, they're always like that. *Il n'y a rien à faire.*" There's nothing to be done. At the time, I believed this was one of the very few mistakes Mémé had made. Now...

"Nathanael would be crazy to cheat on you," I said, to reassure myself as much as Jacinthe. "He wouldn't."

Jacinthe was loyal, funny, gorgeous, stylish and fiercely intelligent, and had an extremely high-profile, cool job, which seemed to count for a lot on Paris.

Now though, she stared down at her cutlery. I saw my sophisticated Parisian girlfriend a different way—unsure and vulnerable.

"No way," I reiterated.

She just shrugged. The waiter whisked away the black cylinders from in front of us. Jacinthe was right, the sorbet was weirdly satisfying after the richness of the *foie gras.*

"How about with your group of friends? Is cheating accepted among them?"

"It's not talked about openly, but behind closed doors, everyone is aware it happens," Jacinthe said.

"Doesn't that bother you?"

The waiter came back with a black plate with three little lumps of what looked like pureed food. I wasn't listening to his explanations of the dish.

"But Laura, is monogamy realistic?" Jacinthe said when he had left. "I'm not so sure. Especially in Paris, where it's an all-you-can-eat buffet of seductive people."

"I don't think I could put up with that," I said, my puritan Canadian soul aghast. "A relationship is all about trust, isn't it? Without trust, I couldn't be myself with Franck and then...well, then what's the point of being in a couple at all?

"Sometimes there isn't another option," Jacinthe said.

"I couldn't stand not being…you know…the only one." As I talked, my mind whirred as I tried to make sense of my visceral reaction to what was apparently accepted practice in Paris.

"I guess in Paris the people on the side are not considered special. The person who is special is the one that you are public with."

"What are the other ones, then?"

"Just…just like scratching an itch. They don't mean anything."

"That's hardly a good advertisement for recruiting mistresses. What's in it for them?" I asked.

"They are *also* just scratching an itch."

I couldn't help but be incredulous. "Do you really believe that?"

"I'm not sure I have a choice. That's the way things are."

Such a compromise made me furious. The waiter came back, taking away my empty plate. I had been so absorbed in our conversation I had eaten the lumps without tasting them.

"*Bien sûr*, you have a choice!" I must have raised my voice, because everyone around us stopped their conversation and turned to stare at us. Jacinthe's cheeks flamed almost as red as the rose between us.

I lowered my voice to a whisper, or more accurately, a hiss. "You don't have to put up with that. You're amazing."

"But Laura, all the other men I know here are the same. I wouldn't be getting anything different with someone else."

"You really think all men in Paris cheat?"

"Yes."

"I'm pretty sure Franck isn't cheating," I said, merely to prove my point.

Jacinthe looked at me, skeptical.

"Franck can't lie to save his life." I said. "I can tell instantly. Besides, he knows that if he did that, I would break up with him. Infidelity is a deal-breaker for me."

"I used to think the same thing," Jacinthe said.

Some sort of tower-like fruit-and-chocolate concoction appeared in front of us, but neither of us paid it attention.

"What if you broke up with Nathanael, you know, just to scare him?"

"That would be overdramatic. Besides, how am I to be sure how it would work out? Besides, I don't have any solid proof at all. Just a hunch...you know...and the fact that I'm aware of how things are with most of my friends."

A possibility flashed through my mind. "Do you have a lover?"

"No."

"Why not?"

"*Jamais dire, 'fontaine, je ne boirais pas de ton eau,'*" Jacinthe quipped. "Not yet."

I had heard Franck use this expression many times. It meant "Never say to the fountain 'I will not drink your waters.'" In a nutshell, never say never.

"I have many girlfriends that do," she said. "I can't say there haven't been interested parties. The thing is... I'm embarrassed to say it."

"What?"

"I don't want to be with anyone else besides Nathanael. I love him. I want to be with him. I know he loves me and wants to be with me...it's just that he has this incorrigible side. I think he will get that out of his system, though. Just hopefully not in Russia."

"Hmm," I said, thinking again of Mémé's maxim that once a man was a philanderer, he would never change.

"Anyway, enough about that. I have something to announce to you."

"What?"

"Nathanael and I are engaged."

chapter **forty-eight**

Jacinthe and I were going together to pick up our men at Charles de Gaulle airport. We had a few hours to kill at her apartment before we left, so we thrashed out her engagement while sipping Champagne on her purple velvet couch.

"How did you decide to say yes?"

"He proposed to me and I accepted. Honestly, I didn't see it coming."

Jacinthe went on to tell me that the wedding was going to be not that summer but the next, at Nathanael's parents' family country home in the rolling hills of the Beaujolais.

It would be a *mariage de campagne*, but a country wedding with hordes of Parisians there. But there would also be both of their families and Franck and me, if we could make it. Besides, Momo would be there. I liked Caroline too. They almost made up for Alexandrine.

Where would Franck and I be the next summer, I wondered. Back in Canada? There in France? Maybe no longer together…

As much as I considered Nathanael my friend, I had significant doubts about the wisdom of Jacinthe marrying him with the whole infidelity issue percolating in the background. Perhaps the problem was I was seeing it from a Canadian perspective, I reminded myself.

Besides, I had expressed my surprise after she announced the engagement when we were out for dinner. Now, as her friend, what was left was for me to discuss her plans with enthusiasm.

Once we had thoroughly dissected her ideas for the wedding, we began discussing the most effective methods of embarrassing our boyfriends on their arrival (or, I guess, technically my boyfriend and Jacinthe's fiancé). Ultimately, we deciced on a welcome banner.

Using an old white sheet and a broken broomstick, we constructed a ridiculously large banner. We kneeled on the floor and began concocting our message in thick black sharpie. We decorated the empty space with a plethora of our best imitation of Russian letters, which ended up looking more like the hieroglyphics of a long-lost civilization than the actual Cyrillic alphabet.

"You have a hidden gift at banner making," I remarked to Jacinthe when we finally stopped laughing.

"Not that hidden," Jacinthe said as we rolled up the banner, one of us at each end. "I spent a good part of my late teens and early twenties going to protests."

"What did you protest?"

"I can't even remember, but it's vital for every French youth to learn how to protest. It's part of our civic education. Besides, they were great places to meet boys."

I thought back to Franck and how he always said that growing up in Villers-la-Faye, the best places to meet girls was the inter-village catechism classes, and, later, serving as an altar boy at the local churches.

In Canada, adolescent romancing had mainly transpired among the trees in a forest or on the beach after some liquor had been consumed and before the police arrived to dump out our beer bottles and tell everyone to go home. My main memories were of being freezing cold.

En route to the airport, Jacinthe decided the fastest way was to drive up the Champs-Élysées and around the Arc de Triomphe. She plunged her car into the five or six lanes of traffic whipping around the Arc de Triomphe and cutting each other off in every direction. I was panicked for a few seconds, then enthralled. Jacinthe honked her horn, making exasperated hand gestures at other drivers. It was like being in the beating heart of Paris itself.

Even though Jacinthe's route was hair-raising, she was right. We arrived at the airport in an amazingly short period of time and avoided traffic jams on the *périphérique*.

Franck and Nathanael's flight direct from Moscow was due to arrive in twenty minutes' time. We quickly discovered, though, that like everywhere else in Paris, there was virtually no parking spaces available at the aéroport Charles de Gaulle.

"What about the parking garage?" I asked after we had circled the arrival zone three times.

Jacinthe glanced over at me. "Have you ever been down there?"

"Yes." Those were not good memories. It was dark and grungy and boasted a permeating scent of urine. It was also falling apart—chunks of the ceiling had been known to fall at unpredictable intervals.

Jacinthe echoed my thoughts. "Every time I go in there, I believe I'm never going to see any of my friends and family ever again. No. It's too awful. *Je refuses.*"

We were on our fourth circuit around the airport. My face was plastered against the car window, trying to find an elusive spot or at least someone lingering near their car with their keys in hand.

"*Merde.* I don't see a single available spot," I said.

"There!" Jacinthe cried, slowing down and pointing to a spot that was about two-thirds the length of her car.

"You'll never fit in there."

"Just wait!" Jacinthe gripped the steering wheel with resolve. "See if I don't."

"The laws of physics forbid it."

"We'll see about that." Jacinthe angled her car in and, with her bumper, pushed the car behind her backwards. Then she moved forward and pushed the car in front of her forwards. The cars had their parking breaks on, so each direction required an enthusiastic application of the accelerator.

The cars Jacinthe shoved, of course, bumped into the cars in front and behind them, setting off a whole domino effect of car alarms in a majestic cacophony. People stopped and stared at us.

I shrank down in my seat and covered my face in shame. "*La honte!*"

"Nonsense," Jacinthe said. "There's no reason to feel shame. Those bystanders are just envious of my technique."

I saw security personnel running toward us just as Jacinthe managed the impossible and wedged her car into the space she had created.

"Let's go!" She grabbed the rolled-up banner from the back seat and leapt out of the car. We dashed into the terminal where we lost the security guards in the crowds of people from around the globe.

Just as I was about to collapse—the Parisian pollution had really done a job on my lungs—Jacinthe slowed to a walk. "I guess we should look at what gate they're arriving at," she said.

"I see a screen," I pointed. Of course, like everything in the airport, the screen wasn't working properly and half of it was black. Luckily, Franck and Nathanael's flight was listed on the lit part, and the gate, we discovered, was only a brisk ten-minute walk through the filthy chaos of the airport.

Jacinthe lit up a cigarette, despite the muffled announcement that came on every minute or so saying that no smoking was allowed in the terminal.

"That always made me laugh," I said to Jacinthe.

"What?"

"How there's no smoking allowed in the terminal but everyone just smokes anyway. The fact that nobody cares says to me, more than anything, "Welcome to France!""

Jacinthe waved around the decay and dirt around us. "For God's sake, look at this place," she said. "What is a little cigarette smoke going to do that hasn't already been done? Besides, if they give us no other option but to fly out of this hellhole, then they have to throw us a bone."

We got to the gate with a few minutes to spare and used them to plan how we would unfurl out banner, or "*banderole*," as Jacinthe called it, as soon as we caught a glimpse of Franck and Nathanael so that they could enjoy its full impact.

A flight from India, from the looks of all the colorful saris that dotted the crowd of tired-looking people, was disembarking, and every time the doors opened and shut, I peered into the distance to try and catch a glimpse of Franck and his duct-taped ski jacket.

We waited, and waited…

"Do you think the flight is late?" I asked Jacinthe.

"Not sure," she mused. "I doubt it. They probably are just taking a long time getting through customs and immigration. There are never enough officers working."

"Or they go on coffee break as soon as they see a crowd of people coming toward them," I said. "That's happened to me before."

"That happens most of the time."

Just then, I spotted Franck nearing the immigration booth. I waved feverishly to get his attention. He looked up, beamed at me, and waved back. My heart thumped oddly in my chest.

"*La banderole!*" Jacinthe snapped me out of dreamland. "Help me with the banner!"

We unrolled it and held it high above our heads. Nathanael was just behind Franck, and when he saw it, he shot Jacinthe an incredulous look.

"*Bienvenue en France!*" Jacinthe shouted.

"*Ty lyubish!*" Jacinthe and I yelled several times. This means "you are loved!" in Russian (we had looked it up in the French-Russian dictionary that Nathanael had forgotten at their apartment).

Before I knew it, I was being lifted off the ground and soundly kissed by Franck. I dropped my half of the broken broomstick and was vaguely aware that my side of the banner had clattered to the ground.

When I emerged, I saw that Jacinthe had dropped her side for the same reasons.

Nathanael eventually bent down to pick the banner from the ground. "Please explain this heinous thing."

"I didn't know you knew how to write in Esperanto." Franck squeezed my shoulder.

I gave his chest a light pound with my fist. "It's Russian."

"It's definitely *not* Russian."

"Well...close to Russian."

"Not even."

"Whatever it is," Nathanael said, "it's an embarrassing welcome banner, but that was the point, wasn't it?" He looked pointedly down at Jacinthe.

"*Bien sûr.*" Jacinthe raised her chin. "That's what you two get for abandoning us for an entire week."

"Left to our own devices, we get creative," I added.

Franck still hadn't let go of me. "I missed you," he whispered in my ear, and the warmth of his breath made me shiver. *We have to still be together next summer at Nathanael and Jacinthe's wedding.* The thought of us broken up reverberated through my bones like a toothache.

"Same."

"Come on." Nathanael put a proprietary arm around Jacinthe and took possession of the rolled-up banner. I was paying closer attention now to the dynamic between our friends. They seemed as happy as before, yet how could they be happy if Nathanael... I was still confused.

"We want to hear all about Moscow," I said.

"And the vodka and the caviar and the Russian girls," Jacinthe added.

"How about we grab some dinner together so you can tell us?" I suggested.

"Where?" Nathanael said.

"A *moules-frites* place," I suggested. "I could demolish some *moules-frites.*"

Paris was dotted all over with pseudo-Belgian restaurants

that specialized in serving the national specialty of mussels and french fries served with mayonnaise.

"There are some good ones in Montparnasse," Jacinthe said. *"Allons!"*

I had forgotten all about Jacinthe's parking job until we got close enough to her car to hear the symphony of several car alarms going off at the same time.

"What idiot—" Nathanael began to say and then stopped short when he saw that his fiancée's car at the center of the din.

"Ah!" He glanced down at Jacinthe, his eyes sparkling with amusement. "I should have known."

As we drew closer, I noticed the crowds of angry-looking people pointing at Jacinthe's car.

None of us rushed to open a car door. With the lynch mob surrounding us, any move we made toward it would have to be fast and coordinated.

"That's a truly majestic parking job," Franck said in a low voice that only the four of us could hear.

"Jacinthe taught me why cars have bumpers," I murmured.

Nathanael ruffled Jacinthe's blond hair. "I don't know if I could have done better myself."

"You couldn't," Jacinthe said.

"We'll debate that later," Nathanael said. "First, we must strategize our getaway. It must be fast. Ready?" He clicked the key fob so the trunk unlocked and popped open.

"You didn't give us any time to get ready!" I hissed. "Honest to God, Nathanael, of all the botched plans..."

People whirled around to locate the origin of the click.

"Hey!" a burly man wearing a blue, nylon Adidas tracksuit yelled. "Is that your car? Do you think we all enjoy going deaf?"

"Our car alarm isn't going off," Jacinthe said. I raised my eyebrows at her nerve. "Anyway, we're leaving."

Franck grabbed Nathanael's bag and shoved it and his own into the small trunk. He gestured at me to get in the back seat—fast. Franck slid in beside me, shut the door, then locked it.

Outside my car window, I saw Nathanael and Jacinthe engaged

in a yelling match with three other people, including the burly
Adidas man.

Finally, Nathanael flicked his fingers skyward, indicating
beyond a shadow of a doubt that he'd had enough of the conversation and that they could shove their complaints where the sun
didn't shine.

Jacinthe passed him the keys and slid in the passenger seat.
She turned to us and laughed. "Can you believe those people?
Getting so riled up... I'm sure they set off other people's car
alarms all the time. *Ce n'est pas leurs oignons, de toute façon.*" It's
wasn't their onions—or business—anyway. We peeled out of the
arrivals area.

On the way back in to Paris, I hardly noticed going around
the Arc de Triomphe, as Franck and I were too busy making
out in the back seat. It felt so wonderful to be surrounded again
by his warmth and his familiar scent. I caught something new
though—a whiff of foreign snow and cold. Something undis-
putedly Russian.

chapter **forty-nine**

"Back to reality," I said to Franck the next morning, just after I had hit snooze on the little alarm clock beside our bed. "Any ideas where you are going to start the job search?"

Franck stretched like an awakening cat. "Not really. I think I'll go for a coffee first and think it over. Do you want to come with me?"

I checked my watch. "Can't. I have one of my medieval classes." I gave him a quick peck on the cheek. "Maybe this afternoon?"

I got dressed quickly, and when I came to kiss him *au revoir*, Franck was still lying in bed, studying the white ceiling. He was usually such a morning person—not one for lounging in bed. *What is the time difference with Moscow anyway?*

I left the building and turned onto the boulevard Saint-Germain, feeling triumphant. The evening before at the Belgian restaurant, neither Jacinthe nor I had stooped to ask any questions about the women in Russia.

We listened to Franck and Nathanael's stories of the huge line to even get inside the McDonalds adjacent to the Red Square and of the dinner they'd had at a former Communist's house where vodka, boiled potatoes, and caviar were the entire menu. They described the imposing mafia types hanging out in their hotel lounge, with their huge guns proudly on display around their waists.

They also mentioned the insanity of the Russian bar scene, but neither Jacinthe nor I asked them who they met in there.

I hadn't been the girlfriend who pressed for learning every detail of his trip. I had my own life there in Paris. I was proud of that.

We had written a test in Madame Renier Bernadotte's medieval French class the week before, and even though I waited through every class, including this one, with apprehension, she still hadn't given us our marks for our oral presentations.

Madame Renier-Bernadotte never gave much feedback to anyone, although she had given a few of the students that went to the podium obviously unprepared a scathing look that I couldn't, to the best of my ability, remember having been given to me.

In the last five minutes of the class, Madame Renier Bernadotte handed back the tests in absolute silence. Everyone received theirs, except me.

Blood rushed to my face. Had I screwed up so badly that it wasn't even worth her time to mark my test or give it back? Maybe she had just thrown it directly into the garbage can. Yet I had studied hard. It was always difficult to tell, but I thought I had acquitted myself well.

"Mademoiselle Bradbury," she said after returning to her podium. "will you stay and see me after class?"

I slumped down further in my seat. My mind raced with nightmare scenarios of one of my role models asking me to please leave her class, informing me that I was unteachable.

Everyone filed out, staring at me as they departed. I got up and made my way down to Professor Renier-Bernadotte's podium on shaking legs. *Chin high. Chin high.*

"Mademoiselle Bradbury," she said as I drew near to her, "if you don't stop gawking at me like I'm a firing squad, I will lose all patience with you."

I took a deep breath. "*Oui*, Professeur."

"Now, I wanted to discuss this with you." Madame Renier-Bernadotte turned over my test paper on her podium. I leaned closer so that I could see my grade.

Madame Renier-Bernadotte marked tests and papers with a crimson pen and a bold scrawl that broadcasted she had better things to do. On my test paper, Madame Renier-Bernadotte had given me a nineteen out of twenty—a grade so good it was practically never achieved in France.

"Your test was exemplary," she said. "I was obliged to subtract a point for your sometimes-awkward turn of phrase, which I assume is from your English background. I wanted to felicitate you in person."

"*Merci*," I said, my voice unreliable. "I studied hard." I was having a hard time coming up with anything more eloquent to say. "I love the material."

"Do you know what grade I gave you on the oral report?" She cocked an auburn eyebrow at me.

"I have no idea," I said.

"Did you find it difficult?"

I could feel sweat beading on my forehead. "Yes. It was intimidating to get up there and speak in front of everyone...and you."

"I could tell you were nervous."

"I'm sure everyone could tell," I said ruefully.

"Yet you performed admirably."

"*Merci*?" I said, a question in it.

"You earned the top mark in the class."

"I did?" This was far and beyond anything I had hoped for.

"You did. I wanted to discuss something with you, Mademoiselle Bradbury. Have you given thought to what you are going to do after this year?"

A laugh escaped me at the irony of her question. All I seemed to do was think about what I would be doing after that year. "I've been contemplating different things." I didn't tell her that my soul searching had been more relationship-focused than academically-focused. I was not proud of this reality.

"And?"

"First, I need to go back to McGill to complete my Bachelor of Arts. My major is English literature and my minor is French literature. After next year, I'll graduate with my BA."

"Could you stay here at the Sorbonne and transfer to a Licence level program?"

"Well…given my experience in transferring between countries, it's complicated—"

"Complicated is resolvable, especially with someone like me as your mentor. What I am saying, Mademoiselle Bradbury, is that I believe you have potential in medieval studies. If you stay here in Paris, I would like you to study under me, possibly toward your *doctorat*. That generally takes about five years. It's a significant commitment, but if you love the work—"

Shock prickled my skin from head to toe. My role model wanted to be my mentor. I never in a million years thought that was even in the realm of possibility.

"I adore the material," I said.

"Such studies require absolute focus," she said. "It must come above everything else in your life."

Everything?

"So?" she said. "Are you interested? Are you ready to—"

"There are a lot of things I have to consider," I said, feeling embarrassed that I couldn't just leap at her offer immediately. "There is my degree at McGill, my boyfriend—"

"Boyfriend?" she said, with no small amount of disgust. "Relationships must come second to this, always. Frankly, I've always found them a waste of intellectual energy."

"Well—"

"I'm not sure if you're completely committed yet," she said and gave me back my test impatiently. "You make up your mind and get back to me."

After two classes, I began to walk home along the rue Monge. My thoughts were whirring. Madame Renier-Bernadotte had raised an entirely new aspect of our end-of-year conundrum. Maybe we could stay there in Paris. Maybe I could become a true Parisian, permanently. *Do I want that?*

"Laura!" I looked up from the pavement. *That was Franck's voice.*

"Laura! *Par ici!*" Franck called me, and I finally saw him about thirty feet down the rue Monge from where I was, walking in my direction. I was supposed to meet him back at the apartment after his job search. Seeing him this early meant that either the search had gone spectacularly well, or spectacularly bad.

I hurried to join him. When I did, he kissed me soundly, then lifted me up and swung me around with a whoop. Was Madame Renier-Bernadotte serious about having to choose between Franck and serious academic study if I pursued a doctorate under her?

Franck had a massive grin on his face.

"It can't be bad news," I said.

"I couldn't wait to tell you," he said. "C'mon. Let's go the Bistro."

By now "the Bistro" meant of course our usual hangout—the Brasserie Le Monge.

The scent of slowly cooking beef and homemade french fries, with that ever-present smell of red wine, welcomed us like a warm hug. We waved and said *bonjour* to everyone as we entered, and now many people in the bistro, including the *tabac* lady, the owner behind the bar, two of the *garçons*, and a few of the patrons who always seemed to be there, greeted us in return.

We sat down at our usual table lodged between the window, the old wooden telephone cabin, and the WC.

"You look happy," I observed.

"I got a job!" Franck grinned.

"Already? That's amazing."

"I told you not to worry."

I needed to tell him my triumph as well, but first I needed to marshal my tangled thoughts about it. "What is it?" I said. "Where? When does it start? How did you find something so quickly?

Franck chuckled, drawing out my anticipation. "No, no. Not yet." He was eyeing the *garçon* who was approaching us.

"*Deux cafés?*" the *garçon* asked.

"*Non,*" Franck answered. "*Deux coupes de Champagne.*"

"Champagne? This must be good. Tell me."

Franck lifted a finger. "Not yet. We need Champagne."

The *garçon* sped away and quickly returned with two bubbling Champagne flutes that he placed in front of us with a flourish.

"*Merci.*" I nodded in thanks. "So?" I prompted Franck.

"First." Franck lifted his glass and gestured at me to do the same, and we clinked them together. "*Santé.*"

"*Santé,*" I said, taking a sip. As always, the bubbles tasted like celebration. "And congratulations," I added, trying to hide my impatience. "Now...details?"

"Yes."

"Tell me!" I almost shrieked.

Franck laughed. "I went for a coffee and a walk first thing. I asked myself this question: Where do I want to spend time while I'm here in Paris?"

"That's an unconventional way to approach a job hunt," I said. Franck always amazed me with his thinking. It was invariably unconventional.

"Maybe, but doesn't it make sense? I hated working at la Défense every day. It's fine to visit occasionally, but it's not the true Paris. It's not why we came here, is it—to work in modern office buildings?"

I understood. Even though I preferred my classes in the New Sorbonne with Madame Renier-Bernadotte, I enjoyed the actual experience of sitting in the historical amphitheaters and classrooms of the old Sorbonne more—even my Dickens class. But Madame Renier-Bernadotte worked out of the New Sorbonne, so if I studied under her...

"No," I agreed.

"So...I thought, what about the Louvre?"

"The Louvre?"

"Of course. I spent tons of time there when I was at the

Sorbonne, but its collections are so rich that you could work there your entire life and not take it all in."

"You know, I read something about people who visit the museums in Paris and experience some kind of bizarre psychosis," I said. "They become overwhelmed by the sheer amount of priceless and incredible artwork they have seen and start hallucinating."

"I can believe it," Franck said. "But what better way to experience the Louvre than to work there? I can enjoy little bits of it every day. Besides, it gives me more free time to spend with you." His thumb caressed my palm.

I was certain Madame Renier-Bernadotte's plans for my academic future did not include leisure time with Franck—this was going to be a problem.

"You got a job at the Louvre? This morning?"

"It was nothing." Franck waved his hand. "As of about one o'clock today, I am officially an employee of the Louvre. I get my laminated card and start tomorrow."

"Amazing. What are you doing there?"

"Coat check," Franck said.

I didn't know what to say exactly. Franck had a master's from the Sorbonne. Didn't that make being a coat-check at the Louvre a little...beneath him?

No, that was ridiculous. Being a coat check *at the Louvre* was different. To spend hours in proximity with all that amazing art... if Franck was thrilled, I should be too.

"I thought all the employees at the Louvre had to be *les fonctionnaires?*" Government jobs were hard to get. There's no way he could have landed one of those coveted positions in the past few hours. Even more than a CDD, it meant full benefits, making it almost impossible to be fired and generally an extremely relaxed attitude to actually working.

"They are." Franck nodded, smiling like the Cheshire cat.

"How did you manage it?"

"I went up to the coat check and asked if they had any jobs available. They shooed me away. I saw someone who looked like a manager come out from an office behind the coat check, so I pushed my way in and handed him my resumé and said I could start immediately. It turned out they had just put an employee on disability an hour before because he had been caught stealing all the furs women left there."

"He wasn't fired?"

"Of course not. He's a *fonctionnaire*. He can't be fired. *De toute façon*, that isn't the point of my story." Franck clinked his flute against mine to bring me back to the conversation at hand.

"It's just so weird that he can't be fired for that."

"Laura…"

"Okay, okay. Sorry. Continue." I took another sip of the Champagne, its fruity effervescence dancing on my tongue, making me feel almost giddy.

"The fur guy was caught loading a bunch of minks and sables into the trunk of his car the night before, after having been suspected for weeks, so putting him on disability was the only way to get rid of him. The manager was stressed because if he didn't rehire someone else right away, he risked having his budget cut. He hired me on the spot. It's only a CDD, but while I am working, I get all the benefits of a civil servant."

"Fantast—" I said.

"I know! Better yet, look at these." Franck pulled a wad of large tickets out of his pocket.

"Wha—"

"Free passes to the Louvre. I can get as many as I want, and I'm allowed to roam around the museum after it closes to the public, while they do the cleaning at night."

Franck ordered us fresh flutes of Champagne. "Do you realize what this means?" he said. "We can go there whenever we want, for free. Isn't that amazing?"

"You can also figure out when the good times are to visit, you know, when there aren't so many people."

"I have high hopes of being able to sneak you in after hours with me."

"Yes. You'll be doing that."

Now was the perfect time to tell him about my triumph, but the words were stuck in my throat. Maybe I needed to think about it on my own before sharing the news. At moments like this, when things with Franck felt so easy, it was hard to remember that there was any uncertainty at all about where we were headed. It felt absurd that we could be anything but a couple.

After our second glasses of Champagne, I grasped Franck's hand, and we decided to head to the Greek *quartier* for a shawarma and a North African pastry for dessert.

As we walked up la rue Monge, I felt like a true Parisian. But did I want to be a true Parisian if that meant putting academics before love? Was Paris the city I wanted to live in for the next five years at least? An icy rain was spitting down from the leaden sky. I would tell Franck, just...not quite yet.

Even though it was March, there were no signs of spring, which meant to me that we could enjoy months of museum-exploring weather and I would have time to consider my options.

Franck, is his own unique way, was a bit of a genius.

chapter fifty

The next day, I walked over to the Louvre after classes and met Franck under the Pyramid after his first shift at work there.

I was amazed at how I.M. Pei's modern architecture somehow melded perfectly with the opulent and ancient Louvre palace. It was something that shouldn't technically have worked, but did.

Once I had made it down to the main entrance floor, where light from the glass pyramid above flooded down over everyone, the noise of many shoes against the marble floor echoed around me. I spotted Franck behind the coat check. His smile told me his first day had gone well.

"So?" I asked and gave him a kiss.

"Come on, let's go up. I'll tell you outside."

"Out of earshot?" I asked, switching to English.

"Exactly," he answered in the same language.

We walked out among the triangular pools of water among the pyramids in the majestic courtyard.

"*Alors*? I asked.

"It was hilarious." He slowed down to sit on one of the ledges of the water triangles and dabbled his finger in it, disturbing the reflection of the Pyramid above. "There are four times more coat check staff members than needed, so we work for about half an hour each, and then get two hours to go and wander around the museum, go back and work for a half hour, then repeat."

"How can they justify doing that with people's tax money?" I watched the gray puffs of scattered cloud move across the pale blue sky in the water's surface.

"Honestly, nobody seems to care."

I looked up at Franck. "That's so…shameless."

He just shrugged. "The first thing I was taught on the job was not how to put away people's coats but rather how I was to act like we were overworked and understaffed at all times."

I thought for a moment about the immense amount of state funds that were wasted every day in France if this same approach to civil servant jobs was spread over several sectors… The numbers quickly became more than my brain could handle.

"Unreal," I managed finally.

"I know," Franck said. "I mean, I do feel guilty—but not much, because this is France, after all."

"What difference does that make?"

Franck stood up and moved closer to wear I sat. He snuck his fingers behind my hair and began to massage the nape of my neck. I shivered with pleasure.

"There is a certain unabashed pride here in milking the system. It is not seen as a bad thing by most people. Everybody does it, and if you don't…well…you are viewed as a bit dumb."

"But it's morally wrong." I said, though I was far too focused on Franck's fingers on the back of my neck to be truly indignant.

"What are morals, after all?"

My mind flashed back to my conversation with Jacinthe. I hoped that Franck's French approach to morality applied to civil servant jobs and jaywalking only.

I sighed, more from pleasure than protest. "Don't go all French philosopher on me."

"I can't help it," he protested. "It's in my DNA. Besides, what am I supposed to do? I don't want to get anyone in trouble. It's just for a few months. It's not like I will be taking advantage of the system for my entire life."

My heart flipped. Did this mean Franck had decided to come back to Montreal with me in a few months? Assuming, of course, that I still wanted to go back after hearing Professor Renier-Bernadotte's offer. I opened my mouth to ask, when Franck said, "Also, guess what?"

"What?"

"I've been asked to work a fashion show under la Pyramid at the beginning of April."

I wanted to go back to the whole "few months" issue. "Great, but I just wanted to see what you—"

"*Oui*, and I think I'll be able to get a free pass for you."

"Awesome, but back to what you said just before—"

"It's just the beginning, *ma belle*," he said, his thumb caressing my palm. "Just the beginning."

One of Franck's new colleagues appeared next to him, full of questions about Franck's first day on the job. The moment was lost.

The beginning of what? I needed to know.

Grace and I were in the café on the rue Monge. She was recounting her further communications with her beau.

"I am friendly but also make it clear I have my own thing going on here in Paris," she said.

"So, how exactly do you do that?" I asked.

Before she could answer, the bell over the door rang. I was shocked to see Madame Fox walk in, supported by her ebony cane and wearing one of her numerous tweed Chanel suits.

She must have seen me staring. She deigned us with a brief nod and said, "*Bonjour*, Mesdemoiselles." Grace's eyes widened at being included in the greeting.

Once we'd echoed timid *bonjours*, Madame Fox turned her back on us and ordered something at the counter.

Grace tore her gaze back to me. "Who is that?" Luckily, we were speaking in English.

"My neighbor," I said, wishing yet again that Madame Fox would make good on that invitation into the inner sanctum of her apartment. To be honest though, I was losing hope.

"She looks…old-school," Grace said. "Anyway…" She continued our interrupted conversation and regaled me with more examples of how she was remaining friendly but aloof, despite the fact that she wanted nothing more than to take the next plane back to Tennessee and fall into her beau's arms. "Also, have you forgotten about your promise to set me up with a French guy?"

"I haven't," I answered, distracted. "I just haven't located the right blind date for you yet. I'm on it though."

I wondered, as I was watching Madame Fox being served a glass of red wine at the bar, whether I was doing the same sort of thing with Franck that Grace was doing with her beau—protecting myself by pretending I cared less than I did.

"Well, at least we've experienced love," Grace said, nodding toward Madame Fox who was sipping her red wine. Her fox stole eyed us beadily over her shoulder. "I don't think some were so lucky."

"I wouldn't be so sure about that," I said. "We all have secrets. Especially Madame Fox."

After our coffee, I went to the stunning *fleuriste* just a few minutes' walk down the boulevard Saint-Germain from our apartment. The day had begun gray and rainy, but when Grace and I emerged from the café, the clouds had cleared and the sun shone. The air felt different. Softer. It smelled of exhaust, as usual, but behind that there was a whiff of freshness.

As I walked along, I felt the sun's warmth on the crown of my head. Spring?

Mémé was coming to stay with us for two days. Franck's aunt and uncle would be dropping her off in about an hour's time.

Franck was working his shift at the Louvre, but the night before, we had cleaned our tiny abode from top to bottom. I couldn't wait for Mémé to see our life there and I also couldn't wait to just see *her*. There was nothing to welcome a guest like fresh flowers, hence my trip to the *fleuriste*.

The thought made my feet feel lighter as I strolled along the pavement. I paused at the vintage bookstore and examined the fascinating ancient texts in its dusty window. I dodged the man on the moped who had just rolled up near me to park it on the sidewalk. He whipped off his helmet to reveal a chiseled face, made even more attractive by what looked like a nose that had been broken in the past.

I reached the *fleuriste* where buckets and baskets of flowers gushed out of the storefront and spilled on to the surrounding sidewalk like a fragrant, floral tidal wave. Inside, I soaked up being surrounded by so many sublime flowers and bouquets. The shopkeeper was tiny and elegant, just like a primrose, and flitted around her shop—a fairy in an enchanted garden.

Eventually, I decided on a bouquet of white roses. I had been sorely tempted by the ranunculus, but white roses were Mémé's favorite flower. There was a sad song she loved entitled "*Les Roses blanches*," sung by Tino Rossi, which she could sing in its entirety at the drop of a hat.

On my walk back home, with my bouquet of white roses wrapped in brown florist paper and tied with a bunch of raffia, I noticed there were now tiny green buds decorating what had been, the week before, bare branches.

Spring. Possibility. The bounce in my step slowed. We were running out of time in Paris. Could we also be running out of time together? I thought back to what Professor Renier Bernadotte had discussed with me. Or maybe we weren't…

An hour later, I had put the vase of white roses in the center of our table and a smaller bouquet of white lilac bunches on the bookshelf. We had made up our bed for Mémé with freshly laundered sheets. Franck and I were planning on sharing a single mattress usually hidden under the bed.

I went downstairs, greeting Monsieur Pierrepont, who was on his way in with his evening baguette. Madame la Gardienne was at the bottom of the stairs on her hands and knees, scrubbing the tiles of our lobby. It smelled of lemon.

"*Bonjour,*" I said.

"*Bonjour,* Mademoiselle." She sat up and nodded, inscrutable as usual.

"My husband's grandmother is arriving today for a short stay," I said. "I'm just going to wait for her outside."

She glanced up at me with an expression that made me ask myself why I was so presumptuous as to think she would care to know the minutiae of my life.

"Right, then," I said, awkward. "I'll just go now."

"*Oui,*" she said, and resumed her scrubbing.

I burst out the front doors of the building and was still fighting the blush in my face when Franck's uncle drove up and double-parked in front of our building.

"There's no parking!" he called out his minivan window. "We've been around the block three times! Can I pass The Package off to you here?"

The van door slid open and Mémé's foot dangled over the side. "Jean! Don't call me a Package!" she said.

Franck's aunt leapt out of the passenger seat and handed Mémé down to me, then passed me a soft-sided, *toile de Jouy* bag and an armful of assorted blankets and shawls and capes.

She kissed me quickly. "We must be off."

"You can't stay for the *apéritif*?" I asked.

"I'm sorry, we've been running late all day. We'll stay when we come to retrieve The Package."

"More kir for us, then!" Mémé squeezed my arm. "Laura, you must not ever refer to me as The Package."

"I would never dare," I said, speaking the absolute truth.

We bid our speedy good-byes, and I tried to help Mémé across the first courtyard, but she shook me off, making it abundantly clear that she needed no assistance, *merci beaucoup.*

We entered our lobby, where Madame la Gardienne was still scrubbing the floor. To my surprise, she stood up.

"*Bonjour,* Madame." She nodded to Mémé. "It is a pleasure having you stay with us."

"The pleasure is mine, Madame," Mémé said, and nodded regally.

The elevator arrived, and *la gardienne* opened the metal door for us.

"*Merci,* Madame." Mémé nodded again.

What was that? I wondered as we stepped into the elevator. I was certain I had missed some crucial French social dynamic, although I had no clue what it was.

"*Bon alors!*" Mémé threw her floral bag down on one of the chairs in the living room once I had given her the "grand tour" and she had rhapsodized for several minutes over the white roses. "I think this calls for a kir," she announced. She unzipped her bag and extracted a large glass bottle of cassis.

"You brought your own cassis?" I asked. "We have some, you know..."

Indeed, a Burgundian could not call themselves a true Burgundian without a bottle of cassis in their home. "Besides, that must have been incredibly heavy. I had never seen such a large cassis bottle."

"Ah, but you don't have cassis like this. I had to bring it to share my newest discovery with you." She thumped her bottle on the table. "*Voici* Supercassis!"

I leaned down and peered at the label. Indeed, emblazoned across the front was "Supercassis."

"What does that mean?" I looked up at her.

"It's more concentrated, thicker, more alcohol...better. We need glasses and some aligoté. Do you have some aligoté?"

I snorted. "Please, Mémé. Have you taught me nothing?"

We quickly settled down, each with a special Burgundian kir glass filled with Supercassis (one-third) and Burgundy aligoté (two-thirds). I had cut up some *saucisson sec* from our favorite *charcutier* on la rue Monge. This humble snack hit all the right notes—sweet, salty, and alcoholic.

On our second glasses, we veered from a discussion about the virtues of black currants for all kind of health complaints (rheumatism, dementia, and stomach disorders, according to Mémé) to how Franck and I were finding our Parisian experience.

"How I would love to be young and smart and independent and living in Paris like you," Mémé rhapsodized. "That wasn't ever an option open to me, you know. I grew up extremely sheltered."

"I know. I'm lucky," I said. "Sometimes, though, I wonder if life wasn't simpler back then."

"Don't be stupid." I wasn't offended, as Mémé was never one to mince words with anyone. "There was nothing simple about it. Do you think it was simple for me to get married when I was eighteen and to not even know about sex until my wedding night? Do you think it was simple for me to divorce my first husband when I was barely twenty because he couldn't stop seducing other women even though he had two babies at home?"

"I guess I never thought of it that way. Yes, that must have been the opposite of simple."

"You have no idea! I divorced in the teeth of opposition from my family, the church, the entire village…it wasn't just complicated. Society was so rigid and judgmental back then. It was impossible."

"But you did it," I said.

"Yes, I did."

"I guess I just keep expecting life to be simpler, you know—"

"But life never had been simple, Laura, for anyone. It never will be. That is not the nature of life, or of people." She clinked her glass against mine. "But cassis…cassis has always been beautifully simple."

"Even Supercassis?" I asked, feeling my ears getting warm with the effects of my second Supercassis kir.

"Especially Supercassis!"

chapter **fifty-one**

When we had emptied our second glasses as well as the plate of *saucisson*, Mémé tapped her palm on the tabletop with that definitive way of hers.

"*Ce nest pas le tout!*" she said. "Franck is going to come home from work and find the two of us giggling over our kirs with nothing made for dinner. Have you planned anything, or should we improvise?"

"Actually, Franck already planned a menu and is picking up what he needed on his way home."

"What is he making?"

"I'm not sure...he cooks more than I do, to be honest." I had always felt ashamed of my lack of culinary expertise compared to Mémé's brilliance.

"If I was smart like you, I wouldn't waste time cooking, either," Mémé said. "I would be going to school and studying hard and stuffing my head full of things like you do. Why on earth would you waste your time in the kitchen?"

"But I like eating so much," I said. "It feels selfish that I still haven't improved my cooking."

"Bah!!" Mémé said. "Besides, I'm here. Do you know if Franck has planned a dessert?"

"I don't know. I don't think so." I tended to have the sweet tooth in our couple.

"Let's make something," Mémé said.

"We don't have much food." Indeed, we never had much food stored in our fridge, as it was only a small, bar-sized one and markets were happening every day in our neighborhood.

"Have you got eggs?"

"Yes."

"Have you got butter?"

"Yes."

"Have you got white sugar?"

I wracked my brain. "Um…I think so,"

"We can make floating islands!"

"Don't you have to whip the egg whites? I don't have any kind of hand mixer, or even a hand whisk."

Mémé stared at me. "No whisk?"

"No." Shame, as well as the kir warmed my ears.

She slapped the table. "*Pas de problème*, we'll improvise. I'll just whip them up with a fork."

We moved our party to the kitchen, where I watched, riveted, as Mémé—with her sinewy eighty-three-year-old arm—whipped up egg whites into stiff peaks with a mere fork.

"All the studying in the world couldn't teach me that," I murmured, in awe.

"Oh this?" she said, without breaking her whipping pace in the slightest. "This is as stupid as cabbage."

"Yet they don't teach it to us at the Sorbonne."

Mémé chuckled.

There was no way I had the arm muscles to do that. I was certain that Franck, even though he was strong, couldn't either. Mémé was truly superhuman in the kitchen.

It hit me at that moment how losing Franck would also mean losing Franck's family. Maybe not Stéphanie—not completely anyway, as she had been my friend before she introduced me to

Franck. Still, Burgundians are nothing if not sticklers for family loyalty. Franck's family felt like my French family now. I couldn't imagine being in France without them being part of our lives. If Franck didn't want a commitment beyond our Paris year, I would lose this crazy, irrational, fiery group of people I had come to love almost as much as I loved Franck.

"*Voilà!*" Mémé showed me her bowl of shiny, firm egg white peaks, which looked like the view seen when flying over the Alps in the middle of winter.

"You're incredible," I murmured, my chest tight.

"You know, sometimes I am," Mémé admitted.

The next day, after Franck left for work, and before I needed to leave for classes, Mémé and I stepped out to grab some ingredients for the *oeufs en meurette* she wanted to make for us that night. Her floating islands—airy and sweet—the night before had been the perfect compliments to Franck's *boeuf bourguignon*.

I was locking the apartment door behind us when Madame Fox stepped out of the elevator. She wheeled her Louis Vuitton grocery cart behind her. It looked full, so she must have been on her way back from her daily shopping.

I introduced Madame Fox and Mémé. Madame Fox lost no time in telling Mémé how I had helped "*cher* Monsieur Pierrepont" after the gas explosion in his apartment. I was rather touched, as up until then, Madame Fox had given me no indication she remembered that day or her promise of an invitation to her apartment.

As if she was a mind-reader, Madame Fox asked, "Would you like to come to my apartment for a *café* or *thé*?"

I glanced over at Mémé, who was nodding.

"It would be with pleasure," I answered for both of us. "*Merci*."

Eyeing the two women, I guessed they were probably of a similar decade. They were very different though—Madame Fox, all old Parisian refinement and Mémé, the respected village matriarch. Still, their erect posture and flashing eyes made me suspect they had many things in common—strength of character being one of them. As for me, I discreetly wanted to uncover a bit more of the mystery of Madame Fox and Monsieur Pierrepont's relationship during the war.

Madame Fox's apartment was exactly as I had expected. Her furniture was almost entirely antiques, and the scent of dried roses enveloped me as soon as I crossed the threshold.

"Please sit." Madame Fox gestured to the damask couch, which looked to be antique Louis something-or-other.

"Mémé and I sat in silence while Madame Fox disappeared down a hallway, presumably into a kitchen. Her apartment was significantly larger than ours and a different footprint. I saw doors to two separate rooms off the room we were in. I caught Mémé's eye, and she widened her gaze meaningfully, nodding to indicate she was impressed by the surroundings. "*Très élégant*," she murmured under her breath.

Madame Fox brought us a tray of coffee in little espresso cups that I could tell, from the smoothness and fineness of the plain white porcelain, were from Limoges.

Madame Fox didn't seem particularly interested in conversing with me, but asked Mémé several questions. Mémé explained that for years she had been the village *boulang*ère. "But I had to retire from that life eventually," Mémé said. "Even though I adored baking, it took its toll—especially during the war."

"Ah. The war," Madame Fox answered, a knowing look in her eye.

Oh yes, please talk about the war.

Mémé went on to explain how she was told by everyone to evacuate her village, which, in the Saône-et-Loire area of Southern Burgundy, was dangerously close to the demarcation line between occupied and unoccupied France.

"But you stayed?" Madame Fox surmised.

"Of course I stayed," Mémé said, with a toss of her chin. "Having a *boulangère* who was...shall we say...*sensitive* to the French cause was useful. Besides, the villagers needed my bread. Many of them were close to starving, as the Germans took anything good to eat.

"She was given a medal for it by Charles de Gaulle after the war," I said to Madame Fox, feeling goosebumps of pride. "But

Mémé refused it because, she always says, she didn't do anything that any decent person wouldn't have done."

"Ah, Laura," Mémé chided me. "There is no need to mention that. You know, no one brags about the war." Her eyes met Madame Fox's.

"Still…," Mémé added slowly, "I wish sometimes that I had accepted it, just to show my children and my great-grandchildren so they could understand."

"You needn't feel embarrassed about that, Madame Menneveau," Madame Fox said. "I did accept a medal. I had lost so many friends and family and loved ones, I reasoned my medal honored them more than it honored me. Regretfully, I don't have any grandchildren to show it to, or any children for that matter. Isn't that a shame?"

"Was your husband killed at the front?" Mémé asked.

"No. We thought he was for a long time. He was away for years—in a German prison camp—but he survived. He came back to me after the war but…he was never the same man again. The Germans managed to kill him, without killing him, do you understand?"

"Yes," Mémé said. "My brother spent three years in a German prison."

If Mémé wasn't going to ask, I was. "What was your medal for?" I asked Madame Fox.

"Laura," Mémé chided, "we don't ask—"

"That's all right, Madame Menneveau." Madame Fox chuckled. I didn't know she was capable of such a sound. "She is far too young to understand. Besides, she's a foreigner. I won't tell you, Mademoiselle, but I'll show you."

Madame Fox went over to a polished mahogany armoire and used a large, metal key with a preposterously huge pink silk tassel attached to open it up with. I caught a glimpse of piles of folded linens and the glint of polished silver. She removed a rectangular velvet box and closed the armoire door again.

She brought the box over to me and opened it up, then placed the open box in my hands. "That is the Resistance medal," she said. "There are a handful of us in this building who received one after the war. This building was an interesting place to be during those years."

I peered down at the medal, nestled in its bed of black silk. It was bronze, with a cross with two bars on its face and a bunch of roman numerals at the bottom. The rosette was striped silk, khaki and a beautiful shade of coral. I sat, robbed of words, in awe of what Madame Fox must have done to deserve this.

Mémé gestured for me to pass it over to her. She took the box and examined it with those sharp eyes of hers. "That is a great honor, indeed," she said. "I can only imagine the kind of things you had to do and the fear you must have felt."

A mysterious look passed between Madame Fox and Mémé. "I have an idea that you know quite well what was involved," Madame Fox said to her.

Mémé simply nodded.

"And Monsieur Pierrepont," I prompted. "He must have been in the Resistance?"

"Yes. He couldn't go to the front because he had tuberculosis as a child, but he was extremely...active...shall we say, here in Paris. He has an identical medal to this one. In fact, we worked together during those years."

The mystery deepened. "Did he have a wife, children?"

Madame Fox shook her head. "No. He never did." She blinked. Were those tears?

"It's so sad seeing him alone," I said, then wished I could take the words back. Madame Fox was alone just as much as Monsieur Pierrepont, from what I could tell.

"He's not alone," Madame Fox snapped, steel back in her eyes. "He has me."

With this, she changed the conversation to recipes and cooking, and no more was said about the war. I cursed my inept questions.

Madame Fox had believed her husband was dead during most of the war, and she and Monsieur Pierrepont lived two doors away from each other. I had a strong hunch that they were much more than neighbors and co-conspirators.

chapter **fifty-two**

Mémé's visit whipped by far too fast, and she wrung every drop of joy out of what she quickly came to call her "Parisian Adventure."

After Franck's aunt and uncle came to pick her up, our apartment felt empty for several days.

Luckily, Franck was as good as his word, and a few weeks later, I found myself dressing for a cutting-edge fashion show underneath the Louvre. My wardrobe seemed to consist mainly of scarves. Racks of them were displayed on almost every street corner in Paris, and they never failed to catch my eye or tempt me to open my wallet.

I decided that everyone there would be too interested in the models, themselves and what other people in the fashion crowd (of which I was definitely not a member) were wearing to pay much attention to me. My goal would be, like our evening at the musée d'Orsay, to dress in such a way that I didn't stand out as a complete hick—more damage control than anything else.

I plucked out a pair of black velvet jeans, added a pair of black patent Doc Marten boots that laced up to my mid-calf in the front, and a black rayon V-neck top that was probably the dressiest thing I owned. I pulled my hair up in a messy chignon and anchored it with a black clip. *Pas mal.*

Franck came home after his shift to pick me up. He was wearing the black pants and white dress shirt required by his job, over which he threw on a uniform blazer. "Musée du Louvre" was embroidered discreetly on the front lapel.

When we arrived near the point of the inverted pyramid underneath the Louvre, where the fashion show was setting up, Franck parked me there.

"I have to work during the first part," he said. "To safely hang up all those haute couture coats, I guess."

"You might get some capes in the mix," I said.

"Dare I dream?" Franck kissed my cheek and hung an accreditation card attached to a lanyard around my neck.

I peered down at it. "Laura Bradbury – Press" was typed in bold black letters.

"It's probably a good idea to come up with a magazine you work for," Franck said. "Go find a spot to stand, and I'll come join you as soon as I can."

I found a gap in the crowd where the runway split into two paths on either side of the point of the inverted pyramid. It was a clever way of integrating this spectacular architectural feature in the show. The entire place reeked of expensive perfume and the waxy undertone of lipstick.

Every available chair had a name written on a piece of paper taped to its seat. I was hardly going to attempt ousting some fashion god from their designated seat. Instead, I stood on the sidelines of the crowd. I recognized Betsey Johnson by her preposterous hair and Karl Lagerfeld by his black suit and fan.

Which imaginary magazine did I write for? I wondered. Was it better to come up with a make-believe publication or a magazine that existed? I couldn't give the name of a French magazine or even a British or American fashion magazine. People knew those too well and there were probably already journalists from those publications in there, in designated chairs no less.

I decided to say I wrote for a Canadian fashion magazine. It would explain my lack of designer outfit (I could safely assume that Canadian fashion was something French people rarely—or never—thought about).

I amused myself catching glimpses of famous people in the crowd. I thought I saw Caroline de Monaco and perhaps her sister, but I couldn't be certain.

"What is your magazine?" The nasal accents of a Parisian came from slightly behind me. I turned around and found myself confronted with a woman who fit in with this crowd perfectly. She was rail thin and wore a loose, sack-like silver lamé dress that highlighted her bony collarbones.

"Um. *Fashion Canada*," I said.

She stared at me down her thin nose in a way that reminded me forcibly of Alexandrine. "Canada?" she questioned.

"Yes." Short answers were probably best if I wanted to keep up my charade.

"But there is no fashion in Canada," she said. "Only dog sleds and such."

"Ah...well. *Fashion Canada* magazine is not about dogsleds."

The woman examined my outfit and her eyes narrowed. "This is all very strange."

I decided to dredge up the lessons I had learned from Dale Carnegie's *How to Win Friends and Influence People*—a book my father had encouraged me to read when I turned ten. *People love talking about themselves.*

"You look every inch Parisian," I said. "There is no need to ask where you are from."

"She ran a hand over her already shiny, smooth hair. "*C'est vrai*," she said. "I was born just one block from the place de l'Étoile."

"It shows," I said. I snuck a peek at her name tag. Her name was Estelle and she worked for *Elle* magazine. Of course. "Being a Canadian," I said, "I would never try to be Parisian."

She looked down at my Doc Martens and sighed. "I am glad to hear that. So many girls and young women idolize us—*les vraies Parisennes*—but one must be born here to understand what being Parisian is all about. All the others…they are just pathetic imposters. So pathetic. I was lucky enough to be born in Paris, so I am *Parisienne*. You were born in…"

"On Vancouver Island," I said.

"So, you are…what does that make you, *enfin?*" she asked.

"An Islander," I said. "And a Canadian." Saying the words, I felt goosebumps ripple down my arms. I stood up straighter. Why had I ever tried to be Parisian. She was a snob, but she was also right: it was *pathetic*.

Why spend my whole life trying to be something I could never be?

I might live in Paris. I might speak French. I might even be studying French in Paris, but I will never be a Parisian. To pretend was an insult to my island, my country, and myself. I wanted Paris—yes—but I wanted more than Paris. I thought I had just found my answer to Madame Renier-Bernadotte's question about my plans for the next year.

The Parisian raised her hand, spotting an acquaintance. *"Tiens!* Alexandrine!"

I squinted. Surely there had to be hundreds of Alexandrines in Paris. But now, I could see through the crowd, it was just my luck that this was the one Alexandrine whom I actually knew in Paris. I turned my head away as Estelle flitted off. I wasn't in the mood to be subjected to the double-whammy of her and Alexandrine's condescending attitude.

My mind was whirring too fast with a new revelation. I needed to see more than just Paris to figure out who I was. I needed to go back to Montreal and finish what I had started.

chapter **fifty-three**

During the last weekend in April, I finally made good on my promise to Grace and set her up with a French guy.

His name was Fabien and he was, according to Jacinthe, freshly arrived in Paris from Nice in the South of France.

He worked at Hennessey Cognac, a sister company to Moet & Chandon. At work functions, he apparently was in the habit of regaling Jacinthe with his goal of living in America, buying a Harley-Davidson, and riding off into the proverbial sunset. I had asked Jacinthe to keep Grace in mind several months before, so Jacinthe asked Fabien if he wanted to meet an authentic American girl.

Fabien did not hesitate.

Hennessy and Moët & Chandon were orchestrating an evening for their big clients on a covered barge that would work its way slowly down the Seine from the Trocadero and Eiffel Tower to the Bastille, then back and forth a few times until the soirée petered out.

I had planned to meet Grace at the Trocadero at six thirty in the evening. Earlier, Momo, Caroline, Franck, and I met at Jacinthe's for a fortifying glass of Champagne prior to putting on our coats and venturing outside. The sun was getting paler in a spring sky. A gusty wind sent clouds scudding behind the Eiffel Tower.

Caroline and Momo were ripe for mischief, having already stopped at a café on their way to Jacinthe's for several *apéritifs.* Alexandrine had been on the barge since that morning, feverishly beautifying it for the Paris elite.

As we rushed along the blustery sidewalks toward the Trocadero, I asked Jacinthe why Nathanael had opted to stay late at work, concerned for my friend about what he might be doing instead.

"There's no way he could come," Franck answered before Jacinthe. "Nathanael gets crazy seasick."

"You said it was on a huge barge though," I said. "It's not like it's the ocean. The Seine is a river. Nobody gets seasick on a *river.*"

"Nathanael does," Jacinthe said. "When my sister was in town once, we went out for a drink on one of those *péniches* that are permanently attached to the *quai* near Notre-Dame. There wasn't any food involved; it was just a drink. Nathanael only lasted about ten minutes before he had to stumble off and throw up in the Seine."

"Ugh," I said, thinking that he would have fared poorly growing up on an island like I had, but I was nevertheless reassured that Nathanael's excuse sounded legitimate.

Momo and Caroline had their heads together, snickering. "Hey you two!" I called to them. "Go easy on Grace. Be nice."

"What about this Fabien person?" Caroline asked. "Do we need to be nice to him too?"

"Yes!" Jacinthe said.

"Damn," Momo muttered. "There's nothing Caroline and I adore as much as matchmaking. I am certain we could do a lot to help them along as a couple."

"*Non, non, non!*" Jacinthe reprimanded, pulling her coat tight against the wind. "The matchmaking has been *done.* I took care of that. Now all we need to do is leave them alone."

Caroline and Momo answered with non-committal sounds that left me far from reassured, but I caught a glimpse of Grace waiting on the breezy Trocadero, so couldn't admonish them further.

"Hi, Grace!" I said in English. I made a quick round of introductions and was pleased to see that everyone was being docile with my Southern Belle friend, so far.

Grace and I fell behind the rest of the group as we hurried toward the pont d'Iéna.

"How do I look?" Grace pulled open her beige trench coat, revealing a pale pink, knee-length taffeta dress. In her hair, she had affixed a matching pale pink taffeta bow. I noticed that her shoes were dyed the same color.

"It was one of my homecoming dresses from college," she explained.

"You look fantastic," I said. If Fabien fantasized about the quintessential American woman, he was not going to be disappointed.

In contrast, I had gone for my usual damage-control Parisian black.

"Ah. Y'all are so sweet," she cooed. "Now, tell me again about Fabien."

"I honestly don't know much more than you," I said as we walked along, buffeted by the wind. "I still haven't met him. He works with Jacinthe, and he'll be waiting for us on the barge. He does have to work a bit tonight, you know, socializing and making sure everyone has a good time and keeping the Cognac flowing."

"Oh Lord." Grace's teeth chattered together. "I'm so nervous. Is he handsome?"

"I guess we'll find out soon." We had made our way to the quai Branly where the barge was docked. It didn't look much like a barge, though—Alexandrine had somehow transformed it into a floating fairyland.

"It's so romantic," Grace breathed.

It was decked out with hundreds upon hundreds of strings of fairy lights, and the entire space sparkled the same way the Eiffel Tower does at night. Alexandrine was talented, I grudgingly realized.

Grace staggered as a squall buffeted us from the side. I took her arm. "Come on," I said. "Let's get on board and meet this sexy Frenchman of yours."

Grace pulled back. "This was a bad idea."

"Nonsense." I pulled her arm harder. "French men can be pretty fantastic."

"I still love my beau."

"Then consider this the perfect opportunity of finding that out for sure," I said, dragging Grace on board.

Inside, I was relieved to see numerous trays of Champagne flutes being circulated. I grabbed two and thrust one in Grace's hand. I peeled off her jacket. "Here, drink this while I go and give these to the coat check."

"Don't leave—"

"I'll be right back."

I managed to quickly divest myself of our coats but had lost Franck and the rest of our friends in the milling crowd. I went back to Grace and found her rooted to the same spot. I was relieved to see she had drained her flute and hadn't bolted. I grabbed another one for her off a tray floating by. "Here," I said. "Enjoy this one too." The barge began to rock gently back and forth. We had cast off the *quai*.

She turned to me, her eyes haunted. "I'm going to get off this barge. I don't think I can do this. I thought I could be interested in someone else if I really, really tried. I told myself I *owed* it to myself, but—"

"The barge is in the middle of the Seine now," I said. "You can't get off right this second."

"Oh no!" Grace stared at me, her eyes huge in her pale face. "What have I done?"

Just then, Jacinthe appeared at my side with an extraordinarily handsome man wearing an exquisitely tailored suit. He was a looker with icy blue eyes under a head of thick brown hair that waved off an alabaster brow. His features were lean and chiseled—his smile, seduction incarnate.

I stood and stared. Could this be…?

"Laura, I'd like you to meet my colleague Fabien," Jacinthe said. I leaned over and Fabien and I gave each other the *bises*. He even smelled delicious, like freshly baked bread and musk combined, so that he exuded the heady combination of comfort and danger.

I gave Jacinthe a look that conveyed my admiration. Maybe it had taken a few months, but when I asked for a Frenchman for Grace, Jacinthe had more than delivered with Fabien.

I tried not to stare as Fabien gave Grace the *bises*, and Grace, blushing and charmingly flustered, said how pleased she was to meet him. They went on to laugh about whether they should speak in English or French.

I sighed with relief that her doubts appeared forgotten.

Jacinthe and I left Fabien and Grace to themselves and made our way over to the Cognac tasting station, where Franck and Momo were arguing over the merits of a particular vintage.

The Cognac in the tasting glasses was sloshing around quite a bit, as was the barge. That brisk wind had picked up. Jacinthe grabbed my sleeve to steady herself. "Thank God Nathanael didn't come," she said. "He would already be spewing all over the place."

I laughed with glee. This was nothing. I had been on ferry rides that were twenty times rougher than this—I loved the thrill of choppy seas.

We were sliding past the Eiffel Tower, and its sparkling lights mirrored the fairy lights inside the barge. Franck and I shared a look. This was one of those perfectly Parisian moments I wanted to capture and hold in my heart forever. Franck winked at me and passed me a glass of Cognac. "We need your opinion, *mon amour.*" My heart expanded with love for him, while my chest ached with longing for us to continue for a very, very long time.

I took a sip. "Nice," I commented, purposely vague. I was no judge of Cognac.

"You see?" Franck said to Momo. "I told you so."

While they continued their debate, I clinked my glass against Jacinthe's. "My friend, you delivered." I fluttered a hand up to my forehead, swooning. "Fabien...*mon Dieu....*"

"I know, right?" Jacinthe smiled like the Cheshire Cat. "I was so frustrated that I couldn't come up with anyone, and then, like a mirage, Fabien walked into our offices and began regaling me with his American dreams. I almost couldn't believe he was real—he is so perfect."

"Better than perfect."

Momo leaned between Jacinthe and me, rubbing his hands together. "Are we discussing Fabien? We met him before Jacinthe strong-armed him over to you and your American friend. What a shame he's not gay."

"Chalk one up for womankind," Caroline said.

I glanced over to where Fabien and Grace were chatting animatedly in the crowd of people, absorbed only in each other.

"Doesn't look like he's gay," I observed ruefully to Momo. "What's happening with your boyfriend by the way? When are we going to meet him?"

Momo's lips clamped tightly together.

"Oh God." I reached out and put my arm around his solid midsection. "Did you break up? I'm so sorry. I didn't know."

"The young whippersnapper met somebody else," Caroline supplied. "Momo is still getting over it. He's been depressing company over the past three weeks. That's why I took him out for a drink before Jacinthe's this evening."

"I'm fine." Momo took a deep breath through his nose. "Better off without him." But, by the way all his features tightened, I could tell he was lying. I wanted to reach out and give Momo a hug, but before I could, Alexandrine bore down on us.

"What have I missed?" she demanded, snatching up a glass of Cognac and swallowing it in a single gulp.

"Nothing," Franck said. "We were just commenting on the stunning decorations."

She smiled at this. "Yes...well...somebody else was going to do it, but I could tell they were planning on doing a completely vulgar theme, so I had to take over."

"It's spectacular," I said, with complete sincerity. "Magical, yet simple. You did a phenomenal job."

Alexandrine stared at me for a moment, perhaps to see if I was being sarcastic, but my compliments were genuine. As much as I had never liked her, I had to give credit where credit was due. Her floating fairyland was perfect.

"Thank you, Laura," she said in a tone I had never heard from her before.

I smiled and passed her another glass of Cognac. "More Cognac?" I said.

"No. No," she said. "Not that vintage! Come with me, I'll show you where they hide the good stuff."

chapter fifty-four

Alexandrine spent the next half hour being nicer to me than I had ever thought possible. She cracked me up with her acerbic humor. I finally saw what Jacinthe, Momo, and the others saw in her.

Finally, Franck came and pulled me away, ostensibly to view the lights of the musée d'Orsay. To my surprise, he led me up the stairs to the roof of the barge, where it was freezing cold and windy. On the plus side, we were alone, and bathed in the glow of the musée d'Orsay lit up at night. Its huge train clock glowed gold.

I buried my back against his chest, and he wrapped his jacket around me. "This is so romantic," I said. "Glacial, but romantic."

He turned me so that I was facing him and wrapped me tighter in his arms. Our breaths mingled, then our lips. Time suspended until we were almost knocked off our feet as the barge was pitched sideways by a big wave.

Once we had steadied each other, I said, "That was probably for the best. I think it may be too precarious—not to mention too cold—up here to continue this the way it was going."

Franck chuckled. "I hate that you're probably right." Yet, he still held me tight against him and neither of us made a move to go back downstairs. We slid under the pont Royal.

"So, do you think Grace likes Fabien?" Franck asked, his mouth close to my ear.

"I don't know what there's not to like," I murmured, resting my cheek against Franck's chest. "He's divine."

"Wait," Franck chuckled. "I'm going to get jealous."

I pushed away from his chest and gazed up at him.

"What?" Franck asked.

"I've been meaning to ask you something, and that reminds me. When you and Nathanael were in Russia, Jacinthe told me that he is not always...well, that sometimes he sleeps with other women, and that's normal in Paris."

Franck stared down at me, a question in his eyes. "That's probably true."

"Why didn't you ever tell me?"

I could feel his back muscles contract in a shrug under my palms. "I assumed you knew."

"Do you think Nathanael's behavior is normal?"

"Normal for him, yes. Normal for Paris too, I guess. Not normal for me. Is that what you're asking?"

I didn't answer right away but instead pressed my ear against his chest again so I could hear his heart. There it was, the heartbeat I knew so well, steady and strong. At that moment, it felt as if I knew Franck through and through, but as I still didn't know what his plans were three months from then, was that just an illusion?

"That hurts," Franck said, finally.

"I told Jacinthe that you wouldn't cheat on me," I murmured. "But still, there are a lot of things going on in that brain of yours that confuse me."

"And you think I know what is going on in your mysterious head?"

"I'm a simple person," I said.

Franck extended his arms, grasping me by the shoulders so he could get a good look at my face. The brisk wind blew a loose strand of my hair between us. "You're joking, right?"

"No."

"Laura, you are the least simple person alive. You have so much going on in your brain all the time—your mind and your imagination are always running on overtime. Don't get me wrong. I admire it. I love it. But sometimes it scares me."

I didn't know what to say. I had never thought I was confusing in the slightest. Franck was the confusing one. The lights of the Louvre that we had been exploring together bit by bit in the evenings slid by on the Right Bank.

"But I love you for that, Laura," Franck continued. "Besides, a bit of mystery is a good thing, isn't it? Surely, it's wonderful that we keep surprising each other?"

"Well, speaking of that, there is something I've been meaning to talk to you about."

"Oh?"

"A while ago, Madame Renier-Bernadotte asked me to stay behind after class. She told me she thought I had potential as a medieval scholar and asked me to consider transferring to Paris and pursuing a doctorate at the Sorbonne under her."

"That's amazing. Wait...when did this happen?"

"I don't know. Some time ago, I guess."

"Why didn't you mention it to me before now?" Franck squeezed my arms.

"I had to think about it myself, first," I said. "Figure it out."

"And?" The barge rocked again, and we clutched on to each other so that we didn't fall over.

"I'm tempted by the offer and flattered. I love Paris. I mean, how could I not love this?" I waved my arm out to take in the lit buttresses of Notre-Dame and the street lamps of Île Saint-Louis. "Still, I realized, too, that I will never be a true Parisian, and to spend years attempting to be one is a waste of my time. I decided I need to go back to McGill and finish my BA before I do anything else."

Franck jerked back, as though I had slapped him.

"What?" I asked.

"This is what I mean when I said your brain scares me. Did

you ever even consider discussing this with me? Sharing with me what Madame Renier-Bernadotte said to you?"

"I thought about it," I said.

"But you just kept it all to yourself and didn't even think of bringing me in until you made your decision."

"You mean you want to stay in Paris?" That was what I feared all along and was exactly why I hadn't brought up Professor Renier-Bernadotte's offer before.

Franck shook his head, clearly frustrated. "No...yes...I don't know, Laura. The thing is, you act as though you're not even part of a couple. Why don't you just talk to me? Why don't you share what is percolating in that brain of yours with me? I just get so—"

"Laura!" I peered into the night, shocked to see Grace emerging from the barge's staircase in just her taffeta dress. "Laura! Help me!"

I was still reeling from what Franck had just said, but Grace looked unsteady on her feet. This was not a safe place for her to be. Franck and I both had steady sea legs. Grace didn't. I had a nightmare vision of her toppling into the black, choppy waters of the Seine.

Franck and I, of one mind for a change, rushed toward her.

"What's wrong?" I yelled over the wind. "Is it Fabien?" I worried that maybe we were all misled and he had tried something inappropriate on my friend.

"No," she said. "I'm just so seasick," she groaned, holding her stomach and crouching down.

"Let's get her back downstairs," Franck said, looking grim.

We each grabbed one of Grace's arms, but before we could move her, she vomited all over her pink taffeta shoes.

Back down in the barge, Grace and I emerged from the tiny bathroom where I had done my best at cleaning off her shoes and her hair with the meager supply of paper towels provided.

Outside, there was a line of haute couture dressed but

extremely bilious-looking Parisians. Grace was far from the only one whose stomach was affected by the wind and waves.

I glanced over at Franck, who was waiting for us a little farther down the barge. He looked fine, like I felt. My mind whirred with how to help Grace, but behind that, I knew I needed to think over Franck's outburst on the roof. The idea that I didn't act as though I was part of a couple appalled me to the core.

"I still feel sick." Grace grabbed hold of the nearest chunk of the bar. "Oh God. I need to get off this thing."

Alexandrine rushed over to me, distress written on every feature. "It's a disaster! Nobody wants to drink any Champagne or Cognac now, and they can't turn the barge around until they reach the Bastille."

The room had taken on a faint whiff of vomit. "Are there any other bathrooms?" I asked. "People need bathrooms."

"There are two in the back for the workers, but I hardly think—"

"Open them," I said.

"They're dirty," she protested, clutching her own stomach. She had never had a healthy complexion at the best of times, but Alexandrine's face was looking particularly sallow.

"It doesn't matter," I said, supporting Grace with one arm and feeling her get heavier and heavier against me. "Also, get out any extra chairs you can find." Alexandrine nodded and rushed off.

Grace moaned. I found a clear spot on the carpet against the wall and gently lowered her down. I had grabbed a bowl that had been full of cloth napkins from the bar and placed it on her lap.

Franck knelt beside us. "What can I do?"

"I think I should stay with Grace," I said. "You're not sick, are you?"

"No."

"Can you find Alexandrine? She needs help getting the barge people to open up any available bathrooms and bringing out as many extra chairs you can find."

Franck was already standing up. "On it," he said.

A few seconds after Franck left, Fabien rushed over. "There you are, Grace!" he said, speaking to me, as Grace had her head down over the bowl and her hair had fallen forward, covering her face. "She disappeared suddenly...I hope I didn't say anything...I thought we were having a lovely time."

Grace mumbled something. I leaned closer. "What?"

"Get rid of him," she hissed.

"What?"

"Please. For the love of God, get rid of him."

I looked back up to Fabien, still handsome and not the slightest bit disheveled—of course he didn't suffer from seasickness. His concern struck me as absolutely sincere, yet Grace had said..."

"Grace is feeling extremely unwell," I said to him. "Besides, I believe Alexandrine and Jacinthe need your help. It is a bit of a crisis, you see, with so many people affected by the waves."

Both Fabien and I scanned the room. A few people laughed and chatted as though nothing was amiss. The seasick ones all seemed to have drawn to the edges of the party, determined to suffer their agonies of nausea and embarrassment alone, like wounded animals.

"*Oui*," he nodded. "*Oui*, of course they need my help. I will be back to check on Grace as soon as I can."

He dashed off. Grace moaned, "Noooooooooooooooo. I don't want Fabien to come back."

"What did he do to you?" I demanded. "You have to tell me. Please. My imagination is way too active, apparently"

"He was a perfect gentleman," Grace whispered. "Fabien was perfect in every way."

"Then, what—"

"The thing is, I started to feel sick, and I realized all I wanted was my beau. I didn't care about how gorgeous or cultured or gentle or sexy Fabien is. When I felt terrible, all I wanted was my beau. He's who I love." She leaned her head back against the wall behind her and closed her eyes. "You must think I'm so stupid, Laura," she moaned.

I took her hand and squeezed it. I thought of Anton and that week after Christmas when Franck and I had been so wretchedly ill together.

"Not even the tiniest bit." I put my arm around her shoulders.

chapter fifty-five

The barge evening was a certified disaster according to Alexandrine and, I supposed, Fabien. In the end, he'd only served as the catalyst for Grace to realize that her beau back in Nashville was still her love, despite everything.

When we had taken Grace back in a taxi to her employer's home in Neuilly, she was weepy and smelled of upchuck. I hadn't done as thorough a job of cleaning her up in the barge bathroom as I had originally thought.

I had managed to get Grace inside her employer's luxurious apartment and to convince her to go straight up to her bedroom. I wondered now whether she had access to a phone in her bedroom and, if she did, whether she had phoned her beau right away.

By the time Franck and I had gotten back to the rue des Fossés Saint-Bernard we were exhausted, and Franck had an early shift at six o'clock the next morning.

I walked up the rue Monge with my straw market basket under one arm. My head was down, and I was hypnotized by my shoes rhythmically hitting the Parisian pavement.

I knew Franck and I needed to talk about what he had said, but I still hadn't decided whether Franck had a point or not.

The mild air caressed my skin. The wind and cold of the night before had given way to our first truly warm day. I glanced up to the clear blue sky. How appropriate that it was May first. I was able to wear one of my favorite white linen tunics, a pair of capris, and some espadrilles I had picked up at a sidewalk stand near the gare de Lyon, without being chilly.

When I arrived at the place Monge the first thing that caught my eye were the bright red, freshly picked Gariguette strawberries from the South of France at my favorite fruit and vegetable stall.

Those strawberries were another sign that spring had arrived, and summer felt close on its heels. Time was running out.

Preoccupied, I moved on to the cheese stall. I was about fifth or sixth in line, comparing the merits of a Livarot topped with straw that smelled of old socks and a Rocamadour, when I heard a familiar, commanding voice demand to know about the eighteen-month-old Comté.

I leaned forward so I had a better view of the front of the line. Sure enough, it was Professor Renier-Bernadotte. It was the first time I had seen her outside the university. Her hair was as well-coiffed as ever and her khaki linen dress reliably chic, yet somehow she looked smaller than she did behind her lectern.

The cheese seller went into detail about how the eighteen-month cheese had been made with the nuttier-tasting winter milk rather than the fruitier summer milk.

"Don't bore me with all that. I'm asking you, which is better, the twelve-month or the eighteen-month?" Her voice was as commanding as ever, but her tone was ill-suited to purchasing cheese. I am the first person to take cheese seriously, but still...

"It's entirely a matter of personal taste," the seller said.

Uh oh.

"I'm asking for an answer, Monsieur. Stop equivocating."

"But they are both excellent," he protested.

"That is *not* an answer," she said. Her lips were pressed together, and her face full of suppressed rage. I glanced around to see if it looked as if she had come with anyone who might calm her down, but she appeared to be alone.

"Well, it is the only one I am able to give you." The seller's face flushed. I knew from experience that notions of customer service did not prevent French people from giving belligerent customers a tongue-lashing.

"That is unacceptable," Professor Renier-Bernadotte sputtered.

"*Tant pis.*" The seller shrugged. Too bad. "Now move along if you can't make up your mind. I have other customers."

Professor Renier-Bernadotte sucked in air, an act that I had come to dread, as I knew it was the preface to one of her majestic take-downs.

I left my place in line and rushed over. I placed my hand on her arm. She jumped. "Professor," I said, "I've made a decision."

"*Quoi?*" she demanded, but I still managed to coax her out of her spot in line and away from the cheese stand.

"It's Laura Bradbury, from your medieval class," I said. Her eyes were darting back and forth so quickly I wasn't certain she recognized me.

"I know," she said, indignant.

"Seeing as we bumped into each other like this, I just wanted to let you know that I made my decision about continuing my studies at the Sorbonne next year."

"*Oui.* And?"

"I may pursue it after my undergraduate degree, but I feel that I need to go back to Montreal next year and finish my degree there first."

She squinted down at me. "Fine," she said, and marched off in the direction of the *charcutier*, looking exasperated.

After I had picked up some Rocamadour, fresh baguettes, some sliced charcuterie, pâté, lamb's lettuce and, of course, strawberries, I made my way toward the Arènes de Lutèce where Franck and I had arranged to meet when he was done his morning shift.

I wandered inside, still in wonder that I was just strolling off the street into a preserved roman amphitheater. I mean, seriously.

I found a seat on one of the stone benches where Romans probably watched people and animals getting devoured. I set down my market bag, which was heavier now with all my purchases.

Shutting my eyes, I leaned against the rock bench behind me and turned my face like a sunflower toward the sunshine. I had forgotten how much I missed feeling warm.

Some local men were playing their usual game of *pétanque*. The clink of the balls was rhythmic and slightly hypnotic.

I reached down in my straw bag and took out a handful of strawberries from the carton perched at the top. I took the green stem off the first one and popped it into my mouth. It was sweet and tangy, and tasted of sunshine and green things, exactly like a strawberry should.

Did Professor Renier-Bernadotte ever take the time to sit outside and savor strawberries? That day, for the first time to me, she had looked out of place—even a bit awkward. Maybe I was imagining it, but at the market, she seemed to radiate loneliness to me, or at least isolation from other people.

That was a perfectly acceptable way to go through the world for some, perhaps even for her, but it was not what I wanted, I realized. I wanted to learn more and follow my passions, but I did not want those things to the exclusion of my personal relationships. I did not want to become an irascible woman at the market, berating the cheesemonger—not when it wasn't warranted, anyway.

I savored another strawberry. Professor Renier-Bernadotte was still a model for me in many ways, with her academic curiosity, her one-minded pursuit of her studies, her devotion to intellect... She was not, however, I realized with clarity, the model for my whole life.

If Franck and I could stay together, I didn't want us to neglect each other.

I wanted to be part of our couple, even though, according to Franck, I hadn't exactly been acting like it. I needed to talk to him about that...and the Montreal thing.

I just had to be brave.

I must have fallen asleep, because the next thing I felt was the familiar pressure of Franck's hand on my shoulder.

"Laura?" His voice floated down and, as I blinked, a beautiful bouquet of lily of the valley floated in front of my line of vision. *"Voilà. Muguet pour mon amour."*

"That's beautiful," I said, still blinking the sleep from my eyes. Franck sat down beside me and passed the bouquet to me. I sniffed its glorious, honeyed scent. I found myself so full of love and regret that the words caught, yet again, in my throat.

"It's the first of May, I had to buy my love a bouquet of lily of the valley." Franck reached over and helped himself to three strawberries from my basket.

"Is that a tradition?"

"Bien sûr. Didn't you see all the people on the street selling bouquets of *muguet?"*

"I didn't notice." Had I been too wrapped up in my thoughts, yet again? With a finger, I jingled the perfect little white bell-shaped flowers. I turned to Franck. "I'm sorry if I'm so much in my own head, it's just that—"

Franck put a strawberry-stained finger in front of my lips. "Hold that thought. I need to warn you. Pauline and Florent came to find me at work today."

"Why?" We hadn't seen them since a family meal at Franck's aunt and uncle's over Christmas. Luckily, there had been a lot of Franck's family there, and I managed to remain civil yet mostly avoid them at the same time.

"Florent had to come into Paris for a meeting, so Pauline tagged along, and they wanted to do something with us this afternoon."

"Merde," I said, then glanced up to the opening of the passageway from the amphitheater that lead to the rue Monge. There was Florent with his loping gait and Pauline jumping up and down and waving, as though she hadn't fleeced us several months earlier.

"You said yes?" I asked.

"I didn't do it for them," Franck said. "I did it for Mémé, who will be happy to hear we did something together. Family is everything to her."

I remembered that family counted a lot for Franck too, so I slapped on a fake smile and went to greet the phonies.

My breath was coming in staccato gasps, but as I stepped up the final stair, triumph rushed through me. I had beat Pauline up the first two flights of the Eiffel Tower.

I thought we were going to take the elevator from the bottom, but Florent suggested climbing the stairs to the second floor instead because it was less expensive.

Franck was a few steps away on the platform, waiting for me. "Well done." He gave me a kiss. "Is Pauline far behind you?"

Florent had already made it up, too, and was standing beside Franck, gazing off into the middle distance.

"I'm not sure." When I'd left her in the dust just after the first-floor platform, I hadn't been inclined to turn around and check on her.

To catch my breath, I went over to the railings and gazed out over the Montmartre hill and the wedding cake confection of Sacré-Coeur.

It had been an odd afternoon. We had dropped off my market purchases and gorgeous lily of the valley at the apartment, and Franck had changed out of his uniform and then we had a street panini for lunch (less expensive than sitting in a restaurant, according to Pauline).

Franck had managed to convince Florent and Pauline to forgo their habitual trek to Häagen-Dazs and instead try a Berthillon ice cream cone on the Île Saint-Louis.

I had chosen a *chocolat et caramel au beurre salé* double scoop and savored it as we walked alongside the Seine toward the Eiffel Tower. The ice cream was as smooth as silk against my tongue and intensely flavored without being too sweet. The dark chocolate and caramel flavors merged together perfectly—the depth of the chocolate highlighted by the savory note of the salted caramel. It was culinary art in a cone.

Pauline had only had a few licks of her lemon and raspberry double scoop when she shrugged and said, "I don't like this at all." She'd then proceeded to chuck her cone in the next trash can. I gasped, and I could hear Franck doing the same behind me. Honestly, I just didn't understand her.

Now she appeared beside me at the railing at the top of the stairs. I could feel her hot breath, coming more rapidly than usual, against my shoulder. As usual, Pauline's presence felt cloying and sticky. Why did she always invade my personal space? I took a few steps away from her along the railing.

"You didn't wait for me!" she said, still breathing hard.

"I didn't know you wanted me to," I said. "Sorry."

I wasn't sorry.

"I'm just going to go around and see if I can find the Arc de Triomphe," I said. "Catch your breath."

After completing a full circuit of the viewing platform, I found Pauline, Florent, and Franck still near the top of the stairs where I had left them. I rubbed my hands together, deliberately staying a few feet away from Pauline. "So. Where do we buy the tickets to the top?"

"Just around the other side," Franck said. "Let's go."

"Wait." Pauline held up one of her tiny hands. "Why do you want to go to the top?"

"We're on the second floor of the Eiffel Tower." I stared at her. "Who wouldn't want to go to the top?"

"It's too expensive," Pauline said. "Anyway, we can see perfectly well from here, and we don't have to spend the extra money."

"Well...that's fine, but I'm going to the top."

"I'm coming with you," Franck said. He turned to his cousin and Pauline. "I mean, it's the Eiffel Tower guys. It's like Everest. We just need to go to the top."

Florent's mouth was pressed into a wavering line. "The view is better from up there," he admitted. "Do you know, Pauline, the third floor viewing platform is actually one hundred and sixty meters higher than this platform?"

Pauline crossed her arms and pouted in that way I certainly didn't miss seeing every day. "It's too expensive."

"All right, then," Franck said, reaching out and taking my hand. "We'll see you when we come back down. Florent?" Franck quirked a questioning brow at his cousin.

"I'll come with..." Florent began to say, and then he looked at Pauline, who narrowed her eyes at him. She shook her head. "I'll stay here, I guess," he said. "We are on a budget."

"Bye!" I said cheerily and headed off hand in hand with Franck.

This was hardly the first time I had been to the top of the Eiffel Tower, but it was always worth the ride.

We were packed like sardines into the tiny elevator, and watching the black rungs of the tower click, click, click past us and seeing it get narrower and narrower was head-spinning.

Franck and I were pressed against each other. His hand roamed across my lower back and then slipped under my waistband. I raised my head and kissed his throat. Come to think of it, Franck also emanated the scent of homey comfort and the spice of risk, a bit like Fabien.

"We could get in trouble in here," Franck murmured for only me to hear.

"So much trouble." I slid my fingers underneath his T-shirt and ran them up the indent of his spine. I knew each warm indent and bump by heart.

A few seconds later, the elevator bumped to a halt and the doors opened. The crowd swept us out to the top viewing platform. Franck kept hold of my hand, and we went to the side of the platform that looked out on to the Seine sparkling under the warm sun. It was so much higher up there and the view was completely different. Paris spread out in miniature at our feet.

"Pauline and Florent are missing out," I said.

"But we're not," Franck squeezed my hand. "That's what's important."

I thought back to Franck's determination not to be like his cousin after they presented us with our bill after staying with them. "Because you're not Florent. You're Franck."

"And because you're not Pauline," Franck said. "You're Laura."

It struck me then as I surveyed the miracle of Paris below that I had never been at any risk of being like Pauline.

I would never throw out a Berthillon ice cream. I love church bells. I might be an overthinker, but I am not miserly and manipulative. I would never have any interest in subjugating Franck, or anyone else for that matter. I have faults, but they are my own.

My frenzy for independence and self-reliance that year was based on a faulty premise. I didn't have to try to be the anti-Pauline, because I had been the anti-Pauline all along. Instead, I could just be Laura.

"I love you," I said to Franck and wrapped my arms around him. He kissed my temple, then the tip of my nose, and at last my lips.

"Thank you for putting up with them this afternoon," he said when we'd come up for air. "I know you did it for me. I can't say I enjoyed it, but it has eased my conscience somewhat in regard to Mémé."

"I would do it for you and for Mémé several times over," I said. "But I still can't believe Pauline tossed out her Berthillon."

"She's unhinged."

"Yup. I may be unhinged too, but in a completely different way."

"Unhinged Laura is rather charming, you know."

We kissed until the elevator bell rang for us to descend back down to earth.

chapter **fifty-six**

Everything seemed right again between Franck and me after that foray to the top of the Eiffel Tower.

The weather was beautiful—we spent most evenings strolling around Paris, finding obscure bookstores, alleyways, and wine bars. Sometimes we would head to the Louvre and run around the place while the cleaners were cleaning, like a couple of kids in the world's most sumptuous playhouse.

I always wanted to go visit the mummies, and it was a gift to be the only one in the room with the *Mona Lisa*, the *Venus de Milo* or Michelangelo's *Dying Slave*. Franck had taught me all the shortcuts to Napoleon's apartments.

Professor Gabrielle had assigned another essay—this time on our last book of the year, *David Copperfield*. At the end of class, she announced she had marked them and, overall, was pleasantly surprised by everyone's work, even mine. We continued to rub along with excess civility on both sides, and I was fine with that as long as the marks she gave me remained fair.

"Did you talk to your beau last night?" I asked Grace as Professor Gabrielle began handing them out.

Two days before Grace had told me how her and her beau—I couldn't believe I still didn't know his actual name—had been talking on the phone almost every night since the barge debacle with Fabien.

Grace blushed and nodded. "He asked me if I wanted to go steady with him again."

"Can you do that if he's there and you're here?"

"Laura, I'm going home in two weeks," Grace reminded me.

Most of the time, I managed to push this reality out of my mind. Grace was going home in mid-June when our classes were over. I was only staying about a month longer than she was. My time in Paris was ticking down as well.

"That's right," I shook my head. "I feel like I'm in some sort of time warp right now. It's like time is suspended or something."

"It's springtime, and maybe it feels suspended because that is what you are longing for it to be," said Grace, wisely.

Professor Gabrielle put my essay on the desk in front of me. "Nice work Laura," she said in her stiff voice.

We would never be friends, but we managed to co-exist. She had stopped having a vendetta against me and I had stopped turning her classroom into a lynch mob. It was, I supposed, a fair deal.

I turned over my essay. She had given it a nineteen out of twenty. I still believed I deserved better, but I had no desire to start another revolution. I had stood up for myself and it had worked.

Grace and I walked out of class onto the boulevard Saint-Michel and decided to go and have a glass of wine on the place de le Contrescarpe at the bottom of the rue Mouffetard.

I had grown to love that odd little *place*, where Hemmingway opened his book *A Moveable Feast* with its description of the cold wind that stripped the leaves off the trees and the permanently sloshed patrons at the Café des Amateurs.

"So...," I said as we took our first sip. It was a house red, but it's heavy robustness made me feel as though I was back in Hemmingway's world, even though the café we sat in was definitively cleaner than the sadly vanished Café des Amateurs. "So how do you feel about you and your beau getting back together when you get home?"

Grace's eyes shone. "I can't wait. In the end, I think this year was good for us—the best thing. We both grew up. We both realized what we wanted."

"Each other?"

Grace blushed and nodded again.

I fiddled with the stem of my wine glass. "I think maybe I figured out what I want this year too. I mean...not completely. Far from it. But I have a clearer idea of where I'm going. I know where I don't want to go, in any case."

"That's something," Grace said.

"It is. I have Paris to thank for that."

Grace raised her glass. "To Paris," she said.

I clinked mine against hers. "To Paris," I said. "*Un grand merci.*"

Grace and I left each other tipsy and jolly.

On my way home, I made a beeline to Notre-Dame. Inside, I went right to my favorite side chapel with my favorite statue of Virgin Mary inside the Cathedral. I put a ten-franc coin in the little copper tin and struck a match. I lit a red candle and sat down on one of the benches.

"*Bonne chance,* Grace," I murmured. "I wish you a life full of love."

I couldn't shake an antsy feeling when I got back to the apartment from Notre-Dame. Franck wasn't back from work yet, and the dreamy haze I seemed to have been residing in during the previous month felt popped like a soap bubble.

I was just making myself a cup of milky tea when the phone rang. It was my dad calling from Canada. "Laura, can you give me your return dates?" He got straight to the point. "Your mom and I need to know so we can plan out the rest of the summer."

"I'm not exactly sure. We'll be back in about six weeks or so," I said, wishing I hadn't picked up the receiver.

"You mean you haven't booked your tickets yet?" my dad demanded, incredulous. Our family are born-and-bred planners—such laxity was unheard of.

"Not exactly. I've been busy with school and—"

"That's not like you, Laura. Mid-July is the high season. In all likelihood, there are no tickets even left for then."

"I'm sure that's not true," I said. "I'll get on it tomorrow."

"Promise?" he said.

"Promise." He tried to chat about this and that, but I wasn't in the mood for talking because the merry-go-round in my brain was spinning too fast.

I hung up, completely forgetting about my tea. All the questions I had been avoiding in the previous month…no, the previous ten months…were encapsulated in the doubt about what I had to do next.

Did I book one ticket or two tickets back to Canada?

The next morning, as the door slammed behind Franck on his way out to the early shift, I had to admit it to myself I'd chickened out.

The pigeons cooing on the roof above me didn't soothe my self-recriminations one bit.

The night before I had prepared myself to ask Franck about the airline tickets, but he had come flying into the apartment telling me that Momo had stopped by the Louvre at the end of his shift. Momo wanted to know if we could go with him to see Corneille's *Le Cid* at the Comédie-Française because he had scored some free tickets at work.

Caroline was going too, and *Le Cid* was one of my favorite French plays, and perhaps I was relieved to procrastinate talking to Franck for just a few hours longer. Heck, I'd procrastinated for months…what difference were a few hours going to make?

Momo had unwittingly provided me with the perfect pretext to avoid asking Franck the plane ticket question.

The evening had been hilarious, and the play in the surroundings of the mythic Comedie-Française was sublime.

When Franck and I finally got back to our place after
après-theatre drinks, Corneille (and perhaps the tiny glasses
of bright green chartreuse alcohol at the Bistro du Théâtre) had
put us in a festive mood and then there were other distractions
behind the door of our bedroom. Then we'd both fallen asleep.

Now the unresolved question pulsed inside me with the
relentlessness of an aching tooth. I had to be done with it, but
Franck wouldn't be finished work for six hours.

I showered and dressed and then decided, as I was going stir
crazy waiting in the apartment with only my thoughts for company, that we needed a fresh baguette. Maybe two.

In the hallway, Madame Fox was chatting in low tones to
Monsieur Pierrepont just outside his door.

"*Bonjour.*" I nodded at my neighbors. Madame Fox hadn't
invited me back to her apartment since Mémé's visit, but I did
earn the occasional smile from her. Well, not exactly a smile, but
an upwards tilt of her lips, as she was doing right then.

"I was just coming in." Monsieur Pierrepont gestured at the
fresh baguette under his arm.

I chuckled. "That's where I'm headed."

"Beautiful day out there," he added.

I had already observed the azure sky outside the apartment
window. "It looks that way."

"What a shame," Madame Fox said to me. "I was just going to
ask you in for a coffee, but seeing as you're on your way out—"

"I have all the time in the world." I didn't even let her finish.
"I can grab a baguette later."

"But there might not be any left," she protested.

I flapped away that consideration. "I still have half a baguette at
home." There was no way I was going to turn down this invitation.
Madame Fox nodded, with the expression of a cornered animal.

We bid our *au revoirs* to Monsieur Pierrepont, and I was ush-ered back onto the same upholstered antique couch where I had sat before. I folded my hands on my lap and waited patiently while Madame busied herself in her kitchen. My gaze tried to take everything in.

The lustrous, orange silk curtains were tied back by a thickly braided, gold rope. Burnished photo frames filled with mostly black-and-white pictures filled the marble fireplace mantle. Beside me was a precarious and ancient-looking table of gilded gold, atop which stood three brightly embellished oriental vases. I would have to be careful not to knock those over.

Everything here, and all of it perfumed with her rose pot-pourri, somehow anchored my flailing brain. It spoke of conti-nuity and history.

It caused me a pang to think Madame Fox might not have any-one to pass on her torch to, not to mention her stories, after she died. From what I had picked up from her so far, like a ravenous bird with scattered crumbs, they were worth being remembered.

chapter **fifty-seven**

She brought in the tray of Limoges espresso cups and saucers, just as she had done on my previous visit. I remained silent, with some sort of reverence I couldn't explain, as she poured the coffee out of a white china coffeepot that matched the cups.

"*Merci*," I said when she was done. "It is lovely of you to have me."

I wondered if I should have perhaps reciprocated and instead invited Madame fox over to our apartment, but the idea seemed so presumptuous that I almost laughed.

"How are you and your boyfriend finding springtime in Paris?" Madame Fox asked me. She sat primly on the opposite loveseat and had adopted her usual formal tone.

I don't know if it was because the question of the plane tickets needed to be verbalized or because I knew I would soon be leaving, but a blunt answer is what popped out. "I'll be leaving soon. My courses at the Sorbonne are almost finished so I'll be returning return to Canada. The problem right now is I don't know if my boyfriend is coming with me."

Madame Fox stared at me, her eyes wide. "Why wouldn't he? He lived with you in Canada prior to Paris, did he not?"

"Yes," I admitted. "But at the beginning of this year, he started to make noises about maybe wanting to stay in France and not return to Montreal. I can't say for sure what he's thinking now—"

"Why on earth haven't you asked him?" Madame Fox interrupted me, her formal tone gone.

I took a few sips of coffee before answering. "I don't know exactly. Pride. Independence. Fear too, I guess…lots of fear."

Madame Fox put her espresso cup and saucer down on the table between us. "Do you love him?"

I couldn't believe I was having this blunt conversation with Madame Fox, particularly as it wasn't about *her* love life during the war, which I was dying to know about, but about *mine*.

"Yes. For a while I was wondering whether it would just be easier for me to be free and single, but then—"

"Then what?" she demanded.

"I realized how much I love Franck and how much I want to be with him."

"Then what on earth are you waiting for to bring it up?" She shook her head, clearly exasperated. I could hardly blame her, as I was exasperated with myself.

"What if he says he wants to stay here in Paris? It would break my heart."

"You can survive a broken heart," Madame Fox answered. "But what you may not survive are regrets."

"Regrets?"

"For things left undone…and especially for things left unsaid."

She was right. I had never thought about the regrets not speaking up could generate. We sat in silence for a minute or two until Madame Fox stood, brushed off her tweed Chanel skirt, and went to her mantle. She took down two photos.

She passed them to me and then sat back down again.

I looked at the black-and-white photos. One of them showed a much younger Madame Fox in a belted, form-fitting dress. She was gorgeous, with waved brown hair and dark lipstick. Beside her was a tall man in a soldier's uniform. She was laughing up at him. It looked to me as though she was trying to get him to laugh for the camera. She hadn't succeeded though. He looked adoringly down at her, but he wasn't laughing. His body seemed to hold back from her—reserved...serious.

The other photo showed Madame Fox, her hair not as coiffed and sitting on a bench wearing a pair of worn, rolled up pants and a utilitarian jacket, but somehow she looked more beautiful.

There, she was smoking a cigarette, and her eyes were full of shared mischief and laughter with the man sitting on the bench beside her, who was shaking a finger at her with one hand and cupping the side of her face tenderly with the other. He wore a pair of pants and a shirt open at the collar. The most notable thing though, was his expression. His smile was wide and full of appreciation and love for this spirited woman on the bench with him. An invisible string of complicity seemed to join them together.

Two different men, but there was only one who the young Madame Fox was meant to be with.

I peered closer at the man on the bench. "That's Monsieur Pierrepont!" I exclaimed.

She slid the photos out of my hands. "Yes." She placed them back on the mantle.

"But—"

She sat down and smoothed out her skirt again. "That was taken during the war when we believed my husband to be dead. I already told you that Monsieur Pierrepont and I fought in the Resistance together. We were part of the same resistance cell."

"You were in love?" I said.

"Yes." She picked up her espresso cup, but it trembled in her grasp. "Once the war was over, we were planning to start a life together. He was the man loved."

"But your husband...?"

"I was only seventeen when I married him. I thought I loved him, but in fact I knew nothing about him or myself then. He was very shy, very reserved. He never understood me or enjoyed the unruly side of my nature. Monsieur Pierrepont—"

"He loved that part of you. *Especially* that part."

Madame Fox shot me a questioning glance.

"I can tell from the photo." I also remembered how Monsieur Pierrepont had pronounced Madame Fox's first name on the day of the explosion—*Berengère.*

"*Oui.* It was with Monsieur Pierrepont that I discovered what love really was. Does your boyfriend love the unruly side of you?"

I remembered Franck's admiration for my admittedly eccentric and often convoluted mind. "Yes," I said. "But what happened with you and Monsieur Pierrepont?"

"Regrets," she said. "So many regrets. My husband returned from the Germain P.O.W. camp...from death itself, it seemed. I should have been happy, but I was devastated. I thought I was doing the right thing by choosing to honor my vows to him. I reasoned that I would grow to love my husband as I did Monsieur Pierrepont, and that Monsieur Pierrepont in time would find someone else to replace me."

"He never did," I murmured.

"No, and my husband remained a stranger to me until he died twenty years later. I returned to Paris a decade ago and moved back into this family apartment that had been shut up during my absence.

"I lived with crushing regrets my whole life because I wasn't brave enough to claim what I truly wanted. If you can learn one thing from an old woman, *ma petite mademoiselle*, learn that."

chapter **fifty-eight**

I forgot all about the baguette and ran straight from Madame Fox's to the Panthéon, where I sat beside Victor Hugo's tomb for a long time.

Just as I was readying to leave to meet Franck as we had planned, I remembered a quote of Hugo's I had memorized in high school: *"Aimer, c'est savoir dire je t'aime sans parler."* Perhaps that had worked for Victor, to believe that love was all about saying "I love you" without speaking. For me, the time for speaking was long overdue.

I rushed into the Brasserie Le Monge ten minutes before Franck was due to show up.

The barman and *tabac* lady and several other regulars greeted me, but I was so distracted that I could only manage a half-hearted wave back.

I couldn't catch my breath. I put my bag down on our usual table and draped my scarf over the chair. I sat down and tapped my fingers on the tabletop. I decided to go the bathroom. Once Franck and I started talking, I didn't want anything to interrupt us. Luckily, I had gotten used to using their goddamn turkish toilet.

When I arrived at *les toilettes*, I noticed they had replaced the sign on the women's door with one that simply said Femmes. Gone was the Fifties lady with her flipped hair and her poodle skirt.

I jerked back, shocked. I had only been there a few days before. When had this change happened? I opened the bathroom door and couldn't believe my eyes.

The confounding hole in the ground had been replaced with a modern toilet and sink. It was sparkling clean and sat on brand new tiles, and its lines were on the modern side. Gone was the chain and porcelain bulb pull attached to the leaky old wall tank. Good God, there was even a toilet paper dispenser on the wall.

It was precisely the type of toilet I had been longing for at our favorite hangout since the beginning of our Paris year, but it made me feel completely furious. How could they just go and change everything? Why had nobody warned me?

I whirled around and marched back to the table.

To my surprise, Franck was just sitting down. "I got off early!" he said. "*Me voilà!*"

"They've taken away the turkish toilet." I pointed, accusing, back to the bathrooms.

"Have they?" Franck said. "I think it's a shame, but you must be thrilled."

"I'm not."

"You're not?" Franck stared up at me.

"No."

"Why?"

"Nobody tells me. Nobody tells me anything. I need to know. I need to know if people are thinking of making big changes."

Franck raised his eyebrows. "How about you sit down?"

I sat down, huffily pulling my chair into the table with unnecessary force. "I need to talk about things! I need things to be talked about!"

"I have a feeling this isn't just about the turkish toilet." Franck cocked his head at me.

"It's not." Tears began to roll, unchecked, down my cheeks. "I don't want things to change."

"What things?"

"I want us to stay together. I don't want to go back to Montreal without you. I want to be buying return tickets for *us*, not just for *me*."

Franck steepled his fingers—a sign that he was having a hard time following me. "Tickets?"

"Plane tickets! Back to Canada. I need to buy them, you know. I can't believe I haven't—I'm usually so organized about that sort of thing, but I was scared to ask you whether I should buy one for you too."

"Why wouldn't you? Or do you want me to buy it myself? I can do that."

After all that, was I hearing what I thought I was hearing? My mouth hung open. I blinked. "You mean you're willing to come back to Montreal with me?"

"Of course I'm coming with you." Franck shook his head. "Why? Do you not want me too?" His face drained of its color.

"I want you to more than anything. I love you. I want us to stay together. I've been so scared to ask you because you had talked about staying on in Paris, and not making choices based on me, and freedom. I've been so scared for months."

"Why didn't you tell me?"

"I was terrified you might say no." I let out a few sobs of relief.

"And you kept that all to yourself?" He reached out and took my hand in his. My hand felt warm wrapped in his, and so much steadier. "*Oui*. It was awful."

"*Ah, ma pauvre chérie.* Never do that again, *d'accord*? Talk to me. Talk to me about anything."

I sniffed. "I'll try."

"Still, I can't tell you how nice it is for you to...you know... actually say that us staying together is what you want."

"It's what I want," I wailed. "Of course it's what I want!" The dam was certainly smashed now.

"Can I ask why?"

"Because I love you and I want to be with you. There. I said it, and I said it first, and I don't care about my pride or being rejected or anything else as much as the fact that I love you so much it scares me."

Franck's hazel eyes kindled. "I love you so much it scares me too. You know, I never seriously thought of us doing the long-distance thing or breaking up. If you're on this earth, I think I have no choice but to do what is necessary for us to be together."

"I'll start doing my part in that too," I said. "After my BA." For the sake of honesty, I had to add that caveat.

"That may be a promise you can't keep. Still, saying that you want it too is a good start. You're ambitious and you're a planner. I love that about you, but it's a fact."

"I know. My unruly side."

"I happen to love your unruly side."

I smiled a secret smile. Madame Fox was right.

We celebrated our last few nights in Paris with a dinner on a *péniche* tied up under Notre-Dame, organized by Jacinthe.

I didn't have the gumption to invite Madame Fox to the *péniche*, but Nathanael, Caroline, Alexandrine, and Momo were there.

When we arrived on the boat, Caroline whisked me away to admire a cast-iron bathtub they had set up on the deck in the back. It was filled to the brim with ice cubes and bottles of Moët & Chandon. It was July, so Paris's lights wouldn't shine down on us for several hours until dusk fell.

Momo had somehow commandeered a small charcoal barbeque and thoroughly burned several rounds of merguez sausage.

We had a long, leisurely dinner and emptied the bathtub bottle by bottle.

Alexandrine, being Alexandrine, had brought an astonishing array of gourmet salads from the finest *traiteur* in Paris. *Bien sûr.* They were delicious. I made sure to tell her so several times.

"You know"—Nathanael leaned over while I was busy putting a forkful of the most delicious *tabouleh* full of fresh winkles, scallops, and tiny shrimp from Brittany into my mouth—"Jacinthe is going to miss you terribly."

"But she has so many friends."

"I know that she felt particularly close with you. She's been quite blue about it, and you haven't even left yet."

"We could be back at some point," I said, even though I was far from certain about that.

It was so odd to think that, all this time, I had considered Jacinthe as one of my main pillars of support in Paris, and that perhaps I had become one of hers as well. I was glad that our friendship was more of a two-way street than I had realized. "I guess, then, you'll need to take care of her even better," I said to Nathanael, with a penetrating look.

I will," he promised.

"You better," I warned.

After we were all digesting the enormous cheese platter (the word had gotten out several months before about my fetish for French cheese—the stinkier the better), I lounged on a deck chair, half on top of Franck.

I was lulled into one of those unforeseen moments of complete joy—by the lapping waves, by the Champagne, by these friends, and by the knowledge that even though I was sad to be leaving Paris, I wouldn't be leaving Franck.

As I was reveling in the moment, Franck sat bolt upright in our seat, almost toppling me to the deck.

"What?" I protested.

"We need to go to the Louvre," Franck declared.

"Now?" Nathanael asked.

"Now!" Franck jumped up. "It'll be empty aside from the cleaners. I can get us all in. When have you ever gone to the Louvre when it's empty?"

There was a chorus of "*Jamais*. Never."

"Then come on!" Franck led us off the boat. We made our way quickly to the Louvre, like a bunch of giddy kids.

Franck quickly managed to sweet-talk the guard at the entrance and then we had the entire Louvre to ourselves. We dashed from room to room, sliding along the freshly polished floors.

Soon, we devised a contest whereby we all tried to do the best imitation of some of the Louvre's most famous portraits. Alexandrine won for her Mona Lisa, although Momo ran a close second. I won with my over-the-shoulder come-hither gaze of *La Grande Odalisque*. Momo was victorious with his *Self-Portrait at an Easel* by Rembrandt, and Nathanael triumphed with his Delacour's *Marquise de la Pompadour*.

After several hours of hilarity, we decided we needed to finish more of the Champagne before all the ice in the bathtub had melted. We made our way back down to the *quai*, the lights of Paris now lit and shining above us.

Then, like a siren's song, on a *quai* not far from ours, came the strains of a musette. Several accordions harmonized in the hot July night. We ran toward it without any consultation. Franck took me in his arms. He was warm against me, and I was so relieved that I had finally claimed what I loved.

That's what mattered—finding love and then, if lucky enough to find the real thing, being brave enough to hold on to it.

"Did you have a good year?" Franck whispered in my ear.

"I had a wonderful year," I murmured back. "We had our Paris year." There would always be roads not taken for both of us, but I highly doubted they would be better than the road we were on.

After all, there we were, spinning under Paris's glowing lights beside the Seine with our friends. The road together had brought us there. I couldn't wait to see where it would take us next.

The accordionists segued into a new tune with a much faster tempo. We held on even tighter and swept each other away.

La Fin

Sneak peek of
Chapter One
My Grape Wedding

chapter **one**

Kathmandu, Nepal

The rickshaw lurched to a stop, throwing Franck and me against the glass partition decorated with posters of Bollywood stars and Hindu deities.

"*Ça va?*" Franck pulled me back and ran a hand over my dusty face, as if to make sure I was more or less intact.

"What was it?" I asked. "Another cow?"

Cows and yaks are kings of the road in Kathmandu. Drivers would much rather cause a major traffic pile-up involving several human fatalities than harm a hair of a sacred bovine. These animals wander through the main streets with impunity, usually with their eyes traced in thick kohl and their necks adorned with necklaces made from threaded orange geraniums.

I peeked out the rickshaw and saw a crowd of gesticulating Nepalis and about thirty screeching monkeys hopping all over the tangle of rickshaws and cars in the road. I leaned back. "Monkeys. If it's not cows, it's monkeys."

It was amazing how, in a matter of weeks, Franck and I had adapted to the chaos of life in Kathmandu, our new home base for the next three months as we volunteered with Operation Eyesight in surgical eye camps in rural Nepal.

Our first camp had been a thirteen-hour bus ride from Kathmandu on the Nepal-Indian border, in a village so isolated most of the villagers had never seen a Caucasian before. We were given a welcome dinner served on lily pads on the porch of the chief's mud hut, and the entire village came to watch us eat. It was breathtaking and disorienting all at once. That village's remoteness had made Kathmandu seem like the epitome of civilization.

I peered at the scribbled address written on a scrap of paper I held in my hand. "The place must be near here."

Franck paid the rickshaw driver—we noticed that the rates the drivers charged us fell at the same speed that our Nepali improved. We weren't paying as little as locals quite yet, but we were paying significantly less than before.

I made my way to the side of the unpaved road, dodging another rickshaw and a cart filled with some type of large green fruit.

Franck joined me. "So, we're close?"

I tried to make out a number—any number—posted on the row of shopfronts in front of us. "Hard to say. It's great to have a street address, but what would make the system work even *better* would be shopkeepers actually putting street addresses on their stores."

"That would make it quicker," Franck mused, "but far less interesting." He took the paper and ducked into the dark doorway closest to us.

"*Namaste!*" Franck bowed his head and pressed his two hands together, a gesture that over the past month had become as natural to us as breathing. The man behind the counter seemed, as far as I could tell, to be selling gold- and jewelry-encrusted horns from enormous yaks. Intriguing, but not what we were looking for. He took the scrap of paper from Franck and read the address.

I was glad for us to have this little project of searching for one of the most under-the-radar jewelry shops in Kathmandu. A hidden treasure, according to the Irish nurse who worked with us.

On coming back to Kathmandu after the camp, we'd found a number of faxes waiting for us—for me, more accurately—with news from my father that he had sent off all the law school applications that I had prepared before leaving Canada.

Franck had shaken his head with obvious frustration when he read the faxes. "Law school in England? I just don't get it, Laura. Why don't we try to work together on the photojournalism thing?"

"We'll never earn enough money to live doing that," I said, thinking about the small checks we had received for the few articles we'd published in magazines over the previous couple of years. "One of us has to be pragmatic."

"And where do I fit in? What am I supposed to do in England while you're busy being pragmatic?"

"Can't you just support my plans?" I said, frustrated. "It's not as if you have a better one that will actually pay for food and a roof over our heads."

"You don't have to go to law school." Franck had tried to convince me. "I know we'll figure something else out. Have faith that we can."

But I wasn't brought up to have faith. Unlike Franck, I knew that life didn't just take care of itself—that was a pipe dream. I had to take care of myself, take care of both of us actually, because I was the designated planner of us, the couple. How could Franck not see that one of us, at least, had to plan and strategize? How could he resent me for that when I was only trying to do what was necessary?

Looking for the jewelry shop was a much-needed distraction from that unresolved conflict that kept bubbling up between us.

The man inside the yak horn shop nodded and gave Franck directions in a fast flow of Nepali, which he embellished with eloquent hand gestures and head tilts, and which I couldn't follow at all.

As we walked out of the shop after thanking him, I whispered to Franck, "Did you catch any of that?"

"Three doors down," he said. "Or maybe thirty. Not entirely sure."

In the end, I was the one who spotted it. Actually, what caught my eye was an exceedingly chic-looking woman sitting in front of a shop counter, appearing entirely out of place. Several gemstones casually scattered on the counter flashed in the dusty afternoon light.

I pulled Franck inside. "This looks promising."

"*Namaste.*" We greeted the two men standing behind the counter, both of whom wore yellowish-white Daura Suruwal—loose pants with a long tunic overtop, which most Nepali men wore.

I tried to explain in my broken Nepali that I was interested in getting a necklace made for my birthday, as a special keepsake from our trip. Franck, in the meantime, sat down on the other available stool and chatted with the chic woman who, *quelle surprise,* turned out to be from Paris.

My eyes opened wide at the sparkling gems splayed out in front of her. Rubies, diamonds, even some emeralds. Franck and I didn't have much money at all. I felt worried—what if this store *looked* like an unassuming hole-in-the-wall, but made only expensive jewelry?

"I've just been in Tahiti," she said to Franck in a nasal Parisian accent. "I bought the most *sublime* black pearls, so I decided to stop by Kathmandu on the way home to Paris to get them set here. They always know what to do. I thought I'd make up a few other little treats for myself as well. I have the idea for the most glorious ring!"

She began inspecting the gems with the tip of her long, manicured fingernail while the other man behind the counter gestured at us to sit farther down.

"What can I help you with?" he asked in heavily accented but excellent English.

"I'm interested in having a necklace made," I said. "Or maybe a ring...I'm not entirely sure."

"A ring?" Franck asked, an odd look on his face. "You hadn't mentioned a ring."

"I thought of it just now. I don't wear necklaces all the time, but I do wear rings every day." I held up my hands to show my silver ring with a cool, opaque purple stone in the middle of some silver squiggles. It wasn't valuable, but I had always liked it. On my other hand, I wore a round, blue flash moonstone set in intricate silver.

Franck peered at my fingers. "You know what would look nice? An engagement ring."

"What are you talking about?" I laughed. "I wouldn't get an engagement ring unless we were going to get mar—"

Franck's eyes widened. He looked as surprised by his suggestion and its implications as I was.

"Are you suggesting what I think you're suggesting?" I asked.

"I think so…*oui*."

I couldn't speak right away. I'd never expected this—especially then, when we had such a fundamental disagreement about the future direction of our lives hovering between us. "Have you been thinking about it for long?" I wondered out loud.

"*Non*," Franck said, "the idea just occurred to me right now. I know we have always said we don't need a marriage certificate to make what we have between us real, but still…what do you think?"

A wedding? Getting married? We had always disdained the concept of taking the traditional route. Still, I realized that I already felt married to Franck in many ways.

"It would be an opportunity for a great party," Franck said.

"Maybe two great parties," I said. "One in Burgundy; one in Victoria."

Franck's eyes lit up, the idea of marrying me or two massive family celebrations—I couldn't be sure which—obviously thrilling him.

The Nepali man was waiting for us, watching this exchange with avid eyes. "This is not how it happens in Nepal," he said.

"How does it happen in Nepal?" Franck asked.

"The families of the young woman and the young man make the match. It is not something that is decided by the couple themselves. Often, they only meet once or twice before the wedding ceremony; sometimes not at all. That is how it was for me and my wife. We are happy. So happy. We have two sons." Pride glowed in his wide smile. From what I had seen so far, sons were the ultimate treasure in Nepali society. "It is the best way," he said. "The Nepali way."

"If we waited for our parents to set us up, we never would have met," I said. "We're from different countries."

"Oh...that does makes it more complicated," the man admitted.

"We had to fight to be together."

"Fight?" the man said. "Did you win?"

I looked over at Franck. *Engagement rings. A wedding. Probably wedding rings as well...* "Did we just get engaged?" I asked him.

Franck's hazel eyes sparkled. "I think so."

Franck and I exchanged shell-shocked looks.

The man clapped his hands together and bowed his head. "I wish you great happiness," he said. "And many, many sons."

To purchase:
My Grape Wedding
http://bit.ly/2v3gy2X

merci

This may be longer than usual, but with good reason.

To Franck and our bevy, who gave me the best reason to keep fighting.

Thank you to my readers who helped me remember that I had a life outside of being a transplant patient. Your support of me and my writing means everything. I am so grateful for the simple act of writing, which proved a lifeline during this turbulent journey. Thank you to Pamela Patchet for always being such an amazing kindred spirit and support.

Thank you to PSC Partners Seeking a Cure and Ricky Safer for continuing to fight for all PSC patients and working so tirelessly to finding a cure for this devastating disease. You are amazing, as is Rachel Ciaves with her incredible work on the PSC Patient Registry, and the much-missed Sandi Pearlman and Philip Burke, my first contacts in the PSC community, who made me feel immediately understood and supported.

To the transplant team at University of Alberta Hospital, for your brilliance, and especially to Mariusz for your skill, knowledge, humor and humanity, as well as your top-drawer restaurant recommendations In Edmonton.

To all the nurses of the ICU and 3G2, you are quite simply amazing. I experienced some rough days on your ward, but you were always around to reassure me and make me laugh. I didn't like the physio team at University of Alberta hospital much when they forced me to get on a recumbent bike a few days after my transplant with multiple IVs hanging off both arms, but I am so grateful they pushed me and showed me I could be strong again.

To all my fellow 3G2 transplantees...you were my comrades, my sounding board and my shoulder(s) to cry on. It was a privilege to go through this experience with you brave souls. I am devastated we lost Mike Rompré this year, but I will never forget his gentle smile and quiet sympathy when one of us was having a rough day. RIP friend.

To the friends and family who quietly rallied around when I had to relocate to Edmonton for three months with only forty-eight hours' notice. You all came quietly, wonderfully together with your child care, driving, dog walking, and meals so I could concentrate on getting through the transplant and then getting well. It does indeed take a village, and I am honored to be part of a wonderful village indeed. Thank you to Lara and Helen, who flew in from London and California so that they could be there when I woke up after the transplant.

I would not have been around to finish this book or, you know, BE ALIVE, if it wasn't for the incomparable Nyssa Temmel, who donated the entire right lobe of her liver to me in an awe-inspiring act of bravery and generosity. I am not only grateful beyond the capacity of words but also honored to have gone through this process with her. I will never forget holding hands and crying before being rolled into our side-by-side ORs. I won't even get started about our majestic shuffles around the ward, both cracking jokes even when we were almost bent over in half with pain.

I am alive today because of Nyssa's organ donation. Also, I walk this earth now with the vessels and ducts donated by an anonymous deceased donor who I will never be able to thank in person. Five people each donated pints of blood to me that kept me alive during this surgery.

If you ever think humanity is not connected, think of me. I am walking, breathing proof that we are all a part of one another, and that people are good. I believe with absolute clarity now that we were put on this earth to help each other. A life in which you love as hard as you can is a good life.

That's all...for now.

a conversation with
laura bradbury

In *My Grape Paris*, it seems quite ambitious to study for a year at the Sorbonne and take almost all your courses in French, even though you are Anglophone. Was it as much of a stretch as it seemed?

Such a stretch! I was terrible in French at high school. I had to have a tutor just to pass, and I dropped it after the mandatory French 11 because my terrible French mark was dragging down my whole GPA. I vividly remember walking out of my Grade 11 French exam and whooping with joy. "I never have to learn French again for the rest of my life!" I yelled triumphantly. Four years after that I found myself doing a year of university at the Sorbonne—in French.

I learned French when I went to Burgundy on the Ursus exchange (recounted in *My Grape Year*). I lived with four French families who spoke no English, so it was sink or swim. I discovered that I can learn a language in a survival situation. Immersion was a completely different process than school, and for me it worked.

I took high school classes that year in France, but I didn't really need to hand in work because I had already graduated in Canada. As a result my written French was far from fluent. Anyone can tell you that written French is almost a completely different language than spoken French—it is far more formal (and difficult). When I signed up for the Sorbonne, I was again taking a leap into the unknown, like when I went to Burgundy on that exchange year in the first place.

It was difficult at first, and I was acutely conscious of the fact that my written essays were clunky and awkward. Still I managed because I loved the subject (especially Professor Renier-Bernadotte's classes). I worked my tail off and benefited from the magical process of osmosis that occurs with immersion. I learned French simply because I was reading, writing, and speaking it every day.

Your conflict with Professor Gabrielle was one of the most dramatic scenes in the book. Why do you think she was so biased against you? How do you view that situation now you are older and have more life experience?

In retrospect I think her attitude toward me was due to the fact she was young to be teaching her own class and insecure about her abilities. To be confronted with me—a native English speaker and a university student in English Literature—must have rattled her already shaky confidence. I still hate the way she attacked me because of her own insecurities. Women can be the most solid support for one another, but the flip side is that we can also be the absolute worst for sabotaging other women.

In my life, and even more so as I age, I do everything I can to support the women in my life. I truly believe a rising tide lifts all boats, and a model of collaboration versus competition is what I choose again and again.

After my friend Nyssa saved my life with the donation of part of her liver, how could I ever feel competitive with anyone again? I mean, I am walking around with Nyssa's liver, an anonymous donor's vessels and ducts, and five pints of anonymously donated blood in my body, keeping me alive. Quite simply, I am here because of the generosity and selflessness of others. I truly believe we are put here on earth to help one another.

Part of me feels bad about how shaken Professor Gabrielle was the day I confronted her. Still, there was no way I could have predicted how my fellow classmates would react—as though I had awoken a sudden, collective thirst for a revolt. It turned into a lynch mob, which I regret, but she did need to be called out for her actions. I often wonder what became of her and whether she grew confident to the point that she could see other women as allies rather than a threat. I hope so.

One thing that creates sustained tension in *My Grape Paris* is the ongoing certainty about whether the Paris year would be the end of you and Franck as a couple. Was that hard to write, seeing as you knew you had, indeed, ended up together?

On the surface, when I thought back on our Paris year, it was so easy to shrug and think, "well, of course we stayed together." However, when I began to write about that time, it came back to me just how tenuous our relationship was at that point. From a practical perspective, we had the deck stacked against us.

Franck was French, and I was Canadian. We both had to deal with the complicated and interminable immigration paperwork. One of us was always far away from our home and family. One of us always felt like a duck-out-of-water in the other's country. Our families didn't disapprove, exactly, but they thought that the chances of Franck and I staying together in the long run were far-fetched. We were still so young, and so many people were sending us the message that we owed ourselves to explore other possibilities before making a serious commitment. In fact, at that juncture, it was far more likely that Franck and I wouldn't last. The uncertainty I wrote about in *My Grape Paris* was real.

Over the course of writing this book, you had a life-saving liver transplant. Did that affect your writing process or the end product of *My Grape Paris*?

Hugely. I began writing *My Grape Paris* about a year before my transplant. I obviously felt extremely sick, but I told myself I was doing all right. In reality, I was suffering from severe hepatic encephalopathy, which involves dementia-like symptoms caused by a sick liver leeching too much ammonia into the bloodstream. I wrote, but one month after my transplant, when I read over my first draft of *My Grape Paris*, I could not make heads or tails of it. It was like Latvian to me (and I don't speak Latvian). I basically wrote this book twice—a hepatic encephalopathy version and then a post-transplant version.

Prior to my transplant I honestly didn't know if I would be alive to finish *My Grape Paris*. There were moments when my chances looked slim. Still, something in me pushed to keep writing every day. I think writing was how I was able to keep faith and hope for a positive outcome. It was my lifeline. I was on the couch writing the pre-transplant draft of *My Grape Paris* when Nyssa, my amazing friend, phoned from Edmonton to say she had been approved as my donor and we had an OR date booked in a week's time. This book is particularly close to my heart, as it has accompanied me through this terrible, wonderful, miraculous journey. The fact that it is now in your hands...well...that is miraculous to me.

The theme of fighting for love was strengthened, I believe, by what I experienced when I was rolled into my transplant surgery. I was informed by every doctor who crossed my path that I could die during the procedure. I was forced to do a reckoning of my life up to that point. I had loved hard and been loved, and if the worst happened, for me that felt like I had lived a good life. It all goes back to love. Always.

Another theme in your book, as introduced by Hemmingway's quote from *A Moveable Feast*, is how this shared daydream of living in Paris was harder and more complicated for you and Franck when it became a reality.

I think a common thread in all my writing—in my books, blogs, and articles—is how real life is always messier than fantasy. This is not necessarily a bad thing, as it means our experiences are far more profound as well. I have always said you can maintain a dream life in a new place for roughly a month, and then, no matter where you are, real life sets in.

I am incurably honest about the crises in my life, including my struggles with anxiety, relationship issues, and health stuff. It turns out I am no good at sustaining a glossy image, unlike many people who excel at that in this age of social media. It just doesn't sit well with me. It feels dishonest and inauthentic. I also think it does a grave disservice to my fellow humans who are often dealing with struggles of their own. I feel a compulsion to let others know they are not alone and that it is possible to get through difficult times, even though it feels impossible in the moment.

There were many aspects of life in Paris that felt like the dream. The picnics on the Seine, going to classes in the ancient amphitheaters at the Sorbonne, discovering our own Roman amphitheater on my route to school, the behind-the-scenes tours of the Louvre, the champagne, the FOOD... However, intermixed was uncertainty and angst. I evolved because of *all* those things, not just the dreamy stuff. Franck and I evolved as a couple because of the challenges more than the fantasy. I personally find the mess far more interesting and beautiful than the gloss.

The subplot of Madame Fox and Monsieur Pierrepont and their romance during the war was one of the most touching parts in *My Grape Paris*. I must ask, did this really happen?

Absolutely. It was such a fabulous and heartbreaking love story that I almost couldn't believe it was real or that I had been privileged to learn some of the details. I changed their names, of course, as I do with most secondary characters because they never asked to be written about. That photo at Madame Fox's apartment—it told a story all by itself.

In France, if a person is interested, they can hear many first-hand stories about life during the last war. I am greedy for these stories, as I know they are a limited commodity. The circumstances of the war meant there were many love stories, and not all of them had happy endings. Madame Fox gave me the final push I needed to be brave and tell Franck what I wanted and how I felt. Every detail of that last conversation with her, and the scent of her apartment, is seared in my memory. Madame Fox and Monsieur Pierrepont won't leave my mind. I think I will end up writing a fictionalized version of their story with the little I know as the spark. Their story just needs to be written, you know?

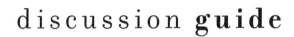

discussion **guide**

1. In *My Grape Paris* Laura goes to the Sorbonne without a solid
    grounding in written French, yet immersion was the best
    method of learning for her. How many languages do you
    speak? How did you learn them? What method of language
    learning works best for you? Is there a language you would
    love to learn?

2. Have you ever experienced women sabotaging other women?
    Conversely, have you seen women supporting women and
    holding one another up? What is your philosophy around
    this? Do you often feel competitive with other people, or do
    you feel an instinct to collaborate?

3. Do you or did you ever have a soul mate in your life? If you
    were in a relationship, did it last? If not, did you find another
    soul mate? Are there any broken relationships from your past
    that you still grieve, or are you grateful they ended?

4. Describe what you think constitutes a soul mate. Is it chem-
    istry? Timing? A shared sense of humor?

5. If you were facing a life-threatening disease, what would prioritize in your life? What would you do, no matter what?

6. If you were put in a situation where you had to make peace with your life so far, what would you be grateful for? What do you think you would regret?

7. Do you agree with Laura's belief that after a month pretty much anywhere in the world, real life starts interrupts and cannot be avoided? If not, why? A myriad of "glossy" life images are shared on social media every day. Do you find this inspiring or anxiety-inducing?

8. Do you, too, find immense value in the messy side of life—the uncertainty, angst, conflicts, and mistakes? What lessons has life taught you in this way?

9. Did you enjoy the subplot of Monsieur Pierrepont and Madame Fox? What about it did you find touching? Do you have a thwarted love in your past? If Madame Fox had the chance to redo her life, do you think she would have done things differently? If you have lived a similar experience, would you?

10. Many of us yearn for travel. Do you dream of going to Paris? Is there someplace else you'd choose instead? What would your ideal setup be in that situation? What complications do you think could arise? What wonderful things could happen?

about **laura**

Bestselling author Laura Bradbury published her first book—a heartfelt memoir about her leap away from a prestigious legal career in London to live in a tiny French village with her Burgundian husband in *My Grape Escape*—after being diagnosed with PSC, a rare autoimmune bile duct/liver disease. Since then Laura has published four more books in the Grape Series about her enchanting adventures in France, with more Grape books in the works. Laura also plans to delve into the worlds of romance and women's fiction. Ooh la la! Now living and writing on the West Coast of Canada with a new liver and three Franco-Canuck daughters (collectively known as "the Bevy"), Laura runs four charming vacation rentals in Burgundy with her husband, has an enviable collection of beach glass, and does all she can to support PSC and organ donation awareness and research.

Find Laura online:

Facebook
https://www.facebook.com/AuthorLauraBradbury/

Twitter
https://twitter.com/Author_LB

Instagram
https://www.instagram.com/laurabradburywriter/

Pinterest
https://www.pinterest.ca/bradburywriter/

BookBub
https://www.bookbub.com/authors/laura-bradbury

CPSIA information can be obtained
at www.ICGtesting.com
Printed in the USA
LVHW090141220720
661257LV00001B/4